AN INTRODUCTION TO

THERMODYNAMICS, THE KINETIC THEORY OF GASES, AND STATISTICAL MECHANICS

BY FRANCIS WESTON SEARS

Department of Physics
Dartmouth College

SECOND EDITION

 ADDISON-WESLEY PUBLISHING COMPANY, INC.

READING, MASSACHUSETTS · PALO ALTO · LONDON

PREFACE

This book was written to bring together under one cover, and at an intermediate level, a presentation of the fundamental principles of Thermodynamics, Kinetic Theory, and Statistical Mechanics. The present edition differs from the first chiefly in that the chapters on the Boltzmann Statistics have been largely rewritten, with more emphasis on the partition function, and a chapter on Fluctuations has been added, following in large part the treatment in Schaefer's *Einführung in die Theoretische Physik*. Some of the material on Low Temperature Physics has been dropped (an excellent discussion is now available in Zemansky's *Heat and Thermodynamics*, fourth edition) and the remainder has been incorporated in appropriate sections throughout the book. Some changes have also been made in the problems.

The author wishes to express his gratitude for the many helpful comments that have been received from both teachers and students who have used the first edition. Further criticisms will be welcomed.

F. W. S.

Cambridge, Mass.
November, 1952

CONTENTS

CHAPTER 1

THERMODYNAMIC SYSTEMS

1-1 Introduction. The science of thermodynamics deals with relations between heat and work. It is based on two general laws of nature, the first and second laws of thermodynamics. By logical reasoning from these laws it is possible to correlate many of the observable properties of matter, such as coefficients of expansion, compressibilities, specific heat capacities, vapor pressures, and heats of transformation.

The principles and methods of thermodynamics are used by the mechanical engineer in the design of steam engines and turbines, internal combustion engines, jet engines, and refrigerators, and by the chemical engineer in practically every process involving a flow of heat or a problem in chemical equilibrium. The sciences of physical chemistry and chemical physics consist in large part of the applications of thermodynamic principles to chemistry.

Thermodynamics makes no hypotheses about the structure of matter. It is an experimental or empirical science, and thermodynamic formulas necessarily have the same general validity as the two laws from which they are derived. The price of generality is a restriction in scope. Thus thermodynamics can predict many relationships between properties of matter but not the actual magnitudes of these properties. The most fruitful approach to the study of the properties of matter therefore combines thermodynamic reasoning with molecular theory and we shall see how the principles of statistical mechanics not only enable us to go beyond the predictions of pure thermodynamics, but to gain a deeper insight into the laws of thermodynamics as well.

1-2 Thermodynamic systems. The term *system*, as used in thermodynamics, refers to a definite quantity of matter bounded by some closed surface. The surface may be a real one, like that of a tank enclosing a certain mass of compressed oxygen gas, or it may be imaginary, like the boundary of a certain mass of liquid flowing along a pipe line and followed in imagination as it progresses. The boundary surface is not necessarily fixed in either shape or volume. When a fluid expands against a moving piston, for example, the volume enclosed by the boundary surface changes. Occasionally it is necessary to deal with systems in which there is a flow of matter across the boundary, into or out of the system, but for the most

1

part we shall consider only systems of constant mass. It is very important that the meaning of the term "system" be kept clearly in mind.

Many problems in thermodynamics involve interchanges of energy between a given system and other systems. Any systems which can interchange energy with a given system are called the *surroundings* of that system.

A system can exchange energy with its surroundings by the performance of mechanical work or by a flow of heat. If conditions are such that no energy interchange can take place, the system is said to be *isolated*. This requires that the system be thermally insulated so that the flow of heat is zero (or negligibly small) and so that no mechanical work can be done on or by the system.

1-3 State of a system. Specification of the state of a thermodynamic system depends to some extent on the nature of the system. The state of a gas in a cylinder is completely specified by giving its pressure, volume, temperature, and mass. The mass and volume need not both be specified, however, since the gas in any portion of the cylinder is considered to be in the same state as that in any other portion. Evidently only the ratio of mass to volume, or the density, is necessary to define the state. In more complicated systems it may be necessary to specify the values of other quantities, such as the concentration of a solution, the charge of an electrolytic cell, the polarization in a dielectric, or the area of a surface film.

The quantities whose values determine the state of a system are called its *thermodynamic coordinates* or its *state variables*. Pressure, density, and temperature are examples.

It is obvious that if one is to be able to speak of *the* temperature or *the* pressure of a system, the temperature or pressure must be the same at all points in the system. When an isolated system is left to itself and the pressure and temperature are measured at various points throughout the system, it is observed that although these quantities may initially change with time, the rates of change become smaller and smaller until eventually no further observable change occurs. The final steady state of an isolated system is called a state of *thermodynamic equilibrium* and we postulate that in such a state *the thermodynamic coordinates of a homogeneous system are the same at all points*. If a system is *heterogeneous*, for example if it consists of a liquid in equilibrium with its vapor, the pressure and temperature are assumed the same at all points, and the density is the same at all points of each portion that is itself homogeneous. That is, the liquid and vapor are at the same temperature and pressure, and while the densities of liquid and vapor are different, the density of the liquid is the same at all points occupied by liquid, and that of the vapor is the same at all points occupied by vapor.

The subject of thermodynamics deals chiefly with systems which are in thermodynamic equilibrium.

1-4 Processes. Any change in the thermodynamic coordinates of a system is called a *process*. If a process is carried out in such a way that at every instant the pressure, temperature, and density of each homogeneous portion of a system remain essentially uniform, the process is called *reversible*. Thus a reversible process can be defined as *a succession of equilibrium states*, or states that depart only infinitesimally from equilibrium. If there are departures from uniformity, the process is called *irreversible*. The significance of the terms reversible and irreversible is only evident in the light of the second law of thermodynamics. The fact that a process is irreversible in the thermodynamic sense does not mean that the system cannot be restored to its original state.

We shall give a few illustrations of reversible and irreversible processes. Consider a gas in a cylinder provided with a movable piston. If the piston is pushed down very rapidly, the pressure, temperature, and density immediately below the piston will be greater than at other points and the process is irreversible. To compress the gas reversibly, the piston must be pushed down very slowly to avoid turbulence and allow time for the pressure and temperature to become the same at all points.

Suppose we wish to heat a beaker of water from a temperature T_1 to a temperature T_2. The water *could* be heated by placing it over a gas flame. This process is highly irreversible, because the temperature of the flame is much greater than that of the water and the water immediately over the flame is much hotter than at other points. To heat the water reversibly from T_1 to T_2, we require a number of other bodies at temperatures $T_1 + dT$, $T_1 + 2\,dT$, $\ldots$ $T_2 - dT$, T_2, as illustrated in Fig. 1-1. These bodies might be large water tanks, containing enough water so that the flow of a small quantity of heat from each one to the beaker will not alter appreciably the temperature of the water in the tank. We shall speak of such bodies as *heat reservoirs*. We first bring the beaker, at a

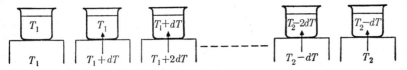

Fig. 1-1. Reversible flow of heat.

temperature T_1, into contact with the reservoir at temperature $T_1 + dT$, and keep the two in contact until thermal equilibrium has been established. The beaker, now at temperature $T_1 + dT$, is then moved to the reservoir at temperature $T_1 + 2\,dT$, thermal equilibrium is established at this temperature, and so on. Thus all transfers of heat take place with only infinitesimal temperature differences between the reservoir and the beaker, or between portions of water in the beaker. The water is at all times essentially in an equilibrium state and, by definition, the process is reversible.

All actual processes are irreversible, because they take place with finite differences of pressure and/or temperature between parts of a system, or between the system and its surroundings. Nevertheless, the concept of a reversible process is a useful and important one in thermodynamics.

1-5 Temperature and thermometry. We have referred to the temperature of a system in the preceding sections without giving a precise definition of this quantity or specifying how it shall be measured. The concept of temperature, like that of force, originated in man's sense perceptions. Just as a force is something we can correlate with muscular effort and describe as a push or a pull, so temperature can be correlated with the sensations of relative hotness or coldness. But man's temperature sense, like his force sense, is unreliable and restricted in range, and out of the primitive concepts of relative hotness and coldness there has developed an objective science of thermometry, just as an objective method of defining and measuring forces has grown out of the naive concept of a force as a push or a pull.

We have already defined *equality* of temperature within a single isolated system. That is, we postulate that all parts of an isolated system eventually come to and remain at the same temperature or, in other words, the temperature is the same at all points of a system in thermodynamic equilibrium. Now suppose we have *two* isolated systems, both in thermodynamic equilibrium. To determine whether they are at the same temperature, we remove the thermal insulating material from a portion of the surfaces of both and bring these portions of the surfaces in contact. If no observable changes take place in the thermodynamic coordinates of either system, the two are at the same temperature. (Although we have not as yet defined the term *heat*, we may use it at this point and say that when two systems are at the same temperature there will be no flow of heat from one to the other when the two are brought in contact.)

Suppose that system A is at the same temperature as system B, as determined by the preceding test, and that A is also at the same temperature as system C. Then we find by the same test that B and C are at the same temperature. That is, *when two systems are at the same temperature as a third, they are at the same temperature as each other.* This statement is sometimes called the *Zeroth law of thermodynamics*, and its truth is tacitly assumed in every measurement of temperature. If we want to know when two beakers of water are at the same temperature, it is unnecessary to bring them into contact and see if their thermodynamic coordinates change with time. We insert a thermometer (system A) in one beaker (system B) and wait until the length of the mercury column in the capillary (a thermodynamic coordinate) becomes constant. The thermometer then has the same temperature as the water in this beaker. We then repeat the procedure with the other beaker (system C). If the thermometer readings are the same, we infer that the temperatures of the beakers are the same and experiment shows that they are; that is, if the two beakers are brought into thermal contact, no changes in their measurable properties take place.

Note that the thermometer used in this test requires no calibration—it is only necessary that the mercury column stand at the same point in the capillary. Such an instrument can be described as a *thermoscope.* It will indicate equality (or inequality) of temperature without determining a numerical value of a temperature.

We now consider the problem of defining a *scale* of temperature, that is, of assigning a numerical value to the temperature of a given body. First we select some measurable property of a body that changes with temperature. Properties commonly used are the length of a column of liquid in a glass capillary connected to a bulb, the resistance of a wire, the emf of a thermocouple, the pressure of a gas kept at constant volume, etc. We also select two fixed temperatures or *fixed points*. Those universally adopted are the *ice point* and the *steam point*. The ice point is defined as the equilibrium temperature of ice and air-saturated water (not pure water) under a pressure of one atmosphere; the steam point is defined as the equilibrium temperature of pure water and water vapor under a pressure of one atmosphere. The numbers assigned to these temperatures are arbitrary. In establishing the centigrade scale, we assign the number 0 to the ice point temperature and 100 to the steam point temperature.

To measure a temperature with a given thermometer, the selected property is measured first with the thermometer at the temperature of one fixed point, then at the other fixed point and finally at the unknown temperature. Let X_i, X_s, and X represent the values of the measured property at the ice point, the steam point, and the unknown temperature respectively. The unknown temperature t is then defined by the equation

$$t = 100 \frac{X - X_i}{X_s - X_i},$$

or

$$(X - X_i) = \frac{t}{100}(X_s - X_i). \tag{1-1}$$

That is, a temperature t on the centigrade scale of a given thermometer is defined as that temperature which results in an increase in the value of the measured property, above its value at the ice point, which is $t/100$ths as great as the increase in this property between the ice and steam points.

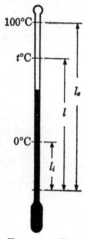

To be specific, let l_i, l_s, and l represent the distances from some reference mark on a mercury-in-glass thermometer to the top of the mercury column in the capillary when the thermometer is at the ice point, steam point, and unknown temperature. (See Fig. 1-2.) Then

$$t = 100 \frac{l - l_i}{l_s - l_i}.$$

This equation defines centigrade temperature *on the scale of this particular thermometer*. To verify the form of the equation, note that if $l = l_s$, $t = 100°$ C, and if $l = l_i$, $t = 0°$ C. The manufacturer of a thermometer has in effect solved the equation above when he divides the distance on the thermometer stem between the ice and steam point readings into 100 parts of equal length, assuming the cross section of the capillary to to be uniform.

FIG. 1-2. Centigrade temperature scale.

Now suppose we construct a second thermometer, using a different kind of glass and a different liquid, calibrate it as we did the first by measuring the lengths l'_s and l'_i, and place it in contact with the same body for which the first thermometer gave a temperature t. The temperature t' determined by the second thermometer is

$$t' = 100 \frac{l' - l'_i}{l'_s - l'_i}.$$

Except in certain special cases, we find that t' is not equal to t, although the two thermometers and the body are all in thermal equilibrium and by definition are at the same temperature. The reason for the difference, of course, is that the two liquids, and the two glasses, do not expand in the same way. One is tempted to say that one or the other (or perhaps both) does not expand "uniformly," but observe that there is no way, using the preceding definition of temperature, to decide this question. Each thermometer expands "uniformly" on the temperature scale determined by that particular thermometer, since by definition equal increments of length correspond to equal increments of temperature. Neither thermometer expands uniformly on the temperature scale determined by the other. Both were constructed and calibrated according to the rules and there is no way (using this definition of temperature) of telling which is "correct." The root of the difficulty is that we have defined a fundamental quantity, temperature, in terms of the properties of a specific instrument. We feel by intuition that there must be such a thing as a "true" or "absolute" scale of temperature and, in fact, there is, but it can be defined only on the basis of the second law of thermodynamics. We shall return to this question in Chapter 7.

Eq. (1-1) defines centigrade temperature as a *linear* function of the property X. There is no *a priori* reason, however, for selecting a linear function rather than any other, and a temperature scale *can* be defined in terms of any function of X. The linear function is simplest and leads to the result that many properties of materials, such as specific heat capacities, coefficients of expansion, etc., are approximately independent of temperature. Some of the consequences of choosing a logarithmic rather than a linear function are explored in problem 1 at the end of the chapter.

1-6 The constant volume gas thermometer. Thermodynamic temperature. The constant volume gas thermometer uses as a measurable physical property the pressure of a fixed mass of gas kept at constant volume. It is possible to define a centigrade temperature scale directly in terms of this thermometer, but instead we shall describe how it is used to define temperatures on a scale which for the present we shall call the "absolute" scale and which we shall show later is identical with the Kelvin or thermodynamic scale, based on the second law. We shall represent a temperature on this scale by T and speak of a temperature as so many degrees Kelvin or °K.

Let p_s and p_i be the absolute pressures exerted by the gas in a constant volume thermometer at the steam point T_s and the ice point T_i. Suppose we make a series of measurements of these pressures, varying the amount of gas in the thermometer. For example, we might start with a mass of gas in the thermometer such that the pressure at the ice point is $p_i = 1000$ mm of mercury. The temperature of the thermometer is raised to the steam point and p_s is measured. We now remove some gas from the thermometer until p_i is reduced to, say, 800 mm of mercury, and again measure p_s. This procedure is repeated for lower and lower values of p_i.

From the data accumulated, we now calculate the ratio $(p_s/p_i)_v$ for each value of p_i. (The subscript v indicates that the volume is constant.)

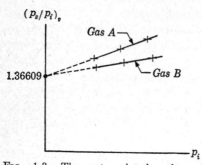

These ratios will not all be the same, but if they are plotted as in Fig. 1-3, as a function of p_i, the points are found to lie on a smooth curve which becomes linear as it approaches the value $p_i = 0$. The experiments, of course, cannot be carried all the way down to zero initial pressure, but the linear portion of the curve can be extrapolated to the vertical axis, as indicated by the dotted line.

FIG. 1-3. The extrapolated value of $(p_s/p_i)_v$ is the same for all gases.

The upper curve in Fig. 1-3 represents the results of a series of measurements with gas A (say hydrogen) in the thermometer. A similar series with a different gas B (say helium) in the thermometer might lead to the lower curve. The ratio $(p_s/p_i)_v$ is different for each gas at each different value of p_i, but it is found experimentally that the extrapolated curves intersect the vertical axis at the same point, whatever kind of gas is used in the thermometer. The numerical value of the ordinate of the common point of intersection is

$$1.36609 \pm 0.00004.$$

We now *define* the ratio of the temperatures T_s/T_i as the limiting value of the ratio $(p_s/p_i)_v$ as p_i approaches zero.

$$\frac{T_s}{T_i} = \lim_{p_i \to 0} \left(\frac{p_s}{p_i}\right)_v = 1.36609.$$

If in addition we set

$$T_s - T_i = 100 \text{ K}°,$$

the preceding equations can be solved for T_s and T_i and we find

$$T_s = 373.16 \pm 0.03,$$

$$T_i = 273.16 \pm 0.03.$$

A temperature other than those of the ice and steam points is determined by making a series of measurements of pressure p at this temperature for different values of p_i, calculating the ratios $(p/p_i)_v$, and extrapolating to $p_i = 0$, as in Fig. 1-3. Then by definition

$$\frac{T}{T_i} = \lim_{p_i \to 0} \left(\frac{p}{p_i}\right)_v,$$

and since T_i is known, T may be computed.

Temperatures defined in this way are therefore independent of the properties of any particular gas, although they do depend on the characteristic behavior of gases as a whole and are thus not entirely independent of the properties of a particular material.

Centigrade temperature t can now be defined by the equation

$$t = T - T_i = T - 273.16,$$

which leads, of course, to the result that

$$t_s = 100° \text{ C},$$

$$t_i = 0° \text{ C}.$$

The centigrade temperature corresponding to the zero point on the absolute scale is

$$t = -273.16° \text{ C}.$$

Notice carefully that the definition of a temperature on the absolute scale does not depend on any assumptions about the pressure or volume of a gas becoming zero at absolute zero, nor does it depend on the existence of a hypothetical ideal gas, nor does it involve any statement about the absence of all molecular motion at absolute zero, nor does it imply that a temperature of absolute zero or less is unattainable. Absolute temperatures can be determined by measurements made entirely with real gases, using the extrapolation process previously described. It turns out that if an ideal gas were available for use in a gas thermometer, the extrapolation procedure would be unnecessary and measurements might be made at any pressure p_i. For this reason absolute temperatures are sometimes described as "ideal gas thermometer temperatures," but the temperatures can be determined even though an ideal gas does not exist.

1-7 The International temperature scale. The International Committee on Weights and Measures, at the Ninth General Conference held in 1948, defined a temperature scale called the International Temperature Scale, which superseded with but slight differences a similar scale defined in 1927. The International Scale is based upon a number of fixed and reproducible equilibrium temperatures (fixed points) to which numerical values are assigned, and upon specified formulas for computing temperatures from the indications of specified instruments. The scale conforms as closely as possible to the centigrade thermodynamic scale. It is not intended as a substitute for the latter, which is accepted as fundamental, and its practical importance lies in its reproducibility rather than its accuracy. The primary and fundamental fixed points are listed in Table 1-1, and a somewhat abbreviated description of the instruments and formulas for computing temperatures follows.

TABLE 1-1.

FUNDAMENTAL AND PRIMARY FIXED POINTS

Fixed point, temperature of equilibrium ($p = 1$ atm)	Temperature, °C
(a) Between liquid oxygen and its vapor (oxygen point)	−182.97
(b) Between ice and air-saturated water (ice point) (*Fundamental fixed point*)	0.00
(c) Between liquid water and its vapor (steam point) (*Fundamental fixed point*)	100.00
(d) Between liquid sulfur and its vapor (sulfur point)	444.60
(e) Between solid and liquid silver (silver point)	960.80
(f) Between solid and liquid gold (gold point)	1063.00

(a) *From 0° C to the freezing point of antimony*, the temperature t is defined by the formula

$$R_t = R_0(1 + At + Bt^2), \tag{1-2}$$

where R_t is the resistance at temperature t of a platinum resistance thermometer. The constant R_0 is the resistance at 0° C, and A and B are determined from measured values of R_t at the steam and sulfur points.

(b) *From the oxygen point to $0°$ C*, the temperature t is defined by the formula

$$R_t = R_0[1 + At + Bt^2 + C(t - 100)t^3], \qquad (1\text{-}3)$$

where R_t, R_0, A, and B are determined as in (a), and C is calculated from the measured value of R_t at the oxygen point.

(c) *From the freezing point of antimony to the gold point*, the temperature t is defined by the formula

$$\mathcal{E} = a + bt + ct^2, \qquad (1\text{-}4)$$

where $\mathcal{E}$ is the emf of a thermocouple of platinum and a platinum-rhodium alloy (90% Pt, 10% Rh) when one junction is at $0°$ C and the other at the temperature t. The constants a, b, and c are calculated from measured values of $\mathcal{E}$ at the freezing point of antimony and at the silver and gold points. The antimony shall be such that its freezing temperature, as determined with a standard resistance thermometer, is not less than $630.3°$ C.

(d) *Above the gold point*, the temperature t is defined by a formula derived from Planck's law,

$$\frac{J_t}{J_{Au}} = \frac{\exp\left[c_2/\lambda(t_{Au} + T_0)\right] - 1}{\exp\left[c_2/\lambda(t + T_0)\right] - 1}, \qquad (1\text{-}5)$$

where J_t and J_{Au} are the radiant powers, per unit area and per unit wave length, at the wave length λ, emitted by an ideal radiator (blackbody) at the temperature t and at the gold point t_{Au}. The constant c_2 equals 1.438 cm-deg K, T_0 is the temperature of the ice point in degrees Kelvin ($= 273.16$) and λ is a wave length in the visible spectrum, expressed in centimeters.

Problems

1. Suppose that instead of defining temperature t as a linear function of some thermometric property X, we defined a temperature t^* as a logarithmic function,

$$t^* = a \ln X + b.$$

(a) Let X be the length l of the column of liquid in a liquid-in-glass thermometer, as in Fig. 1-2, and let $l_i = 5$ cm, $l_s = 25$ cm, $t_i^* = 0°$, $t_s^* = 100°$. Find the distance in centimeters between the divisions $t^* = 0°$ and $t^* = 10°$, and between $t^* = 90°$ and $t^* = 100°$. (b) The pressure of an ideal gas kept at constant volume is given by the equation

$$p = KT,$$

where T is the absolute temperature and K is a constant. If the pressure p is taken as the thermometric function X in the equation above, find the value of t^* when $T = 0°$.

2. The table below lists observed values of the pressure p of the gas in a constant volume gas thermometer at an unknown temperature T, for a series of values of the pressure p_i at the ice point. Determine to four significant figures the limiting value of the ratio p/p_i as p_i approaches zero, and find the unknown temperature to the nearest 0.1°.

p_i (mm of mercury)	100.0	200.0	300.0	400.0
p (mm of mercury)	127.9	256.5	385.8	516.0

3. (a) Find the temperature of the ice and steam points on the Rankine or Fahrenheit absolute scale, in which $T_s - T_i = 180$ degrees. (b) Find the temperature of absolute zero on the Fahrenheit scale, where $t_i = 32$ degrees and $t_s - t_i = 180$ degrees.

4. Centigrade temperature on the scale determined by a platinum resistance thermometer is called *platinum temperature,* t_{pt}, and is defined from Eq. (1-1) as

$$t_{pt} = 100 \frac{R - R_i}{R_s - R_i}, \tag{1-6}$$

where R_i, R_s, and R are the resistances of the thermometer at the ice point, the steam point, and the platinum temperature t_{pt}. The resistance of a certain platinum resistance thermometer is 10.000 ohms at the ice point, 13.861 ohms at the steam point, and 26.270 ohms at the sulfur point (where $t = 444.6°$ C on the International scale). (a) Find the platinum temperature of the sulfur point. (b) Find the platinum temperature at which the resistance is 21.000 ohms. (c) Find to the nearest 1/10 degree the International temperature at which the resistance is 21.000 ohms. *Note:* To obtain International temperature t from Eq. (1-2), one must first determine A and B and then solve a quadratic equation for t. It was shown by Callendar that the calculations could be simplified if Eq. (1-2) were put in the form

$$t = t_{pt} + \delta \left[\left(\frac{t}{100} \right)^2 - \left(\frac{t}{100} \right) \right], \tag{1-7}$$

which expresses t as the sum of the platinum temperature t_{pt} (which is easily computed) and a small correction term. The Callendar equation is solved by successive approximations. One first computes t_{pt}, which is the first approximation to t. Inserting t_{pt} instead of t in the correction term gives a second approximation, and so on. The coefficient δ can be expressed in terms of the constants A and B in Eq. (1-2), but it is simpler to find it directly from Eq. (1-7), using the values of t and t_{pt} at the sulfur point.

CHAPTER 2

EQUATIONS OF STATE

2-1 Intensive and extensive variables. An *intensive* variable is one whose value is independent of the mass of a system. Examples are pressure, temperature, and density, which, for a homogeneous system in equilibrium, are the same for the entire system as they are for any part of it. The volume, on the other hand, is proportional to the mass of the system considered and is an example of an *extensive* variable. Other extensive variables, which we shall discuss later, are the internal energy and the entropy of a system.

Any extensive variable, when divided by the mass or the number of moles of a system, becomes an intensive variable, and in many instances it is more convenient to write thermodynamic equations wholly in terms of intensive variables, since the equations are then independent of the mass of any particular system.

The ratio of an extensive variable to the mass of a system is called the *specific* value of that variable. We shall use capital letters for extensive variables and small letters for the corresponding specific values. Thus the total volume of a system is represented by V, and the specific volume, or the volume per unit mass, by v.

$$v = \frac{V}{m}.$$

The specific volume is evidently merely the reciprocal of the density ρ, since by definition

$$\rho = \frac{m}{V} = \frac{1}{V/m} = \frac{1}{v}.$$

Since the density of a substance in a given state is independent of the mass considered, density is obviously an intensive variable and hence the specific volume is also.

The ratio of an extensive variable to the number of moles of a system is called the *molal specific value* of that variable. We shall use small letters also to represent molal specific values and, for example, write the molal specific volume as v, where

$$v = \frac{V}{n}.$$

13

No confusion arises from the use of the same letter to represent both the volume per unit mass, say, and the volume per mole. In (nearly) every equation in which such a quantity occurs there will be some other quantity that will indicate which specific volume is meant or, if there is no such indication, the equation will hold equally well for either.

Since the number of moles n of a system equals the total mass m divided by the so-called molecular weight M (molecular mass is the correct term), the molal specific volume can be written

$$v = \frac{V}{m/M} = M \frac{1}{\rho}.$$

The molal specific volume is therefore the reciprocal of the density, multiplied by the molecular weight.

Note that in the mks system, the term "mole" implies *kilogram-mole*, that is, a mass in kilograms numerically equal to the molecular weight. Thus one mole of O_2 means 32 kilograms of O_2.

2-2 Equations of state. The equation of state of a substance is a relation between its pressure, specific volume, and temperature. We know by experience that an equation of state *exists* for every homogeneous substance —solid, liquid, or gas. Thus the density of a block of copper is completely determined when the temperature of the block and the pressure on it are specified. While it may not be possible to express this equation in any simple analytic form, a function of the type

$$F(p,v,T) = 0$$

exists for every substance, and the substance knows how to solve the equation for v (or ρ) when p and T are specified, even if we do not. The exact form of the function is, in general, extremely complicated and it is often expressed as a power series. A general idea of the nature of the function is often better conveyed by presenting the data in graphical form.

2-3 Equation of state of an ideal gas. Suppose one has measured the pressure, volume, temperature, and mass of a certain gas, over wide ranges of these variables. Instead of the actual volume V, we shall use the molal specific volume, $v = V/n$. Let us take all data collected at a given absolute temperature T, calculate for each individual measurement the ratio pv/T, and plot these ratios as ordinates against the pressure p as abscissae. We shall use the mks system of units, in which pressure is

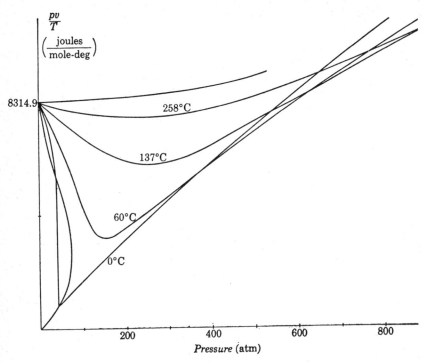

FIG. 2-1.   The limiting value of pv/T is independent of T.

expressed in newtons/meter² and molal specific volume in m³/kgm-mole. It is found experimentally that these ratios all lie on a smooth curve, whatever the temperature, but that the ratios at different temperatures lie on different curves.   The data for carbon dioxide are plotted in Fig. 2-1, for a number of different temperatures.   (The region in the lower left corner can be disregarded for the present.   It corresponds to values of pressure and temperature where the gas condenses to a liquid.)   The remarkable feature of these curves is (a) that they all converge to exactly the same point on the vertical axis, whatever the temperature, and (b) that the curves for all other gases converge to exactly the same point.   This limit of the ratio pv/T, common to all gases, is called the *universal gas constant* and is denoted by R.

In mks units,

$$R = 8.3149 \times 10^3 \text{ joules/kgm-mole-deg.} \qquad (2\text{-}1)$$

It follows that at low pressures we can write, for all gases,

$$pv/T = R, \quad pv = RT, \quad \text{or} \quad pV = nRT, \tag{2-2}$$

where R has the value above.

The numerical value of R depends, of course, upon the system of units employed. Chemists commonly express pressure in atmospheres, volume in liters, and use the gram-mole rather than the kilogram-mole. In this system,

$$R = 0.08206 \text{ liter-atm/gm-mole-deg.}$$

In cgs units, pressure is expressed in dynes/cm², volume in cm³, and the gram-mole is used. Then

$$R = 8.3149 \times 10^7 \text{ ergs/gm-mole-deg.}$$

At low pressures, the ratio pv/T has by experiment the same value R for all gases. It is convenient to postulate an *ideal gas* for which by definition the ratio pv/T is exactly equal to R at all pressures and temperatures. The equation of state of an ideal gas is therefore

$$\boxed{pv = RT,} \tag{2-3}$$

and for such a gas the curves in Fig. 2-1 all coalesce to a single horizontal straight line at a height R above the pressure axis. It follows from Eq. (2-3) that at "standard conditions," ($p = 1$ standard atmosphere $= 1.01325 \times 10^5$ n/m², $T = 273.16°$ K $= 0°$ C) the molal specific volume of an ideal gas is

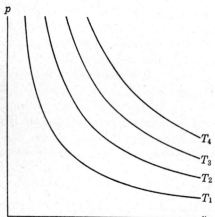

$$v = \frac{RT}{p}$$

$$= \frac{8.3149 \times 10^3 \times 273.16}{1.01325 \times 10^5}$$

$$= 22.4146 \text{ m}^3/\text{kgm-mole.}$$

At constant temperature, the product of pressure and specific volume of an ideal gas is constant. If we plot the pressure as a function of the volume, as in Fig. 2-2, we obtain at any given temperature a rectangular hyperbola, with different hyperbolas for different

FIG. 2-2.   Isotherms of an ideal gas.

temperatures. Real gases, of course, approximate to this behavior at low pressures, a fact that was discovered in 1660 by Robert Boyle and known as *Boyle's law.*

If the pressure is kept constant, the specific volume of an ideal gas increases linearly with temperature or, if the volume is constant, the pressure increases linearly with temperature. (The latter is a necessary consequence of our definitions of absolute temperature and of an ideal gas.) The fact that real gases approximate to this behavior has also been known for many years and is often referred to as the law of Charles and Gay-Lussac.

2-4 Other equations of state. Many equations have been proposed which describe the p-v-T relations of real gases more accurately than does the equation of state of an ideal gas. Some of these are frankly empirical while others are derived from assumptions regarding molecular properties. The Dutch physicist van der Waals, in 1873, derived the following equation:

$$\left(p + \frac{a}{v^2}\right)(v - b) = RT. \tag{2-4}$$

The quantities a and b are constants for any one gas but differ for different gases. Some values are listed in Table 2-1. We shall show in a later chapter that the term a/v^2 arises from the existence of intermolecular forces and that the term b is proportional to the volume occupied by the molecules themselves, but for the present we shall consider the equation as an empirical one.

TABLE 2-1.

Constants a and b in van der Waals equation. p in n/m², v in m³/kgm-mole, T in deg K, $R = 8.31 \times 10^3$ joules/kgm-mole-deg K.

Substance	a n-m⁴/(kgm-mole)²	b m³/kgm-mole
He	3.44×10^3	0.0234
H_2	24.8	.0266
O_2	138	.0318
CO_2	366	.0429
H_2O	580	.0319
Hg	292	.0055

$= N v_0$

good to $\pm 10\%$

It will be seen that at sufficiently large specific volumes the term a/v^2 becomes negligible in comparison with p and that b becomes negligible in comparison with v. The van der Waals equation then goes over into the equation of state of an ideal gas, which any equation of state must do at large specific volumes.

Another useful form of the equation of state of a real gas is

$$pv = A + \frac{B}{v} + \frac{C}{v^2} + \cdots, \tag{2-5}$$

where A, B, C, etc. are functions of the temperature and are called the *virial coefficients*. Theoretical derivations of the equation of state, based on an assumed law of force between the molecules of a gas, usually lead to an equation in virial form.

For an ideal gas, it is evident that $A = RT$ and that all other virial coefficients are zero.

The van der Waals equation can be put in virial form as follows. We first write it as

$$pv = RT \left(1 - \frac{b}{v}\right)^{-1} - \frac{a}{v}.$$

By the binomial theorem,

$$\left(1 - \frac{b}{v}\right)^{-1} = 1 + \frac{b}{v} + \frac{b^2}{v^2} + \cdots.$$

Hence

$$pv = RT + \frac{(RTb - a)}{v} + \frac{RTb^2}{v^2} + \cdots, \tag{2-6}$$

and for a van der Waals gas

$$A = RT, \quad B = RTb - a, \quad C = RTb^2, \text{ etc.}$$

The *Beattie-Bridgman equation*, which fits experimental data extremely well over a wide range of pressure, volume, and temperature, is a modified virial equation. This equation is

$$p = \frac{RT(1 - \epsilon)}{v^2} (v + B) - \frac{A}{v^2}, \tag{2-7}$$

where

$$A = A_0(1 - a/v), \quad B = B_0(1 - b/v), \quad \epsilon = c/vT^3,$$

and A_0, a, B_0, b, and c are constants having different values for different gases. A few are listed in Table 2-2.

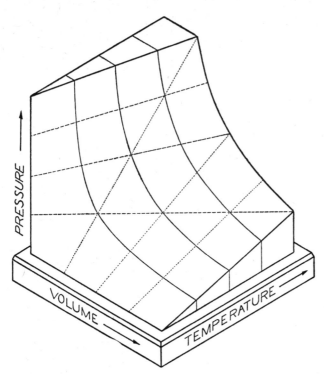

Fig. 2-3. p-v-T surface for an ideal gas.

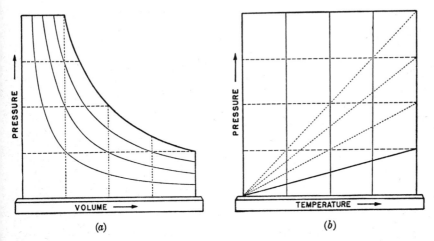

Fig. 2-4.   Projections of ideal gas p-v-T surface on (a) the p-v plane, (b) the p-T plane.

TABLE 2-2.

Constants in the Beattie-Bridgman equation of state. p in atm, v in liters/gm-mole, T in deg K, $R = 0.08206$ liter-atm/gm-mole-deg.

Gas	A_0	a	B_0	b	$10^{-4}c$
He	0.216	0.05984	0.01400	0.0	0.0040
H_2	0.1975	-0.00506	0.02096	-0.04359	0.0504
O_2	1.4911	$+0.02562$	0.04624	$+0.004208$	4.80
CO_2	5.0065	0.07132	0.10476	0.07235	66.00
NH_3	2.3930	0.17031	0.03415	0.19112	476.87

2-5 p-v-T surfaces. The equation of state is a relation between the three variables p, v, and T, and if these variables are plotted along three mutually perpendicular axes the equation defines a surface called the p-v-T surface. A portion of this surface for an ideal gas is shown in Fig. 2-3. Every possible equilibrium state of an ideal gas is represented by a point on its p-v-T surface and, similarly, every point on the surface represents a possible equilibrium state. A reversible process, i.e., a succession of equilibrium states, is represented by a line on the surface. The lines on the surface in Fig. 2-3 are the intersections with the surface of planes perpendicular to the three coordinate axes. The intersections with planes perpendicular to the temperature axis represent processes at constant temperature or *isothermal* processes. Intersections with planes perpendicular to the volume axis represent processes at constant volume or *isometric* processes, and intersections with planes perpendicular to the pressure axis represent processes at constant pressure or *isobaric* processes.

Figs. 2-4(a) and 2-4(b) are projections of the lines in Fig. 2-3 onto the p-v and p-T planes.

Fig. 2-5 is a diagram of a portion of the p-v-T surface of a van der Waals gas, and Fig. 2-6 is a projection of a number of isotherms onto the p-v plane. When expanded in powers of v, van der Waals' equation takes the form

$$pv^3 - (pb + RT)v^2 + av - ab = 0.$$

It is therefore a cubic in v and for given values of p and T has three roots, of which only one need be real. For low temperatures, such as that lettered T_1, three positive real roots exist over a certain range of

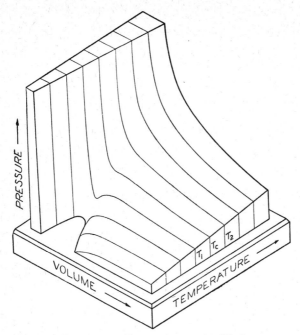

FIG. 2-5.   *p-v-T* surface for a van der Waals gas.

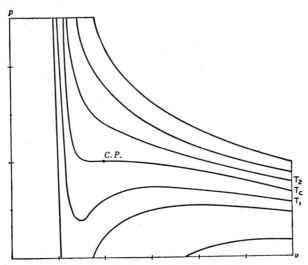

FIG. 2-6.   Isotherms of a van der Waals gas.

values of p. At pressures above and below this range two of the roots are imaginary and only one real root exists. As the temperature increases above T_1 the three real roots approach one another and at the temperature T_c they become equal. Above this temperature only one real root exists for all values of p.

We shall show later that the region in which the equation has three roots can be correlated with the range of values of p, v, and T at which real gases condense to the liquid phase.

Problems

1. The density of water in cgs units is 1 gm/cm³. Compute (a) the density in mks units, (b) the specific volume in m³/kgm, (c) the mks molal specific volume. (d) Make the same computations for air at standard conditions where the density in cgs units is 0.00129 gm/cm³. The mean molecular weight of air is 29, that is, the mass of 1 kgm-mole of air is 29 kgm.

2. The table below lists corresponding values of the pressure and specific volume of steam at the three temperatures of 700° F, 1150° F, and 1600° F. The ice-point temperature on the Fahrenheit absolute scale is 492° F abs. Pressures are in lb/in² abs and specific volumes in ft³/lb. Without converting to mks units, compute the ratio pv/T at each temperature and pressure, and for each temperature plot these ratios as a function of pressure. Estimate the extrapolated value of pv/T as p approaches zero, and find the value of R in joules/kgm-mole-deg K.

	$t = 700° F$	$t = 1150° F$	$t = 1600° F$
p	v	v	v
500	1.304	1.888	2.442
1000	0.608	0.918	1.215
2000	.249	.449	0.601
3000	.0984	.289	.397
4000	.0287	.209	.294
5000	.0268	.161	.233

3. At standard conditions, how many kilograms of air are there in a room measuring 10m × 10m × 3m? The mean molecular weight of air is 29, that is, the mass of 1 kgm-mole of air is 29 kgm. What is the weight of the air, in pounds?

4. Fig. 2-7 shows five processes, ab, bc, cd, da, and ac, plotted in the p-v plane for an ideal gas. Show the same processes (a) in the p-T plane, (b) in the T-v plane. (c) Locate four points of intersection of the lines on the p-v-T surface in Fig. 2-3 that correspond to a, b, c, and d in Fig. 2-7.

5. In Fig. 2-7, let $p_2 = 10 \times 10^5$ n/m², $p_1 = 4 \times 10^5$ n/m², $v_1 = 2.5$ m³/kgm-mole. Find (a) the temperature T; (b) the temperatures at points b and d; (c) the specific volume v_2; (d) the actual volume V at point a if the system consists of 4 kgm-moles of hydrogen; (e) the mass of gas if it is oxygen and if $V_1 = 5$ m³.

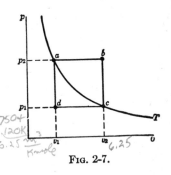

FIG. 2-7.

6. A tank of volume 0.5 m³ contains oxygen at an absolute pressure of 150 atm and a temperature of 20° C. Assume that oxygen behaves like an ideal gas. (a) How many kilogram-moles of oxygen are there in the tank? (b) How many kilograms? (c) How many pounds? (d) Find the pressure if the temperature is increased to 500° C. (e) At a temperature of 20° C, how many moles can be withdrawn from the tank before the pressure falls to 15 atm?

7. A cylinder provided with a movable piston contains an ideal gas at a pressure p_1, specific volume v_1, and temperature T_1. The pressure and volume are simultaneously increased so that at every instant p and v are related by the equation

$$p = kv,$$

where k is a constant. (a) Express the constant k in terms of the pressure p_1, the temperature T_1, and the gas constant R. (b) Construct the graph representing the process above in the p-v plane. (c) Find the temperature when the specific volume has doubled, if $T_1 = 200°$ K.

8. One standard atmosphere is defined as the pressure produced by a column of mercury exactly 76 cm high, at a temperature of 0° C, and at a point where $g = 980.665$ cm/sec². (a) Why do the temperature and the acceleration of gravity have to be specified in this definition? (b) Compute the pressure in n/m² produced by a column of mercury 76 cm in height, of density 13.6 gm/cm³, at a point where $g = 980$ cm/sec².

9. The U-tube in Fig. 2-8, of uniform cross section 1 cm², contains mercury to the depth shown. The barometric height is 75 cm of mercury. The left side of the tube is now closed at the top, and the right side is connected to a good vacuum pump. How far does the mercury level fall in the left side? The temperature remains constant.

10. The left side of the U-tube in Fig. 2-8 is closed at the top. (a) If the initial temperature is 300° K, find the temperature T at which the air column at the left is 60 cm long. The barometric height remains constant at 75 cm of mercury. (b) Sketch the isotherms at 300° K and at the temperature T, in the p-v plane, and show the curve representing the process through which the left side is carried as its temperature increases.

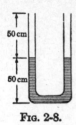

FIG. 2-8.

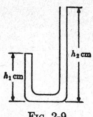

FIG. 2-9.

density × height = pres.

11. The J-shaped tube in Fig. 2-9, of uniform cross section, contains air at atmospheric pressure. The barometric height is h_0. Mercury is poured into the open end, trapping the air in the closed end. What is the height h of the mercury column in the closed end when the open end is filled with mercury? Assume that the temperature is constant and that air is an ideal gas. Neglect any effect of the curvature at the bottom. As a numerical example, let $h_0 = 75$ cm of mercury, $h_1 = 20$ cm, $h_2 = 200$ cm.   14.5 cm

12. (a) Estimate as accurately as you can from Fig. 2-1 the molal specific volume of CO_2 at a pressure of 300 atm and a temperature of 60° C. (b) At this pressure and temperature, how many moles of CO_2 are contained in a tank of volume 0.5 m³? (c) How many moles would the tank contain if CO_2 were an ideal gas?

13. A vessel contains CO_2 at a temperature of 137° C. The specific volume is 0.0700 liter/gm-mole = 0.0700 m³/kgm-mole. Compute the pressure in atmospheres, (a) from the ideal gas equation, (b) from the van der Waals equation, (c) from the Beattie-Bridgman equation. (d) Calculate the ratio pv/T, in joules/kgm-mole-deg K, for the three pressures found above, and compare with the experimental value as read from Fig. 2-1.

14. In all so-called diatomic gases, some of the molecules are dissociated into separate atoms, the fraction dissociated increasing with increasing temperature. The gas as a whole thus consists of a diatomic and a monatomic portion. Even though each component may act as an ideal gas, the mixture does not, because the number of moles varies with the temperature. The degree of dissociation δ of a diatomic gas is defined as the ratio of the mass m_1 of the monatomic portion to the total mass m of the system.

$$\delta = m_1/m.$$

(a) Show that the equation of state of the gas is

$$pV = (\delta + 1)(m/M_2)RT,$$

where M_2 is the molecular "weight" of the diatomic component. Assume that the gas obeys Dalton's law, i.e., the measured pressure p is the sum of the pressures each component would exert if it alone occupied the total volume V.

(b) The table below lists measured values of the ratio pV/m, for iodine vapor, at three different temperatures. Compute and show in a graph the degree of dissociation as a function of temperature.

$t(°C)$	800	1000	1200
$\dfrac{pV}{m}$, $\dfrac{\text{joules}}{\text{kgm}}$	3.72×10^4	5.08×10^4	7.30×10^4

CHAPTER 3

WORK

3-1 Work. The term work refers to an interchange of energy between a system and its surroundings. When the hot gases in the cylinders of an automobile engine push against the moving pistons, work is done by the gases. When air is forced into a bicycle tire by a pump, work is done on the air. The work may be mechanical, as in the examples above, or it may be electrical, magnetic, or of many other types. For the present we shall consider mechanical work only. While the work can always be expressed as $\int F \cos \theta \, ds$, in most cases of practical interest the work is associated with a change in volume, and it is more convenient to put the relation above in a different form.

Suppose that we have a system of arbitrary shape as in Fig. 3-1, acted upon by an external hydrostatic pressure p_e, and that the original boundary of the system, shown by full lines, is displaced outward against the external pressure to a new position shown by dotted lines. The external force dF exerted against a portion of the surface of area dA is

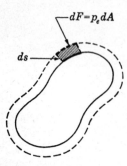

$$dF = p_e dA,$$

and if this portion moves out a distance ds the work done against the external force is

$$dW = dF ds = p_e dA ds.$$

Integration over the boundary surface gives

$$dW = p_e A ds,$$

where A is the total area of this surface.

But $A ds$ is the increase in volume of the system, dV, so the external work is

Fig. 3-1.

$$dW = p_e dV. \tag{3-1}$$

In this equation, dV is the change in volume of the *system* and p_e is the *external* pressure. The work is expressed in joules when p_e is in newtons/m² and dV is in m³.

If the process is *reversible*, then by definition the boundary walls are essentially in equilibrium at all instants and the *external* pressure p_e equals the *internal* pressure p. Under these conditions we can replace p_e by p in Eq. (3-1), and express p in terms of V and T by the equation of state of the system.

$$d'W = pdV. \qquad (3\text{-}2)$$

We write $d'W$ in this equation, rather than dW, to indicate that this quantity is not an exact differential. That is, while $d'W$ represents a small quantity of work, it is *not* the differential of a function W of the state of the system. The distinction between exact and inexact differentials is very important in thermodynamics and we shall consider it in more detail later.

The work $d'W$ is positive when work is done *by* a system *on* its surroundings. In such a case the volume of the system increases and dV is positive. When work is done *on* a system, the volume decreases, and dV and $d'W$ are negative.

When Eq. (3-2) is divided through by the mass m or the number of moles n of a system, the left side becomes the work done per unit mass or per mole, $d'w$, and the right side becomes pdv, the product of the pressure and the change in specific volume.

$$d'w = pdv. \qquad (3\text{-}3)$$

Any *reversible* process can be represented by a line in the p-v plane. This line is the projection onto the p-v plane of the line representing the process on the p-v-T surface. The work $d'w$ (per unit mass or per mole) done in a small (specific) volume change dv is represented graphically by the *area* of a narrow vertical strip such as the one shown shaded in Fig. 3-2. The total work w done in the finite increase in volume from state a to state b is

$$w = \int_{v_a}^{v_b} pdv, \qquad (3\text{-}4)$$

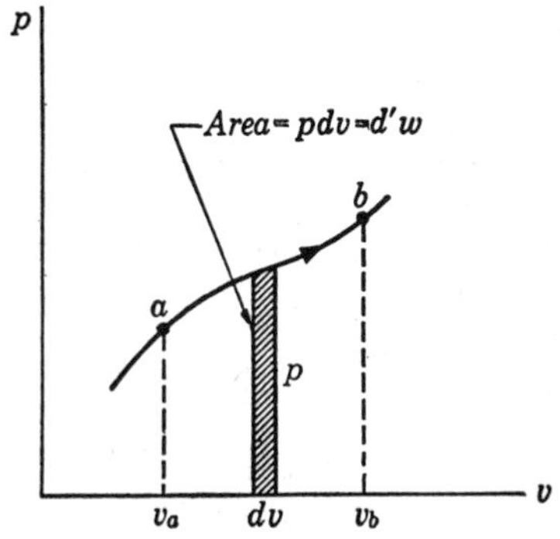

Fig. 3-2. Area represents work in a p-v diagram.

and this is evidently proportional to the area bounded by the curve representing the process, the volume axis, and the vertical lines at v_a and v_b. The work is positive if the process proceeds in the direction shown, i.e., from state a to state b. If the process proceeds in the opposite direction, work is done *on* the system and w is negative.

Cyclic processes play an important part in thermodynamics. A cyclic process is one in which a system goes through certain changes and returns to its initial state. Such a process is represented in the p-v plane in Fig. 3-3. The work done by the system is represented by the area shaded ▨, the work done *on* the system by the area shaded ▨. The *net* work done *by* the system evidently is proportional to the area bounded by the closed curve representing the process.

We next evaluate $\int pdv$ for a number of processes.

The work done in any *isometric* process is obviously zero, since in such a process $v = $ constant.

In an *isobaric* process the pressure is constant and the work is

$$w_p = p \int_{v_a}^{v_b} dv = p(v_b - v_a), \tag{3-5}$$

which evidently is the area of the shaded rectangle in Fig. 3-4. The subscript p means that the pressure is constant and calls attention to the fact that Eq. (3-5) applies to an isobaric process only.

Consider next an *isothermal* process, carried out at the constant temperature T. *If the system is an ideal gas,*

$$p = \frac{RT}{v}$$

and

$$w_T = \int_{v_a}^{v_b} \frac{RT}{v} dv = RT \ln \frac{v_b}{v_a}. \tag{3-6}$$

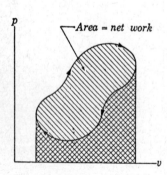

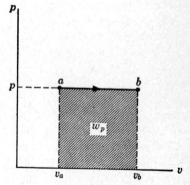

FIG. 3-3. The net work done in a cyclic process is represented by the area bounded by a closed curve in the p-v plane.

FIG. 3-4.

The work w_T is represented by the shaded area in Fig. 3-5. The subscript T implies that Eq. (3-6) holds for an isothermal process only. This equation can be put in a number of different forms with the help of the equation of state. Since T is constant it follows that

$$p_a v_a = p_b v_b = RT,$$

and hence

$$w_T = p_a v_a \ln \frac{v_b}{v_a} = RT \ln \frac{p_a}{p_b},$$

and so forth.

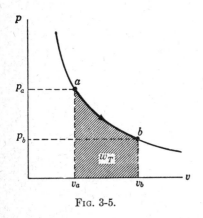
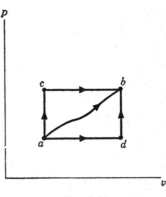

FIG. 3-5.   FIG. 3-6.

3-2 Work depends on the path. Obviously, there are an infinite number of different processes by which a system can be taken from a given initial state to a given final state. Three possible processes connecting states a and b are shown in Fig. 3-6. The work done *by* the system is greatest along the path *acb*, least along the path *adb*, and has some intermediate value along the third path. Conversely, if the processes are reversed in direction, the work done *on* the system is different along the three paths. It is therefore meaningless to speak of the "work in a system" or the "work of a system," in the way we can speak of the temperature, pressure, or volume of a system. Suppose we assigned some arbitrary value W_0 to the "work of a system" in some arbitrary state such as that represented by point b in Fig. 3-6. The "work" W in some other state would then equal that in the reference state plus the additional work done on the system in going to the second state. But the work done on the system depends on the particular process by which it is taken from the reference state to the second state and has no unique value. Hence the "work in the system" has no unique value either, and work is not a property of a system.

In mathematical language, we say that the quantity $d'W$ (or $d'w$) is not an exact differential. By definition, the integral of an exact differential is a function of the limits of integration only and is independent of the path. Obviously, this is not true of $\int d'W$. The symbol $d'W$ can only be interpreted to mean "a small quantity of work"; it does not mean "a small change in the value of W," since it is impossible to assign any unique value to W. To emphasize the point, the inexact differential is written $d'W$ or $d'w$.

3-3 Partial derivatives. In general, the pressure and temperature, as well as the volume, change in a process and it is sometimes more convenient to express the work in terms of pressure and temperature changes. Because of the functional relationship between pressure, volume, and temperature, expressed by the equation of state, one can make any arbitrary small changes in any two of the state variables but not in all three simultaneously, since the change in the third variable must be such that the values of the variables after the change still satisfy the equation of state. For example, in a system consisting of a fluid under pressure in a cylinder provided with a movable piston, one can change the volume by any arbitrary amount dV and at the same time change the temperature by any arbitrary amount dT. When this has been done, the pressure will be found to have changed by just such an amount dp that the new values of p, V, and T also satisfy the equation of state. We now show how the change in any one of the state variables can be expressed in terms of the changes in the other two.

The general form of the equation of state is

$$F(p, v, T) = 0,$$

or, if it is solved in turn for each of the state variables,

$$p = f_1(v, T),$$

$$v = f_2(T, p),$$

$$T = f_3(p, v). \tag{3-7}$$

For generality, suppose we have any three variables x, y, z, connected by a functional relation $F(x, y, z) = 0$. Any two of the variables can be considered independent. Let us solve the equation above for z, obtaining

$$z = f(x, y).$$

Then

$$dz = \frac{\partial f}{\partial x} dx + \frac{\partial f}{\partial y} dy$$

$$= \frac{\partial z}{\partial x} dx + \frac{\partial z}{\partial y} dy$$

$$= \left(\frac{\partial z}{\partial x}\right)_y dx + \left(\frac{\partial z}{\partial y}\right)_x dy. \tag{3-8}$$

The symbols $\frac{\partial f}{\partial x}$, $\frac{\partial z}{\partial x}$, and $\left(\frac{\partial z}{\partial x}\right)_y$ are different ways of writing the same thing, namely, the partial derivative of z or $f(x,y)$ with respect to x. This derivative is obtained in the ordinary way except that in taking it the other variable, y, is to be held constant. The first two notations are commonly used in mathematics and the third in thermodynamics. The subscript y indicates that y is to be kept constant in forming the derivative. It also indicates that z is a function of both x and y, which is obvious in this particular example but which has certain advantages in other instances to be discussed later.

The partial derivative of z with respect to x, when y is constant, is the rate of change of z with x at constant y. The first term on the right of Eq. (3-8) is the product of the rate of change of z with x at constant y, by the change dx in x, and is therefore equal to the change in z due to the change in x alone. Similarly, the second term on the right of Eq. (3-8) gives the change in z due to the change in y alone. The sum of these two changes equals the total change in z, or dz.

We next derive some useful relations between the partial derivatives of three variables satisfying the relation $F(x, y, z) = 0$. Suppose we solve for x and for y, obtaining

$$x = f_1(y, z), \quad y = f_2(x, z).$$

Then

$$dx = \left(\frac{\partial x}{\partial y}\right)_z dy + \left(\frac{\partial x}{\partial z}\right)_y dz,$$

$$dy = \left(\frac{\partial y}{\partial x}\right)_z dx + \left(\frac{\partial y}{\partial z}\right)_x dz.$$

Let us now eliminate dy between the latter two equations and collect the coefficients of dx and dz. The result is

$$\left[1 - \left(\frac{\partial x}{\partial y}\right)_z \left(\frac{\partial y}{\partial x}\right)_z\right] dx = \left[\left(\frac{\partial x}{\partial y}\right)_z \left(\frac{\partial y}{\partial z}\right)_x + \left(\frac{\partial x}{\partial z}\right)_y\right] dz.$$

But the changes dx and dz are independent, that is, we can assign any value to dz and any other value to dx. Suppose we let $dz = 0$, $dx \neq 0$. Then to satisfy the equation above we must have

$$1 - \left(\frac{\partial x}{\partial y}\right)_z \left(\frac{\partial y}{\partial x}\right)_z = 0,$$

or

$$\boxed{\left(\frac{\partial x}{\partial y}\right)_z = \frac{1}{(\partial y/\partial x)_z}.}$$
(3-9)

Similarly, since we can set $dx = 0$, $dz \neq 0$, it must be true that

$$\left(\frac{\partial x}{\partial y}\right)_z \left(\frac{\partial y}{\partial z}\right)_x + \left(\frac{\partial x}{\partial z}\right)_y = 0.$$
(3-10)

By combining Eqs. (3-9) and (3-10), the latter may be put in the more symmetrical cyclical form

$$\boxed{\left(\frac{\partial x}{\partial y}\right)_z \left(\frac{\partial y}{\partial z}\right)_x \left(\frac{\partial z}{\partial x}\right)_y = -1.}$$
(3-11)

We have shown in the preceding section that work cannot be expressed as a function of the state of a system. It follows that partial derivatives such as $(\partial w/\partial T)_p$ or $(\partial w/\partial p)_T$ have no meaning, since w cannot be expressed as a function of p and T. However, a ratio such as

$$\frac{d'w_T}{dp_T}$$

does have a meaning, since it is merely the ratio of the small quantity of work done in an isothermal process to the corresponding change in pressure.

Eqs. (3-9) and (3-11) are readily verified for an ideal gas. Let $x = p$, $y = v$, $z = T$. Then

$$\left(\frac{\partial z}{\partial x}\right)_y = \left(\frac{\partial T}{\partial p}\right)_v = \left[\frac{\partial}{\partial p}\left(\frac{pv}{R}\right)\right]_v = \frac{v}{R},$$

$$\left(\frac{\partial x}{\partial z}\right)_y = \left(\frac{\partial p}{\partial T}\right)_v = \left[\frac{\partial}{\partial T}\left(\frac{RT}{v}\right)\right]_v = \frac{R}{v},$$

in agreement with Eq. (3-9).
    Also,

$$\left(\frac{\partial x}{\partial y}\right)_z = \left(\frac{\partial p}{\partial v}\right)_T = \left[\frac{\partial}{\partial v}\left(\frac{RT}{v}\right)\right]_T = -\frac{RT}{v^2},$$

$$\left(\frac{\partial y}{\partial z}\right)_x = \left(\frac{\partial v}{\partial T}\right)_p = \left[\frac{\partial}{\partial T}\left(\frac{RT}{p}\right)\right]_p = \frac{R}{p},$$

and

$$\left(\frac{\partial p}{\partial v}\right)_T \left(\frac{\partial v}{\partial T}\right)_p \left(\frac{\partial T}{\partial p}\right)_v = \left(-\frac{RT}{v^2}\right)\left(\frac{R}{p}\right)\left(\frac{v}{R}\right) = -\frac{RT}{pv} = -1,$$

in agreement with Eq. (3-11).

The geometrical meaning of the three partial derivatives $\left(\frac{\partial p}{\partial v}\right)_T$, $\left(\frac{\partial p}{\partial T}\right)_v$, and $\left(\frac{\partial v}{\partial T}\right)_p$, is illustrated in Fig. 3-7. The diagram shows the intersection with the p-v-T surface of an ideal gas, of three planes perpendicular to the p, v, and T axes. The slopes of the lines of intersection, at point a, are equal to the three partial derivatives at point a. At other points the slopes are, in general, different. It will be seen that the partial derivatives represent properties of the *surface* (or better, of the substance for which the surface is constructed) and do not depend on any particular *process* the substance may undergo.

3-4 Coefficient of expansion and compressibility. Even if the equation of state of a substance is not known or cannot be expressed in any simple analytic form, the partial derivatives $(\partial v/\partial T)_p$ and $(\partial v/\partial p)_T$ can be found from tabulated properties of materials, namely, the coefficient of cubical expansion β and the compressibility κ.

The definition of the coefficient of cubical expansion given in elementary texts is

$$\bar{\beta} = \frac{V_2 - V_1}{V_1(T_2 - T_1)},$$

where V_2 and V_1 are the volumes of a specimen of the material at temperatures T_2 and T_1. $\bar{\beta}$ is the mean fractional increase in volume, per degree rise in temperature.

The *true* coefficient of volume expansion β, at any temperature T, is the limiting value of the expression above when the increase in temperature and the corresponding volume change become infinitesimal.

$$\beta = \frac{dV}{VdT} = \frac{1}{V}\frac{dV}{dT},$$

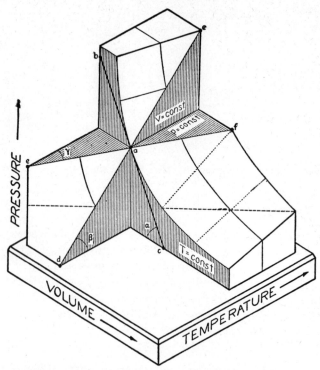

Fig. 3-7. Geometrical meaning of partial derivatives.
$(\partial p/\partial v)_T = -\tan \alpha$, $(\partial p/\partial T)_v = \tan \beta$, $(\partial v/\partial T)_p = \tan \gamma$.

where V is the volume at temperature T. The mks units of β are deg^{-1}. However, the volume of an object depends upon pressure as well as upon temperature and it is implied in the definition above that the pressure is to be kept constant. We should therefore write

$$\beta = \frac{1}{V}\frac{(dV)_p}{(dT)_p},$$

where the subscript p means that the pressure is kept constant during the changes in volume and temperature. But V is a function of T and p, and the ratio of a small change in volume to a small change in temperature, both at constant pressure, is the same thing as the partial derivative of V with respect to T at constant pressure. Hence

$$\frac{(dV)_p}{(dT)_p} = \left(\frac{\partial V}{\partial T}\right)_p$$

and

$$\beta = \frac{1}{V}\left(\frac{\partial V}{\partial T}\right)_p,$$

or, in terms of specific volumes,

$$\beta = \frac{1}{v}\left(\frac{\partial v}{\partial T}\right)_p,$$

$$\boxed{\left(\frac{\partial v}{\partial T}\right)_p = \beta v.}$$

(3-12)

It follows from Eq. (3-12) that the coefficient of cubical expansion of an ideal gas is

$$\beta = \frac{1}{v}\frac{R}{p} = \frac{1}{T}.$$

(3-13)

The van der Waals equation is a cubic in v but can be solved explicitly for p. Hence in computing β it is simplest to use Eqs. (3-9) and (3-11) and write

$$\left(\frac{\partial v}{\partial T}\right)_p = -\frac{\left(\frac{\partial p}{\partial T}\right)_v}{\left(\frac{\partial p}{\partial v}\right)_T}$$

Then, since

$$p = \frac{RT}{v - b} - \frac{a}{v^2},$$

we have

$$\left(\frac{\partial p}{\partial T}\right)_v = \frac{R}{v - b},$$

$$\left(\frac{\partial p}{\partial v}\right)_T = -\frac{RT}{(v - b)^2} + \frac{2a}{v^3},$$

and for a van der Waals gas,

$$\beta = \frac{1}{v}\left(\frac{\partial v}{\partial T}\right)_p = \frac{Rv^2(v - b)}{RTv^3 - 2a(v - b)^2}.$$

(3-14)

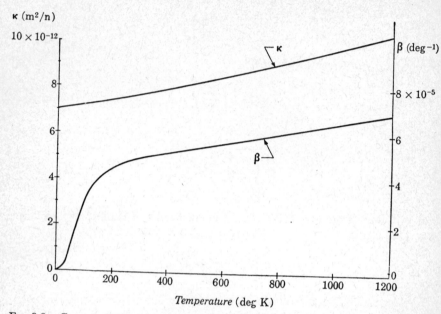

FIG. 3-8.   Compressibility κ and coefficient of cubical expansion β of copper, as functions of temperature at a constant pressure of 1 atm.

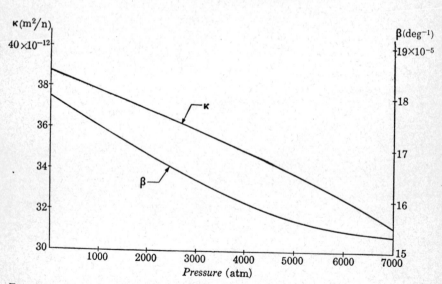

FIG. 3-9.   Compressibility κ and coefficient of cubical expansion β of mercury, as functions of pressure, at a constant temperature of 0° C.

Coefficients of expansion of solids and liquids cannot be computed from an equation of state, but can, of course, be measured experimentally. In elementary courses in physics a single value is usually listed for these coefficients but actually they vary widely with both temperature and pressure. Fig. 3-8 shows how the coefficient of cubical expansion of copper varies with temperature, over a range from 0° K to 1200° K. Fig. 3-9 shows the variation with pressure of the coefficient of cubical expansion of mercury, at a temperature of 0° C. Other metals show similar variations. Liquid water has a maximum density at 4° C, and in the range between 0° C and 4° C its coefficient of cubical expansion is negative, while at 4° C it is zero. Hence β is a function of temperature and pressure and may be positive, negative, or zero.

The mean compressibility of a material, $\bar{\kappa}$, is defined by the equation

$$\bar{\kappa} = -\frac{V_2 - V_1}{V_1(p_2 - p_1)},$$

where V_2 and V_1 are the volumes at pressures p_2 and p_1. The *true* compressibility κ is the limiting value of the expression above when the changes in pressure and volume become infinitesimal.

$$\kappa = -\frac{dV}{V\,dp} = -\frac{1}{V}\frac{dV}{dp}.$$

The negative sign is included in the definition of κ because an increase in pressure always results in a decrease in volume. Thus if dp is positive, dV is negative and κ is a positive quantity. The mks units of κ are $(newtons/m^2)^{-1}$.

The change in volume accompanying a change in pressure depends not only upon the pressure change, but also upon any change in temperature that may have occurred simultaneously. If the temperature is constant, the corresponding value of κ is called the *isothermal* compressibility and the derivative becomes the partial of V with respect to p at constant temperature.

$$\kappa = -\frac{1}{V}\left(\frac{\partial V}{\partial p}\right)_T,$$

or,

$$\kappa = -\frac{1}{v}\left(\frac{\partial v}{\partial p}\right)_T,$$

$$\boxed{\left(\frac{\partial v}{\partial p}\right)_T = -\kappa v.}$$
(3-15)

From Eq. (3-15), the compressibility of an ideal gas is

$$\kappa = -\frac{1}{v}\left(-\frac{RT}{p^2}\right) = \frac{1}{p},\qquad(3\text{-}16)$$

and that of a van der Waals gas is

$$\kappa = \frac{v^2(v-b)^2}{RTv^3 - 2a(v-b)^2}.\qquad(3\text{-}17)$$

The compressibilities of solids and liquids must be determined experimentally. The experimental techniques, which are not simple, are described in P. W. Bridgman's book, *The Physics of High Pressures*. Like the coefficient of expansion, the compressibility is a function of both temperature and pressure. The compressibility of copper over the temperature range from 0° K to 1200° K is plotted in Fig. 3-8, and that of mercury over a pressure range from 0 to 7000 atm is plotted in Fig. 3-9.

Let us now return to the question of computing the work done in a reversible volume change, in terms of the changes in pressure and temperature. We have

$$d'w = pdv = p\left[\left(\frac{\partial v}{\partial T}\right)_p dT + \left(\frac{\partial v}{\partial p}\right)_T dp\right]$$

$$= pv(\beta dT - \kappa dp).\qquad(3\text{-}18)$$

For an ideal gas, this reduces to

$$d'w = pdv = RdT - vdp,$$

a relation which could have been written down at once from the equation of state, since

$$pdv + vdp = RdT.$$

For a van der Waals gas, the expressions for β and κ may be substituted from Eqs. (3-14) and (3-17).

For solids and liquids, empirical equations expressing β and κ in terms of p and T must be inserted in Eq. (3-18). However, if the ranges of pressure and temperature are not too great, we may assume that β and κ are constant. Furthermore, since these quantities are very small for solids and liquids the volume will change but slightly and we may assume v constant also. With these approximations Eq. (3-18) can be integrated to find the work done in a finite process, but in carrying out the integration it must be remembered that $d'w$ is not an exact differential and that the work depends on the path and not merely on the end points.

As an example, suppose that a solid or liquid is taken from state 1 to state 2 in Fig. 3-10, first along path 1-3-2 and then along path 1-2, where for the latter path,

$$p = p_0 + aT.$$

Along path 1-3, $p = p_1 = $ const, $dp = 0$, and

$$w_{1-3} \approx p_1 v \beta \int_{T_1}^{T_2} dT \approx p_1 v \beta (T_2 - T_1). \tag{3-19}$$

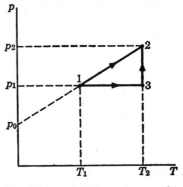

FIG. 3-10.   Work depends on path.

This is the general expression for the work done in any isobaric process by a system having the properties assumed above.

Along path 3-2, $T = $ const, $dT = 0$, and

$$w_{3-2} \approx -\kappa v \int_{p_1}^{p_2} p\,dp \approx \frac{\kappa v}{2}(p_1^2 - p_2^2). \tag{3-20}$$

This is the general expression for the work done in any isothermal process by a system having the properties assumed.

The total work along the path 1-3-2 is

$$w_{1-3-2} = w_{1-3} + w_{3-2} \approx \beta v p_1 (T_2 - T_1) - \frac{\kappa v}{2}(p_2^2 - p_1^2).$$

Along the direct path 1-2,

$$w_{1-2} \approx \beta v \int_{T_1}^{T_2}(p_0 + aT)dT - \kappa v \int_{p_1}^{p_2} p\,dp$$

$$\approx \beta v p_0 (T_2 - T_1) + \frac{\beta v a}{2}(T_2^2 - T_1^2) - \frac{\kappa v}{2}(p_2^2 - p_1^2).$$

Expressing the constants p_0 and a in terms of p_1, p_2, T_1, and T_2, this reduces to

$$w_{1-2} \approx \beta v \frac{p_1 + p_2}{2}(T_2 - T_1) - \frac{\kappa v}{2}(p_2^2 - p_1^2).$$

As another illustration of the usefulness of the relations between partial derivatives, as derived in Sec. 3-3, suppose we wish to find the increase in the pressure exerted by a solid or a liquid when it is heated but not allowed to expand. In elementary courses in physics this problem is solved by first computing the increase in volume, assuming the system free to expand, and then finding the pressure necessary to compress the system to its original volume. From the thermodynamic viewpoint, however, the quantity desired is the rate of increase of pressure with temperature at constant volume, or the partial derivative

$$\left(\frac{\partial p}{\partial T}\right)_v.$$

It follows from Eqs. (3-9) and (3-11) that

$$\left(\frac{\partial p}{\partial T}\right)_v = -\frac{(\partial v/\partial T)_p}{(\partial v/\partial p)_T},$$

or

$$\left(\frac{\partial p}{\partial T}\right)_v = -\frac{\beta v}{-\kappa v} = \frac{\beta}{\kappa}. \tag{3-21}$$

Then for a solid or a liquid, and to the degree of approximation to which the ratio β/κ can be considered constant, the increase in pressure $p_2 - p_1$, when the temperature is increased from T_1 to T_2 and the volume is kept constant, is

$$(p_2 - p_1)_v \approx \frac{\beta}{\kappa}(T_2 - T_1). \tag{3-22}$$

It is left for the reader to show that this is the same as the result obtained by the elementary method described above. Thus the methods of thermodynamics do not involve any new principles or physical concepts but they enable problems such as this to be handled in a more systematic manner and with greater "economy of thought."

Problems

1. Steam at a constant (absolute) pressure of 20 atm is admitted to the cylinder of a steam engine. The length of the stroke is 60 cm and the diameter of the cylinder is 20 cm. How much work in joules is done by the steam per stroke?

2. 1 kgm of water, when converted to steam at atmospheric pressure, occupies a volume of 1.67 m³. Compute the work done against atmospheric pressure.

3. 5 kgm of oxygen occupy a volume of 10 m³ at a temperature of 300° K. Find the work necessary to decrease the volume to 5 m³, (a) at constant pressure, (b) at constant temperature. (c) What is the temperature at the end of process (a)? (d) What is the pressure at the end of process (b)? (e) Show both processes in a p-V diagram.

4. An ideal gas originally at a temperature T_1 and pressure p_1 expands reversibly against a piston to a volume equal to twice its original volume. The temperature of the gas is varied during the expansion so that at each instant the relation $p = kV$ is satisfied, where k is a constant. (a) Draw a diagram of the process in the p-V plane. (b) Find the work done by the gas, in terms of n, R, T_1, and p_1.

$k - slope$?

$\dfrac{3nRT_1}{2}$

5. An ideal gas at an initial pressure p_1 and volume V_1 is heated at constant volume until the pressure is doubled, allowed to expand isothermally until the pressure drops to its original value, and then compressed at constant pressure until the volume returns to its initial value. (a) Sketch the process in the p-V plane and in the p-T plane. (b) Compute the net work done in the process, if $n = 2$ kgm-moles, $p_1 = 2$ atm, $V_1 = 4$ m^3.

6. Compute the work done by the expanding air in the left side of the U-tube in Problem 9, Chapter 2. Assume the process to be reversible.

7. Compute the work done by the expanding gas in the left side of the U-tube in Problem 10, Chapter 2. The process is reversible. Explain why the work is not merely that required to raise the center of gravity of the mercury.

8. (a) Derive the general expression for the work done per mole by a van der Waals gas in expanding reversibly and at a constant temperature T from a specific volume v_1 to a specific volume v_2. (b) Using the constants in Table 2-1, find the work done when 2 moles of steam expand from a volume of 30 m^3 to a volume of 60 m^3 at a temperature of 100° C. (c) Find the work done by an ideal gas in the same expansion.

9. The Clausius equation of state is

$\beta = (1/T)[1 - (b/v)]$

$$p(v - b) = RT.$$

$\kappa = (1/p)[1 - (b/v)]$

(a) Compute the coefficient of cubical expansion, and the compressibility, for a substance obeying this equation. (b) Show that if $a = 0$, the corresponding quantities for a van der Waals gas reduce to the expressions derived in (a).

10. The Dieterici equation of state is

a) $\beta = (1/T)[1 + (\frac{a}{v RT})]$

$$p(v - b)e^{a/vRT} = RT,$$

$[(\frac{1}{v-b}) - (\frac{a}{v^2 RT})]$

where a and b are constants, different for different gases. (a) Making use of the cyclic relation, Eq. (3-11), find the coefficient of cubical expansion of a substance obeying this equation. (b) At high temperatures and large specific volumes, all gases approximate ideal gases. Verify that for large values of T and v, the Dieterici equation and the expression for β derived in (a), both go over into the corresponding equations for an ideal gas.

11. Express the coefficient of cubical expansion and the compressibility, in terms of the density ρ and its partial derivatives.

12. A cylinder provided with a piston contains 1 m^3 of a fluid at a pressure of 1 atm and a temperature of 300° K. The pressure is increased reversibly to 100 atm and the temperature is kept constant. Find the work done on the system, (a) if the fluid is an ideal gas, (b) if it is a liquid of compressibility $5 \times 10^{-10}(\text{n/m}^2)^{-1}$, about equal to that of water. (c) Find the change in volume of each fluid.

where did they get this eq. of state

13. (a) Making use of the fact that

$$\frac{\partial^2 v}{\partial T \partial p} = \frac{\partial^2 v}{\partial p \partial T},$$

prove that

$$\left(\frac{\partial \beta}{\partial p}\right)_T = -\left(\frac{\partial \kappa}{\partial T}\right)_p.$$

(b) From Fig. 3-8, obtain a linear equation that gives approximately the relation between κ and T for copper, at a constant pressure of 1 atm. (c) Compute the rate of change of the coefficient of cubical expansion of copper with pressure, at constant temperature. (d) Read from Fig. 3-8 the coefficient of cubical expansion of copper at 1200° K and 1 atm, and compute the fractional change in its value when the pressure is increased to 1000 atm, the temperature being kept constant.

14. Compute the work done in compressing 1 liter ($= 10^{-3}$ m³) of mercury at a constant temperature of 0° C from a pressure of 1 atm to a pressure of 4000 atm, (a) assuming that κ is constant and equal to its value at atmospheric pressure, and (b) taking into account the variation of κ with pressure. See Fig. 3-9. (c) Justify the assumption that the volume may be considered constant by computing the fractional change in volume.

15. If mercury is heated and not allowed to expand, what temperature rise is necessary to produce a pressure of 4000 atm? An approximate calculation is sufficient, but state carefully any approximations you make.

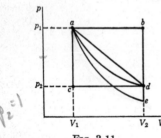

FIG. 3-11.

16. Fig. 3-11 applies to an ideal gas. At point a, $T = 300°$ K, $p_1 = 3$ atm, $V_1 = 8$ m³. The curve ad is an isotherm, and $V_2 = 24$ m³. Along the curve ae,

$$pV^{1.4} = \text{constant}.$$

(This curve is an adiabatic. See Sec. 5-7.)

(a) Find the temperature at points b, c, and e.

(b) Find the work done by the gas in the five processes abd, acd, aed, and the isothermal and linear processes ad.

CHAPTER 4

THE FIRST LAW OF THERMODYNAMICS

4-1 The first law of thermodynamics. The first law of thermodynamics is a statement of the principle of conservation of energy. In very general terms, it asserts that the net flow of energy across the boundary of a system is equal to the change in energy of the system. For the purposes of thermodynamics it is sufficient to consider only two types of energy flow across a boundary. One of these consists of work done on or by the system, discussed in the preceding chapter. The other is a flow of heat, either by conduction or radiation. (For reasons which are evident only in light of the second law, a flow of radiant energy can be classed as heat only if the frequency distribution is Planckian, that is, like that emitted by a blackbody or ideal radiator.)

In the days of the caloric theory of heat, before the universal validity of the principle of conservation of energy had been established, various units of "quantity of caloric" such as the gram-calorie and the Btu were defined. When it became evident, about the middle of the last century, that these were merely arbitrary units of energy, any justification for their continued use disappeared. Nevertheless much time and effort were devoted to precise measurements of the so-called "mechanical equivalent of heat." It is true that the experimental proof that a definite ratio existed between the joule and the gram-calorie played a large part in establishing the principle of conservation of energy, but we can now see that these measurements were exactly analogous to, say, determining the ratio of the British standard yard to the standard meter. The futility of maintaining these two standards of length was eventually recognized, and the legal yard is now, by definition, a certain fraction of the meter. Similarly, the Btu and the calorie are now defined as certain fractions of the joule and measurements of the "mechanical equivalent of heat" can now be recognized in their true light as determinations of the specific heat capacity of water.

In spite of the fact that the Btu and the calorie are anachronisms, they are still widely used both in engineering and in science, and their use will in all probability continue indefinitely. An understanding of the *principles* of thermodynamics, however, is hindered rather than helped by a superfluity of units of quantities of the same physical nature, and we shall therefore (except in some of the problems) use the mks energy unit, the joule, for energy in any form, including that flowing across the boundary of a system by conduction or radiation. To distinguish this type of energy transfer from work, we shall speak of it as "a flow of heat," and represent the energy thus transferred by the symbol Q (or $d'Q$ if the quantity is infinitesimal), but both Q and W will be expressed in joules.

From the principle of conservation of energy, whenever there is any net transfer of energy inward across the boundary of a system, the energy of the system increases by an amount just equal to the net energy transferred. If U_1 represents the energy of the system at the start of a process, U_2 its energy at the end of the process, Q the net heat flowing *into* the system during the process, and W the net work done *by* the system during the process, then the increase in the energy of the system, $U_2 - U_1$, equals the difference between Q and W, or,

$$U_2 - U_1 = Q - W. \qquad (4\text{-}1)$$

This equation is one form of the *first law of thermodynamics*. We call U the *internal energy* of the system.

To state the law as we have done above assumes that the internal energy is a function of the state of the system only. (It may be recalled at this point that "state" implies "state of thermodynamic equilibrium.") That is, the fact that we write the energy in state 1 as U_1 and the energy in state 2 as U_2 carries the implication that the system *has* a definite internal energy in a definite state, and carries also the further implication that the change in energy, $U_2 - U_1$, depends only on the end states and not at all on the process by which the system is taken from one state to the other. The entire structure of the science of thermodynamics is consistent with this assumption. Hence in a process whose end states differ only infinitesimally, the change in internal energy can be written as dU, that is, as the differential of a function of the state of the system.

4-2 Heat depends on the path. We have shown that the work W may be very different when a given system is taken by different processes from one state to another. Since the change in internal energy is independent of the process, it follows that the heat Q is different for different processes also and that as a consequence Q is *not* a function of the state of the system and it is meaningless to speak of the "heat in a system," or the "heat of a system." Suppose some arbitrary reference state is selected, such as one at absolute zero, and we say that the "heat in the system" is zero in this state. Then the "heat in the system" in any other state would be the heat flowing into the system when it is brought from absolute zero to this state.   But the heat is different for every different process by which the system is brought from the reference state and so no unique value can be assigned to the "heat in a system."   It is for this reason that we have written $d'Q$, rather than dQ, to represent an infinitesimal quantity of heat flowing into a system.   The symbol $d'Q$, like $d'W$, is an inexact differential. It cannot be interpreted as "a small change in Q" since a function Q cannot be uniquely defined.   Similarly, partial derivatives such as $(\partial Q/\partial p)_T$ have no meaning.   However, a ratio such as

$$\frac{(d'Q)_T}{(dp)_T}$$

does have a meaning, since it is merely the ratio of a small quantity of heat flowing into a system in an isothermal process, to the corresponding change in pressure.

It follows from the preceding discussion that for an infinitesimal process the first law becomes

$$dU = d'Q - d'W. \tag{4-2}$$

That is, although $d'Q$ and $d'W$ are both inexact differentials, their difference dU is an exact differential.

When both sides of the equation above are divided by the mass or the number of moles of a system, we get

$$du = d'q - d'w. \tag{4-3}$$

One more aspect of the first law should be mentioned at this point. When a system is carried through a cyclic process (not necessarily reversible) $U_2 = U_1$ and $Q = W$.   That is, the net heat flowing into the system equals the net work done by the system.   This means that it is impossible to construct a machine operating in cycles which, in any number of complete cycles, will put out more energy in the form of work than is absorbed in the form of heat.   A machine which *would* do this is called a *perpetual motion machine of the first kind* (see Chapter 7 for a discussion of perpetual motion machines of the second kind).   The first law is sometimes stated, "A perpetual motion machine of the first kind is impossible."   The experimental fact that no one has ever constructed such a machine is one justification of the assumption made at the beginning of the chapter that the internal energy of a system is a function of its state only and not of its past history.

It is important to note that *the internal energy of a system cannot be identified with either work or heat.* The terms heat and work are used only in connection with a *flow* or *interchange* of energy between a system and its surroundings. Consider two possible methods of increasing the temperature of a resistor. We could surround it with a thermal insulator such as rock wool so as to eliminate any flow of heat from it (or at least to reduce the flow to negligible proportions), and raise its temperature by the input of a certain amount of electrical energy. Or, with the resistor disconnected from the power line, we could produce exactly the same rise in temperature by placing the resistor in a gas flame. In the first process the change in state was brought about by doing work W; in the second, by a flow of heat Q. The end state of the resistor is exactly the same in both processes and it is meaningless to assert that as a result of the first process the resistor contains more "work," while at the end of the second process it contains more "heat." What it does contain is more *energy* and we say that the increase in its internal energy is the same in both processes if its initial and final states are the same in both.

4-3 Heat capacity. In any process in which the state of a system does not change, the net heat Q flowing into the system equals the net work W done by the system, or, the net heat flowing out of the system equals the net work done on the system. Now the most precise experimental measurements of work or energy can be made if the energy is electrical. We therefore take as our system a resistor, in which there is a current I and across the terminals of which there is a potential difference V. In a time interval $t_2 - t_1$, the electrical work "flowing" into the resistor is given by

$$W = \int_{t_1}^{t_2} IV dt, \qquad (4\text{-}4)$$

and this work can be measured with a high degree of precision. To speak of work as "flowing" into the resistor is not as peculiar as it might seem. According to electromagnetic theory, energy flows into the resistor across its surface at a rate given by $E \times H$ (the Poynting vector) per unit of area.

If the resistor is kept at constant temperature by a fluid flowing over it, and if its other thermodynamic coordinates do not change, then $U_2 = U_1$ and the quantity of heat flowing out of the resistor is just equal to the electrical energy supplied to it. But the heat flowing out of the resistor equals the heat flowing into the fluid, so the latter can be very precisely

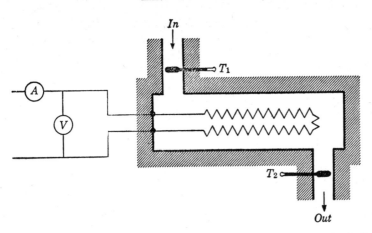

FIG. 4-1. Continuous flow method for determining heat capacity of a fluid.

determined. The method above, or some modification of it, is now almost invariably used in precision methods of measuring heat flow.

Fig. 4-1 is a schematic diagram of an apparatus known as a continuous flow calorimeter, with which the experiment described above can be performed. The rate of flow of fluid through the calorimeter and the temperature T_1 at which it enters, are kept constant. The current in the resistor is turned on and eventually a steady state is reached in which the temperature T_2 of the fluid as it leaves the calorimeter no longer changes with time. Let m represent the mass of fluid flowing through the apparatus in the time interval $t_2 - t_1$, after the steady state has been established. The heat Q that has flowed into the fluid is equal to the work W done on the resistor, as computed from Eq. (4-4). We now define the *mean heat capacity* of the mass m of fluid, over the temperature range $T_2 - T_1$, by the equation

$$\bar{C} = \frac{Q}{T_2 - T_1}. \tag{4-5}$$

In mks units, heat capacity is expressed in joules/deg.

The *true* heat capacity C, at any temperature T, is defined as the limit of the ratio above, when the temperature increases from T to $T + dT$ and the corresponding flow of heat is $d'Q$.

$$C = \frac{d'Q}{dT}. \tag{4-6}$$

The true heat capacity is a function of temperature. That is, if a number of experiments are performed in which equal quantities of heat are supplied to the same mass of fluid originally at different temperatures, the increases in temperature are different for different initial temperatures.

Both the mean and true heat capacities of a system depend on the nature of the process during which heat flows into the system. We shall return to this question in Sec. 4-5.

Heat capacities of solids cannot of course be determined by a continuous flow calorimeter. They can be measured (and those of liquids and gases also) by embedding a resistor in a sample of the material under investigation, supplying a measured quantity of energy to the resistor, and measuring the temperature rise of the sample. In such an experiment the temperature of the resistor increases along with that of the sample so that its internal energy does not remain constant and the heat flowing out of it into the sample is not exactly equal to the electrical work done on it. The difference, however, can be made negligibly small or a correction can be made for it.

In either method of measuring heat capacity, precautions must be taken that the sample exchanges heat only with the resistor, or if not, that any "leakage" is corrected for. Thus the apparatus may be surrounded by a thick layer of heat insulating material, or suspended in a vacuum, or surrounded by a jacket whose temperature is independently controlled so as to be at all times equal to that of the sample.

Once the heat capacity of a system has been determined experimentally as described above, the heat flowing from this system to any other can be computed by measuring the change in temperature of the first system. Thus if a cylinder containing a gas is immersed in a tank of water, and the gas is compressed or expanded, the heat flowing into or out of the gas can be determined from the heat capacity of the water and its change in temperature. The larger the heat capacity, the smaller the change in temperature, and by making the heat capacity very large indeed, the temperature change can be made as small as we please. A system of very large heat capacity is referred to as a *heat reservoir*, with the implication that any quantity of heat desired can be withdrawn from it or added to it without appreciable temperature change. Thus any reversible process carried out by a system in contact with a heat reservoir is isothermal.

4-4 Specific heat capacity. The heat capacity C is a property of a *system*. To obtain a quantity characteristic of a *substance*, and which does not depend on how much of a substance one considers, we define the *specific heat capacity* c of a substance as the ratio of the true heat capacity of a system composed of that substance, to the mass of the system.

$$c = \frac{C}{m}.$$

From the definition of C, and defining $d'q$ as $d'Q/m$, we can also write

$$c = \frac{d'Q}{mdT} = \frac{d'q}{dT}. \tag{4-7}$$

The true molar specific heat capacity is defined as

$$c = \frac{C}{n} = \frac{d'Q}{ndT} = \frac{d'q}{dT}. \tag{4-8}$$

In what follows, we shall omit the word "true" with the understanding that it is always implied unless otherwise stated. Specific heat capacities are expressed, in the mks system, in joules/kgm-deg or joules/mole-deg.

The total quantity of heat Q flowing into a system when its temperature increases from T_1 to T_2 is

$$Q = \int d'Q = \int_{T_1}^{T_2} CdT.$$

If the system is composed of a homogeneous substance of mass m and specific heat capacity c,

$$Q = m \int d'q = m \int_{T_1}^{T_2} cdT.$$

The specific heat capacity of a substance is defined as the ratio of the heat $d'q$ flowing into the substance, per unit mass or per mole, to the rise in temperature dT. To state only the temperature increase in a process, however, does not completely define the process. For example, if a system is under a constant external hydrostatic pressure it will, in general, increase in volume as its temperature increases. If it is enclosed in a rigid container its volume remains constant but its pressure increases, and in general the pressure may be caused to vary in any arbitrary way during the process. A few possibilities are shown in Fig. 4-2, which is drawn for an ideal gas, although the same principles apply to any substance whatever. The initial state of the system is represented by point a, and the lines ab, ac, ad, and ae represent four different processes in which the temperature of the system is increased by the same amount, from T to $T + dT$. One finds experimentally that the heat $d'q$ supplied to the system is different in each of these processes and hence *the specific heat capacity*

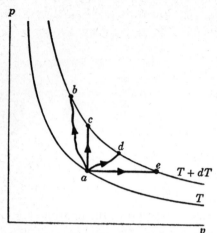

FIG. 4-2. Heat depends on the path.

$c = d'q/dT$ is different in each process. Since there are obviously an infinite number of different processes by which the system could go from a state at temperature T to another state at temperature $T + dT$, it follows that a substance has an infinite number of specific heat capacities. As we shall show later, these range from $+\infty$ to $-\infty$.

Most measurements of specific heat capacity are made with a system subjected to a constant hydrostatic pressure, as in process ae in Fig. 4-2. This will be atmospheric pressure if the system is in the open, or the measurements may be made in a pressure chamber at pressures greater or less than atmospheric. The specific heat capacity obtained under these conditions is called the specific heat capacity at constant pressure, and is represented by c_p. The value of c_p depends, in general, on the pressure as well as the temperature.

If a system is kept at constant volume while heat is supplied to it, the corresponding value of c is called the specific heat capacity at constant volume and is represented by c_v. Because of the large stresses set up when a solid or a liquid is heated and not allowed to expand, direct experimental determinations of c_v for a solid or a liquid are difficult, and c_p is the quantity generally measured. However, as we shall show later, if c_p is known, the value of c for any other process can be calculated if we know in addition the coefficient of cubical expansion and the compressibility. It is therefore unnecessary to measure c for all possible processes.

Fig. 4-3 shows the variation with temperature of the molar specific heat capacities c_p and c_v for copper, at a constant pressure of 1 atm. At low temperatures the two are nearly equal, and near absolute zero both decrease rapidly to zero. This behavior is characteristic of most solid substances, although the temperature at which the sharp drop occurs varies widely from one substance to another. At high temperatures c_p continues to increase while c_v becomes nearly constant and equal to about 25×10^3 joules/mole-deg or 6 cal/gm-mole-deg. It is found that this same value of c_v is approached by many solids at high temperatures, and it is called the Dulong and Petit value, after the men who first discovered this fact. Although there seems to be little connection between the heat capacity

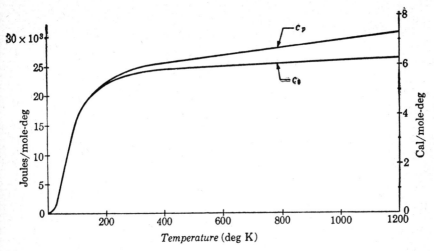

FIG. 4-3. c_p and c_v for copper, as functions of temperature at a constant pressure of 1 atm.

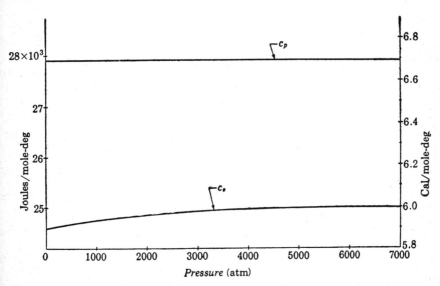

FIG. 4-4. c_p and c_v for mercury, as functions of pressure at a constant temperature of 0° C.

of solids and the properties of gases at low pressure, it will be recalled that the gas constant R equals 8.31×10^3 joules/mole-deg, and 25×10^3 joules/mole-deg is almost exactly 3 times this. We shall show later that on theoretical grounds a value of $3R$ is to be expected for c_v for solids at high temperatures.

Fig. 4-4 shows the change with pressure of c_p and c_v for mercury, at constant temperature. The curves are typical of most substances. The pressure variation is relatively much smaller than the temperature variation.

Some values of c_p and c_v for gases, also expressed in terms of R, are given in Table 12-3, for temperatures near room temperature. It will be noted that for monatomic gases $c_p \approx \frac{5}{2}R$, $c_v \approx \frac{3}{2}R$, and for diatomic gases, $c_p \approx \frac{7}{2}R$, $c_v \approx \frac{5}{2}R$.

4-5 More relations between partial derivatives. The (specific) internal energy of a system, u, is one of a number of quantities of importance in thermodynamics which are functions of the state of a system. Specifically, if the system can be completely specified by the three state variables p, v, and T, then u is a function of these variables. But the equation of state imposes a certain relation between the state variables, so that the state can be specified by values of any two of the variables. Hence *the internal energy can be expressed as a function of any two of the state variables,* and in general it is a *different* function of each pair of variables.

As a specific example, let the equation of state be that of an ideal gas, $pv = RT$, and consider a function of the state of the system, given by

$$aT + bv,$$

where a and b are constants. Making use of the equation of state, we have

$$aT + bv = aT + \frac{bRT}{p} = \frac{apv}{R} + bv.$$

The first of these expressions is an explicit function of T and v, the second is a function of T and p, and the third is a function of p and v. The forms of the functions are all different, although of course each has the same value for any given set of values of p, v, and T.

In mathematics, the three functions would ordinarily be distinguished by *different* symbols and we would write, say,

$$X_1 = aT + bv,$$

$$X_2 = aT + \frac{bRT}{p},$$

$$X_3 = \frac{apv}{R} + bv. \tag{4-9}$$

In thermodynamics, it is customary to use the *same* symbol for each function, regardless of the variables in terms of which it is expressed, and we write

$$x = aT + bv,$$

$$x = aT + \frac{bRT}{p},$$

$$x = \frac{apv}{R} + bv.$$

In mathematics, the six partial derivatives of the three functions are written

$$\frac{\partial X_1}{\partial T}, \quad \frac{\partial X_1}{\partial v}, \quad \frac{\partial X_2}{\partial T}, \quad \frac{\partial X_2}{\partial p}, \quad \frac{\partial X_3}{\partial p}, \quad \frac{\partial X_3}{\partial v}.$$

To carry out these differentiations, say to obtain $\partial X_1/\partial T$, we look at the definition of X_1, observe that it is a function of T and v, realize that v is to be kept constant, and obtain

$$\frac{\partial X_1}{\partial T} = \frac{\partial}{\partial T}(aT + bv) = a.$$

The derivative $\partial X_2/\partial T$, on the other hand, is

$$\frac{\partial X_2}{\partial T} = \frac{\partial}{\partial T}\left(aT + \frac{bRT}{p}\right) = a + \frac{bR}{p}.$$

There is no ambiguity as to the different meanings of $\partial X_1/\partial T$ and $\partial X_2/\partial T$, since X_1 and X_2 are explicitly defined in Eqs. (4-9) as different functions of different pairs of variables. On the other hand, to write merely $\partial x/\partial T$ does not indicate which of the partial derivatives above is meant, since the same symbol x is used for the function expressed in terms of any pair of variables. It is here that the thermodynamic notation,

$$\left(\frac{\partial x}{\partial T}\right)_v, \quad \left(\frac{\partial x}{\partial T}\right)_p, \quad \text{etc.,}$$

serves its most-useful purpose, since it is evident that the first implies that x is to be expressed as a function of T and v, and the second that x is expressed as a function of T and p. The mathematical notation,

X_1, X_2, etc., does not give this information directly unless some convention is adopted for the order in which pairs of variables are to be selected. Thus $(\partial x/\partial T)_v$ indicates both that (a) x is to be expressed as a function of T and v (in other words, $x = X_1$) and (b) that we are to differentiate, keeping v constant. On the other hand, $(\partial x/\partial T)_p$ means that (a) x is to be expressed as a function of T and p (that is, $x = X_2$) and (b) that we are to differentiate, keeping p constant. Of course,

$$\left(\frac{\partial x}{\partial T}\right)_v = a = \frac{\partial X_1}{\partial T},$$

$$\left(\frac{\partial x}{\partial T}\right)_p = a + \frac{bR}{p} = \frac{\partial X_2}{\partial T}.$$

In thermodynamics, the six partial derivatives of x are written,

$$\left(\frac{\partial x}{\partial T}\right)_v, \quad \left(\frac{\partial x}{\partial v}\right)_T, \quad \left(\frac{\partial x}{\partial T}\right)_p, \quad \left(\frac{\partial x}{\partial p}\right)_T, \quad \left(\frac{\partial x}{\partial p}\right)_v, \quad \left(\frac{\partial x}{\partial v}\right)_p.$$

We now derive some useful relations between these partial derivatives and the partial derivatives of the state variables with respect to one another. If we consider x expressed as a function of T and v, then

$$dx = \left(\frac{\partial x}{\partial T}\right)_v dT + \left(\frac{\partial x}{\partial v}\right)_T dv.$$

But since T is a function of p and v,

$$dT = \left(\frac{\partial T}{\partial p}\right)_v dp + \left(\frac{\partial T}{\partial v}\right)_p dv.$$

Substituting this expression for dT in the preceding equation gives

$$dx = \left[\left(\frac{\partial x}{\partial T}\right)_v \left(\frac{\partial T}{\partial p}\right)_v\right] dp + \left[\left(\frac{\partial x}{\partial T}\right)_v \left(\frac{\partial T}{\partial v}\right)_p + \left(\frac{\partial x}{\partial v}\right)_T\right] dv.$$

On the other hand, if we consider x expressed as a function of p and v then

$$dx = \left(\frac{\partial x}{\partial p}\right)_v dp + \left(\frac{\partial x}{\partial v}\right)_p dv.$$

The differentials dp and dv are independent, and the two preceding equations can always be satisfied only if the coefficients of dp and dv are equal. Hence

$$\left(\frac{\partial x}{\partial p}\right)_v = \left(\frac{\partial x}{\partial T}\right)_v \left(\frac{\partial T}{\partial p}\right)_v, \tag{4-10}$$

$$\left(\frac{\partial x}{\partial v}\right)_p = \left(\frac{\partial x}{\partial T}\right)_v \left(\frac{\partial T}{\partial v}\right)_p + \left(\frac{\partial x}{\partial v}\right)_T. \qquad (4\text{-}11)$$

Had we started with x as a function of T and p, we would have obtained

$$\left(\frac{\partial x}{\partial p}\right)_v = \left(\frac{\partial x}{\partial T}\right)_p \left(\frac{\partial T}{\partial p}\right)_v + \left(\frac{\partial x}{\partial p}\right)_T. \qquad (4\text{-}12)$$

Eqs. (4-10) and (4-12) are special cases of two alternate expressions for the partial derivative of any function of the state of the system, with respect to any one of the state variables with any other state variable constant. To put these in general form let us change the notation and let x, y, and z represent the state variables while w (not to be confused with work) represents any function of the state of the system. Then

$$\boxed{\left(\frac{\partial w}{\partial x}\right)_y = \left(\frac{\partial w}{\partial z}\right)_y \left(\frac{\partial z}{\partial x}\right)_y,} \qquad (4\text{-}13)$$

$$\boxed{\left(\frac{\partial w}{\partial x}\right)_y = \left(\frac{\partial w}{\partial z}\right)_x \left(\frac{\partial z}{\partial x}\right)_y + \left(\frac{\partial w}{\partial x}\right)_z.} \qquad (4\text{-}14)$$

Problems

1. An inventor claims to have developed an engine which takes in 100,000 Btu from its fuel supply, rejects 25,000 Btu in the exhaust, and delivers 25 kilowatt-hours of mechanical work. Do you advise investing money to put this engine on the market? *No*

2. When a system is taken from state a to state b, in Fig. 3-6, along the path acb, 80 joules of heat flow into the system, and the system does 30 joules of work. (a) How much heat flows into the system along path adb, if the work done is 10 joules? (b) The system is returned from state b to state a along the curved path. The work done on the system is 20 joules. Does the system absorb or liberate heat and how much? (c) If $U_a = 0$, $U_d = 40$ j, find the heat absorbed in the processes ad and db. *a) 60 j, b) 70 j liberated, c) Q_{ad}: 50 j, $Q_{db} = 10$ j*

3. The true molar specific heat capacity c_p of most substances (except at very low temperatures) can be satisfactorily expressed by the empirical formula

$$c_p = a + 2bT - cT^{-2},$$

where a, b, and c are constants and T is the Kelvin temperature. (a) In terms of a, b, and c, find the heat required to raise the temperature of n moles of the substance at constant pressure from T_1 to T_2. (b) Find the mean specific heat capacity between T_1 and T_2. (c) For magnesium, the numerical values of the constants are $a = 25.7 \times 10^3$, $b = 3.13$, $c = 3.27 \times 10^8$, when c_p is in joules/kgm-mole-deg K. Find the true specific heat capacity of magnesium at $300°$ K, and the mean specific heat capacity between $300°$ K and $500°$ K.

a) $Q = m[a(T_2 - T_1) + b(T_2^2 - T_1^2) + c(\frac{1}{T_2} - \frac{1}{T_1})]$

b) $c_p = a + b(T_2 + T_1) - \frac{c}{T_1 T_2}$,   c) $c_p = 24 \times 10^3$

$c_p = 24.1 \times 10^3$

4. At very low temperatures the true molar specific heat capacity at constant volume of rock salt, NaCl, varies with temperature as follows:

$$c_v = k(T/\theta)^3,$$

a relation known as Debye's law. The quantity k is a constant equal to 19.4×10^5 joules/kgm-mole-deg and θ is the "characteristic temperature," equal to 281° K for NaCl.

What is the true molar specific heat capacity at constant volume of NaCl (a) at 10° K, (b) at 50° K? (c) How much heat is required to raise the temperature of 2 moles of rock salt from 10° K to 50° K, at constant volume? (d) What is the mean specific heat capacity at constant volume over this temperature range?

5. The *Handbook of Chemistry and Physics* lists the following values of the specific heat capacity of aluminum at constant pressure:

$t(°C)$	c_p(cal/gm-deg)
−240.6	0.0092
−233	0.0165
−190	0.0889
−190 to −82	0.1466
−76 to −1	0.1962
17 to 100	0.217
15 to 435	0.236
500	0.274

From these values, construct a graph of c_p as a function of temperature, and estimate the number of calories required to raise the temperature of 1 gram of aluminum at constant pressure from 0° K to 800° K.

6. Electrical energy is supplied to a thermally insulated resistor at the constant rate of P watts, and the temperature T of the resistor is measured as a function of time τ. (a) Derive an expression for the true heat capacity of the resistor in terms of the slope of the temperature-time graph. (b) By means of a heating coil, heat is supplied at a constant rate of 31.2 watts to a block of cadmium of mass 500 gm. The temperature is recorded at certain intervals as follows:

τ (sec)	0	15	45	105	165	225	285	345	405	465	525
T (°K)	34	45	57	80	100	118	137	155	172	191	208

Construct a graph of T vs τ, and measure the slopes at a sufficient number of points to plot a graph of the true molar specific heat capacity of cadmium, at constant pressure, as a function of temperature. The atomic weight of cadmium is 112.

CHAPTER 5

SOME CONSEQUENCES OF THE FIRST LAW

5-1 The energy equation. The energy equation of a system is the relation expressing the internal energy u in terms of the state variables. This equation cannot be derived analytically from the equation of state of the system, but experimental measurements of heat capacity must be made in addition to collecting p-v-T data. From this information, the partial derivatives of u with respect to other variables can be determined and the energy equation can then be found by integration. We now show how the partial derivatives of u can be expressed in terms of specific heat capacities, together with the state variables and their partial derivatives. In order to proceed systematically, we consider each pair of state variables in turn as independent, and derive the relations referred to above and a number of other important equations as well.

5-2 T and v independent. Let us consider the specific internal energy of a system to be expressed in terms of T and v. Then

$$du = \left(\frac{\partial u}{\partial T}\right)_v dT + \left(\frac{\partial u}{\partial v}\right)_T dv. \tag{5-1}$$

If we consider only systems for which $d'w = pdv$, the first law, Eq. (4-3), can be written

$$d'q = \left(\frac{\partial u}{\partial T}\right)_v dT + \left[p + \left(\frac{\partial u}{\partial v}\right)_T\right] dv. \tag{5-2}$$

This equation is perfectly general, applying to any substance whatever and to any reversible process. For a process at constant volume,

$$dv = 0, \quad d'q_v = c_v dT_v.$$

Hence

$$c_v dT_v = \left(\frac{\partial u}{\partial T}\right)_v dT_v,$$

and

$$c_v = \left(\frac{\partial u}{\partial T}\right)_v. \tag{5-3}$$

Thus an experimental measurement of c_v gives the rate of change of internal energy with temperature at constant volume, and $(\partial u/\partial T)_v$

57

may be replaced by c_v in any equation in which it occurs, even if the equation refers to a process in which the volume is *not* constant. Hence for any reversible process the first law can be written,

$$d'q = c_v dT + \left[p + \left(\frac{\partial u}{\partial v} \right)_T \right] dv. \tag{5-4}$$

Consider next a process at constant pressure. Then

$$d'q_p = c_p dT_p$$

and Eq. (5-4) becomes

$$c_p dT_p = c_v dT_p + \left[p + \left(\frac{\partial u}{\partial v} \right)_T \right] dv_p.$$

Dividing through by dT_p, we get

$$c_p = c_v + \left[p + \left(\frac{\partial u}{\partial v} \right)_T \right] \left(\frac{\partial v}{\partial T} \right)_p. \tag{5-5}$$

For a process at constant temperature, $dT = 0$, and Eq. (5-4) becomes

$$d'q_T = \left[p + \left(\frac{\partial u}{\partial v} \right)_T \right] dv_T$$

$$= p\,dv_T + \left(\frac{\partial u}{\partial v} \right)_T dv_T. \tag{5-6}$$

This equation merely states that the heat supplied to a system in an isothermal reversible process equals the sum of the work done by the system and the increase in its internal energy. Note that it serves no useful purpose to define a specific heat capacity at constant temperature, c_T, by the equation $d'q_T = c_T dT$, because $d'q_T$ is not zero while $dT = 0$. Hence $c_T = \pm \infty$ (since $d'q_T$ can be positive or negative). In other words, a system behaves in an isothermal process as if it had an infinite heat capacity, since any amount of heat can flow into or out of it without producing a change in temperature.

Finally, we consider a reversible *adiabatic* process, that is, one in which the system is thermally insulated and $d'q = 0$. The changes in the state variables in such a process will be designated by the subscript s, the reason being that the entropy s remains constant in such a process. Eq. (5-4) becomes

$$c_v dT_s = - \left[p + \left(\frac{\partial u}{\partial v} \right)_T \right] dv_s, \tag{5-7}$$

giving the relations between the changes in temperature and volume in an adiabatic process.

Dividing through by dv_s, we get

$$c_v \left(\frac{\partial T}{\partial v}\right)_s = -\left[p + \left(\frac{\partial u}{\partial v}\right)_T\right]. \tag{5-8}$$

Using the definitions of β and κ, the results derived above can be put in the following form,

$$\left(\frac{\partial u}{\partial T}\right)_v = c_v, \tag{5-9}$$

$$\left(\frac{\partial u}{\partial v}\right)_T = \frac{c_p - c_v}{\beta v} - p, \tag{5-10}$$

$$d'q_T = \frac{c_p - c_v}{\beta v} dv_T, \tag{5-11}$$

$$\left(\frac{\partial T}{\partial v}\right)_s = \frac{c_v - c_p}{\beta v c_v}. \tag{5-12}$$

5-3 T and p independent. Let us next consider T and p as independent variables and write

$$du = \left(\frac{\partial u}{\partial T}\right)_p dT + \left(\frac{\partial u}{\partial p}\right)_T dp,$$

$$dv = \left(\frac{\partial v}{\partial T}\right)_p dT + \left(\frac{\partial v}{\partial p}\right)_T dp.$$

The first law then becomes

$$d'q = \left[\left(\frac{\partial u}{\partial T}\right)_p + p\left(\frac{\partial v}{\partial T}\right)_p\right] dT + \left[\left(\frac{\partial u}{\partial p}\right)_T + p\left(\frac{\partial v}{\partial p}\right)_T\right] dp. \tag{5-13}$$

In a process at constant pressure,

$$dp = 0, \quad d'q = c_p dT_p,$$

and

$$c_p = \left[\left(\frac{\partial u}{\partial T}\right)_p + p\left(\frac{\partial v}{\partial T}\right)_p\right]. \tag{5-14}$$

Note that while c_v is equal to $(\partial u/\partial T)_v$, it is not true that c_p equals $(\partial u/\partial T)_p$.

The general expression for c_p in Eq. (5-14) can be inserted in Eq. (5-13) to give

$$d'q = c_p dT + \left[\left(\frac{\partial u}{\partial p}\right)_T + p\left(\frac{\partial v}{\partial p}\right)_T\right] dp, \tag{5-15}$$

which is the analog of Eq. (5-4).

In a constant volume process, $d'q = c_v dT_v$ and

$$c_v dT_v = c_p dT_v + \left[\left(\frac{\partial u}{\partial p}\right)_T + p\left(\frac{\partial v}{\partial p}\right)_T\right] dp_v,$$

or

$$c_v = c_p + \left[\left(\frac{\partial u}{\partial p}\right)_T + p\left(\frac{\partial v}{\partial p}\right)_T\right]\left(\frac{\partial p}{\partial T}\right)_v,$$

a relation analogous to Eq. (5-5) and which expresses $(\partial u/\partial p)_T$ in terms of c_p, c_v, and state variables.

If the temperature is constant,

$$d'q_T = \left[\left(\frac{\partial u}{\partial p}\right)_T + p\left(\frac{\partial v}{\partial p}\right)_T\right] dp_T, \tag{5-16}$$

which, like Eq. (5-6), states (in terms of different variables) that the heat supplied equals the sum of the increase in internal energy and the work done.

In an adiabatic process,

$$c_p dT_s = -\left[\left(\frac{\partial u}{\partial p}\right)_T + p\left(\frac{\partial v}{\partial p}\right)_T\right] dp_s, \tag{5-17}$$

$$c_p\left(\frac{\partial T}{\partial p}\right)_s = -\left[\left(\frac{\partial u}{\partial p}\right)_T + p\left(\frac{\partial v}{\partial p}\right)_T\right]. \tag{5-18}$$

Again using the definitions of β and κ, we obtain

$$\left(\frac{\partial u}{\partial T}\right)_p = c_p - p\beta v, \tag{5-19}$$

$$\left(\frac{\partial u}{\partial p}\right)_T = pv\kappa - \frac{\kappa}{\beta}(c_p - c_v), \tag{5-20}$$

$$d'q_T = \frac{\kappa}{\beta}(c_v - c_p)\, dp_T, \tag{5-21}$$

$$\left(\frac{\partial T}{\partial p}\right)_s = \frac{\kappa(c_p - c_v)}{\beta c_p}. \tag{5-22}$$

5-4 p and v independent. Equations similar to the foregoing can be derived by expressing u as a function of p and v, combining with the first law, and applying the result to the special cases of isometric, isobaric, isothermal, and adiabatic processes. The same equations can also be derived from those worked out in the two preceding sections and Eqs. (4-13) and (4-14). It is left as an exercise for the reader to show that:

$$\left(\frac{\partial u}{\partial p}\right)_v = \frac{\kappa c_v}{\beta}, \tag{5-23}$$

$$\left(\frac{\partial u}{\partial v}\right)_p = \frac{c_p}{\beta v} - p, \tag{5-24}$$

$$d'q_T = \frac{c_v \kappa}{\beta} dp_T + \frac{c_p}{\beta v} dv_T, \tag{5-25}$$

$$\left(\frac{\partial p}{\partial v}\right)_s = - \frac{c_p}{\kappa v c_v}. \tag{5-26}$$

We have therefore expressed all six of the partial derivatives of u in terms of the experimentally measurable properties of a substance, c_p, c_v, β and κ, together with the state variables p and v. We have also obtained three expressions for the heat flowing into a system in an isothermal process, and three forms of the differential equation of an adiabatic process. All of the equations above are entirely general in that they are not restricted to any particular substance such as an ideal gas. The expressions for $d'q_T$ are limited to *reversible* processes. The expressions for the partial derivatives, however, do not have this restriction, since they do not refer to a *process* at all. That is, if we think of u as a function of p and v, as in Eqs. (5-23) and (5-24), this function defines an energy surface in a three-dimensional rectangular coordinate system and the partial derivatives give the slopes of curves lying in this surface along which v and p are respectively constant. The shape of this surface is determined by the nature of the particular substance for which it is constructed, and the partial derivatives, geometrically speaking, represent properties of the *surface*. This question is discussed further in Sec. 5-5, in connection with the energy surfaces of a real and a van der Waals gas.

5-5 Internal energy of gases. The equations derived in Sec. 5-2 all contain the expression $p + \left(\frac{\partial u}{\partial v}\right)_T$ as a factor. If the heat capacities c_p and c_v and the coefficient of expansion β could be experimentally determined with sufficient precision, the variation of internal energy with volume at constant temperature, $(\partial u/\partial v)_T$, could be computed from Eq. (5-10). The difficulty of making precise measurements of c_v renders this impractical. We shall show in Sec. 5-8 that there is a direct method, although not of high precision, for measuring $(\partial u/\partial v)_T$ for a gaseous system. These experiments show that this quantity is very small for real gases and we might arbitrarily set it equal to zero for an ideal gas. However, let us at this point depart from a strictly logical development of the subject (and from the implications of the title of this chapter) and anticipate a result that can only be derived with the help of the second law. We shall prove in Chapter 9 that for any substance whatever,

$$p + \left(\frac{\partial u}{\partial v}\right)_T = T\left(\frac{\partial p}{\partial T}\right)_v = \frac{T\beta}{\kappa}.$$ (5-27)

Therefore $(\partial u/\partial v)_T$ can be computed for any substance whose equation of state is known, or for which β and κ have been measured, independently of measurements of c_p and c_v.

For an ideal gas,

$$p = \frac{RT}{v}, \quad \left(\frac{\partial p}{\partial T}\right)_v = \frac{R}{v},$$

and

$$\left(\frac{\partial u}{\partial v}\right)_T = \frac{RT}{v} - p = 0.$$ (5-28)

Hence at constant temperature, the internal energy of an ideal gas is independent of the specific volume or density. It is independent of the pressure also, since from Eq. (4-13),

$$\left(\frac{\partial u}{\partial p}\right)_T = \left(\frac{\partial u}{\partial v}\right)_T \left(\frac{\partial v}{\partial p}\right)_T = 0.$$

The internal energy of an ideal gas is therefore a function of its temperature only, and at a given temperature is the same whether the gas occupies a large or a small volume, or whether it is subjected to a large or a small pressure. This is in agreement with the predictions of the molecular theory of an ideal gas, and also with experiments performed on real gases in states where they approximate an ideal gas (described in Sec. 5-8). By hypothesis, the molecules of an ideal gas do not attract or repel one another. There is therefore no mutual potential energy between them, and their total energy, which we identify with the internal energy of the gas, is the sum of their kinetic energies. The kinetic energy, however, depends only on the temperature, and hence the internal energy is a function of temperature only. It is true that as an ideal gas is compressed to smaller and smaller volumes, keeping its temperature constant, it exerts a greater and greater pressure on the walls of its container, but this is only because more molecules collide with the wall per unit time, not because the energies of the molecules are larger.

For an ideal gas, therefore, the subscript in Eq. (5-3) can be dropped and the partial derivative written as a total derivative, since u is a function of T only.

$$c_v = \frac{du}{dT} \text{ (ideal gas)}.$$

Hence

$$du = c_v dT$$

and

$$u = u_0 + \int_{T_0}^{T} c_v dT, \tag{5-29}$$

where u_0 is the internal energy at some arbitrary reference temperature T_0, not necessarily equal to absolute zero. This is the energy equation of an ideal gas, insofar as it can be determined by thermodynamic principles alone. The constant u_0 is unknown, and there is no thermodynamic justification for setting it equal to zero at $0°$ K. To evaluate the integral, c_v must be known as a function of T but thermodynamics alone can provide no information about the magnitude of c_v.

For a van der Waals gas,

$$p = \frac{RT}{v-b} - \frac{a}{v^2}, \quad \left(\frac{\partial p}{\partial T}\right)_v = \frac{R}{v-b}$$

and from Eq. (5-27),

$$\left(\frac{\partial u}{\partial v}\right)_T = \frac{a}{v^2}. \tag{5-30}$$

Inserting this expression for $(\partial u/\partial v)_T$ in Eq. (5-1) and integrating, we get for the energy equation of a van der Waals gas, expressed as a function of T and v,

$$du = c_v dT + \frac{a}{v^2} dv,$$

$$u = u_0 + \int_{T_0}^{T} c_v dT + a \left(\frac{1}{v_0} - \frac{1}{v}\right), \tag{5-31}$$

where u_0 is the specific internal energy at a temperature T_0 and a specific volume v_0.

The internal energy of a van der Waals gas therefore depends on its specific volume as well as on its temperature. Note that only the van der Waals constant a appears in the energy equation. The reason, as we shall show later, is that this constant is a measure of the forces of attraction between the molecules, or of their mutual potential energy, while the constant b is a measure of molecular diameters and does not affect the energy.

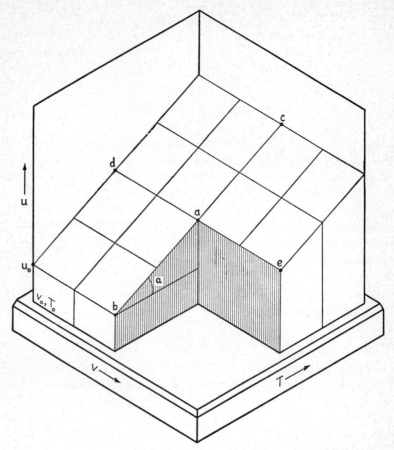

FIG. 5-1. Energy surface of an ideal gas (c_v constant).

In a temperature range over which c_v can be considered constant, the energy equations become

$$u = (u_0 - c_v T_0) + c_v T \text{ (ideal gas)},$$

$$u = \left(u_0 - c_v T_0 + \frac{a}{v_0} \right) + c_v T - \frac{a}{v} \text{ (van der Waals gas)}.$$

These equations can be represented graphically as in Figs. 5-1 and 5-2, in which u is plotted vertically and T and v horizontally. The partial derivatives $(\partial u/\partial T)_v$ and $(\partial u/\partial v)_T$, at any point such as a, are the slopes of lines in the surface passing through the point, formed by the intersec-

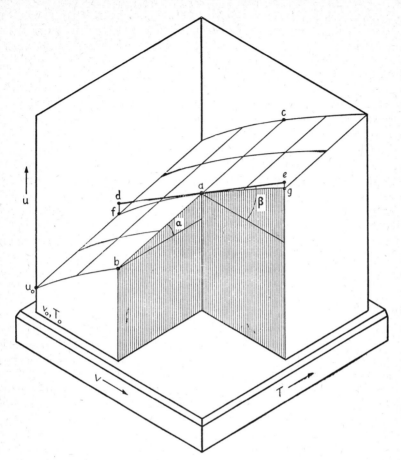

FIG. 5-2.   Energy surface of a van der Waals gas (c_v constant).

tion with the surface of planes perpendicular to the v- and T-axes.   Thus in Fig. 5-1, the value of $(\partial u/\partial T)_v$ at point a is the slope of the line bc at point a, or $\tan \alpha$.   Since this slope equals c_v, which we are assuming constant, bc is a straight line having the same slope at all points.   The same is true of all other lines at constant volume.   The value of $(\partial u/\partial v)_T$ at point a is the slope of the line de, which is zero at all points, since for an ideal gas u does not vary with v when T is constant.

In Fig. 5-2, for a van der Waals gas, the value of $(\partial u/\partial T)_v$ at point a is the slope of the line bc.   Since this equals c_v, assumed constant, bc is a straight line, as are all other lines at constant volume.   The value of

$(\partial u/\partial v)_T$ at point a is the slope of the curve fag at point a, or it is the slope of the tangent to this curve at a, the line de. From Eq. (5-30), this slope, at point a, is equal to a/v_a^2. It is the same for all points at the same volume but decreases as v increases.

Although drawn for a van der Waals gas, Fig. 5-2 represents the general nature of the u-v-T surface for any real gas, in a region of constant c_v. The internal energy increases both with increasing temperature and with increasing volume.

Notice, as mentioned in Sec. 5-4, that the partial derivatives are properties of the *surface* (or better, of the *substance* for which the surface is constructed) and do not refer to any particular *process* the substance may undergo.

5-6 Difference between specific heat capacities. The special forms taken by some of the general equations derived in the preceding section can now be written down for an ideal gas and for a van der Waals gas. Thus Eq. (5-10) becomes

$$c_p - c_v = \beta v p \text{ (ideal gas)},$$

$$c_p - c_v = \beta v \left(p + \frac{a}{v^2} \right) \text{ (van der Waals gas)}.$$

For an ideal gas,

$$\beta = \frac{1}{T}.$$

For a van der Waals gas,

$$\beta = \frac{Rv^2(v - b)}{RTv^3 - 2a(v - b)^2}, \quad p + \frac{a}{v^2} = \frac{RT}{v - b}.$$

Hence

$$c_p - c_v = R \text{ (ideal gas)}, \tag{5-32}$$

$$c_p - c_v = R \frac{1}{1 - \dfrac{2a(v - b)^2}{RTv^3}} \text{ (van der Waals gas).} \tag{5-33}$$

Table 12-3 gives experimental values of $(c_p - c_v)/R$ for a number of real gases at temperatures near room temperature. This ratio, exactly unity for an ideal gas at all temperatures, is seen to differ from unity by less than 1 percent for nearly all of the gases listed.

5-7 Adiabatic processes. We next consider a reversible adiabatic process. Eq. (5-7) becomes

$$c_v dT_s = -\,pdv_s = -\,\frac{RT}{v}\,dv_s \text{ (ideal gas)},$$

$$c_v dT_s = -\left(p + \frac{a}{v^2}\right)dv_s = -\,\frac{RT}{v-b}\,dv_s \text{ (van der Waals gas)}.$$

These equations are readily integrated to obtain the relation between T and v in an adiabatic process. Dropping the subscript s, we have for an ideal gas

$$\frac{dT}{T} + \frac{R}{c_v}\frac{dv}{v} = 0,$$

$$\ln T + \frac{R}{c_v}\ln v = \ln \text{const},$$

$$Tv^{\,R/c_v} = \text{const}, \tag{5-34}$$

and for a van der Waals gas,

$$\frac{dT}{T} + \frac{R}{c_v}\frac{dv}{v-b} = 0,$$

$$\ln T + \frac{R}{c_v}\ln (v-b) = \ln \text{const},$$

$$T(v-b)^{\,R/c_v} = \text{const}. \tag{5-35}$$

Since the gas necessarily obeys its equation of state in *any* reversible process, the relations between T and p, and between p and v, can be found from the equations above by eliminating v or T between them and the appropriate equation of state. They can also be found by integrating Eqs. (5-22) and (5-26). For an ideal gas, we find

$$Tp^{-\frac{R}{R+c_v}} = \text{const},$$

$$pv^{\frac{R+c_v}{c_v}} = \text{const}.$$

These equations can be put in a more familiar form if we use the fact that for an ideal gas $c_p - c_v = R$, and define a quantity γ by the equation

$$\gamma = \frac{c_p}{c_v}.$$

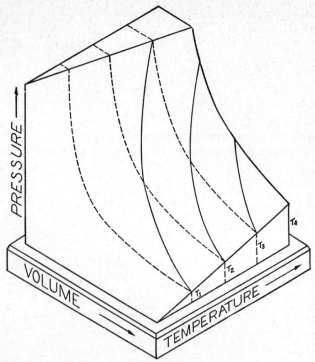

FIG. 5-3.   (a) Adiabatic processes (full lines) on the ideal gas p-v-T surface.

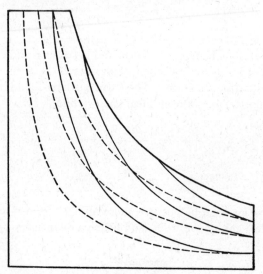

FIG. 5-3.   (b) Projection of adiabatic processes in (a) on the p-v plane

Then for an ideal gas in a reversible adiabatic process,

$$Tv^{\gamma-1} = \text{const}, \tag{5-36}$$

$$Tp^{\frac{1-\gamma}{\gamma}} = \text{const}, \tag{5-37}$$

$$pv^{\gamma} = \text{const}. \tag{5-38}$$

The derivation of the corresponding equations for a van der Waals gas is left for a problem.

The curves representing adiabatic processes are shown on the ideal gas p-v-T surface in Fig. 5-3(a) and their projections on the p-v plane in Fig. 5-3(b). The adiabatic curves projected onto the p-v plane have at every point a somewhat steeper slope than the isotherms. The temperature of an ideal gas increases in a reversible adiabatic compression, as will be seen from an examination of Fig. 5-3, or from Eqs. (5-36) or (5-37). This increase in temperature may be very large and it is utilized in the Diesel type of internal combustion engine, where on the compression stroke, air is compressed in the cylinders to about 1/15th of its volume at atmospheric pressure. The air temperature at the top of the compression stroke is so high that fuel oil injected into the heated air burns without the necessity of a spark to initiate the combustion process.

The work done in an adiabatic expansion of an ideal gas is

$$w = \int_{v_1}^{v_2} p\,dv$$

$$= C \int_{v_1}^{v_2} v^{-\gamma}\,dv$$

$$= \frac{1}{1-\gamma}\left[Cv^{1-\gamma}\right]_{v_1}^{v_2}, \tag{5-39}$$

where C is the constant in Eq. (5-38). But to state that $pv^{\gamma} = \text{const} = C$ means that $p_1v_1^{\gamma} = p_2v_2^{\gamma} = \text{const} = C$. Hence when inserting the upper limit in Eq. (5-39) we let $C = p_2v_2^{\gamma}$, while at the lower limit we let $C = p_1v_1^{\gamma}$. Then

$$w = \frac{1}{1-\gamma}(p_2v_2 - p_1v_1). \tag{5-40}$$

The work can also be found by realizing that since no heat flows into or out of a system in an adiabatic process the work is done wholly at the expense of the internal energy of the system.   Hence

$$u_2 - u_1 = -w,$$

and for an ideal gas

$$w = u_1 - u_2$$

$$= c_v(T_1 - T_2), \tag{5-41}$$

if c_v is constant.

The work done by a van der Waals gas can be found most simply by the latter method.   If c_v is constant, then from Eq. (5-31),

$$w = c_v(T_1 - T_2) - a\left(\frac{1}{v_1} - \frac{1}{v_2}\right). \tag{5-42}$$

5-8 The Joule experiment.   The internal energy of real gases has been studied experimentally by Joule and others.   One experimental technique consists of allowing the gas to perform a *free expansion,* that is, to expand into an evacuated vessel.   The apparatus used by Joule is shown schematically in Fig. 5-4.   The gas under investigation is contained in vessel A, connected to a second evacuated vessel B by a tube in which there is a valve V.   The experimental procedure is to allow the system to come to thermal equilibrium, open the valve, wait for the re-establishment of thermal equilibrium, and observe the final temperature.

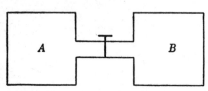

FIG. 5-4.   The Joule experiment.

In a free expansion, no work is done by the gas *on its surroundings.* It is true that while the expansion is taking place the gas remaining in vessel A is doing work on the gas that has already flowed into vessel B, but this work is done by one part of the system (i.e., the gas) on another part and is not done by the system as a whole on its surroundings.

It would be desirable also to prevent any flow of heat from the gas to its surroundings, or to reduce the flow to negligible proportions, but practically this is impossible.   If the space outside the vessels is evacuated, or if they are surrounded by a poor heat conductor, the heat loss or gain from the vessels to *their* surroundings may be very small, but the vessels themselves constitute the immediate surroundings of the gas, and if the temperature of the gas changes in the expansion there will be a flow of heat between the gas and the vessels.   The heat capacity of the latter is always large compared with that of the gas and the resulting temperature change is therefore much smaller and more difficult to observe precisely than if the gas could be truly isolated.   However, if the heat capacities of gas and containers are known, then in principle one can compute what the temperature change of the gas would have been had there been no flow of heat from it.   We shall therefore consider an idealized experiment in which the flow of heat, as well as the work, is zero.   Then from the first law there is no change in the internal energy of the gas.

Since the change in volume in a free expansion is large, we should use the integrated form of the energy equation.   Experimental results are best interpreted in terms of some assumed form of the equation of state, so let us take for illustration the van der Waals equation, although it may not fit the data as well as some more complicated expression.   Over any range of temperature occurring in a free expansion the specific heat c_v can be considered constant.   Let T_1, v_1, and u_1 refer to the state of the gas before the expansion and T_2, v_2, and u_2 to the values after the expansion. From the conditions of the experiment, $u_2 = u_1$, and from Eq. (5-31)

$$c_v(T_2 - T_1) = a\left(\frac{1}{v_2} - \frac{1}{v_1}\right).\tag{5-43}$$

All of the quantities in this equation except a can be measured experimentally, so that a can be computed from experiment and information thus obtained regarding the intermolecular forces.   Conversely, we can use values of a obtained in other ways to estimate the temperature change expected.   Note that the van der Waals constant a is positive for all gases (indicating a force of attraction between the molecules) and since $1/v_2$ is necessarily smaller than $1/v_1$, T_2 is necessarily less than T_1 and the temperature of a van der Waals gas drops in a free expansion.   From the molecular viewpoint this is explained as follows.   The total energy of the molecules, kinetic plus potential, remains constant in the expansion. Since the molecules are farther apart after the expansion, and since they attract one another, their potential energy has increased.   Their kinetic energy has therefore decreased and this is observed as a lowering in temperature.

Let us estimate the lowering of temperature when carbon dioxide expands from a specific volume of 2 m^3/mole (corresponding approximately to 10 atm pressure and 0° C) to a specific volume of 4 m³/mole, which means that vessels A and B in Fig. 5-4 are of approximately equal volume. The constant a for CO_2, from Table 2-1, is 366×10^3, and c_v, from Table 12-3, is $3.38R$. Hence

$$T_2 - T_1 = \frac{a}{c_v}\left(\frac{1}{v_2} - \frac{1}{v_1}\right)$$

$$= \frac{366 \times 10^3}{3.38 \times 8.31 \times 10^3}\left(\frac{1}{4} - \frac{1}{2}\right)$$

$$\approx -3 \text{ deg.}$$

This is the temperature drop expected if the gas does not exchange heat with its surroundings, but the temperature change actually measured would be very much smaller, perhaps a few hundredths of a degree. Hence the experiment is not well suited for a direct determination of a or, more generally, for determining the dependence of internal energy on volume. All experiments agree, however, in the conclusion that the temperature change is very small and we may postulate from these experiments, even if we could not compute it from the second law and the equation of state, that the temperature change is zero for an ideal gas and hence that $(\partial u/\partial v)_T$ is zero for such a gas.

5-9 The Joule-Kelvin or porous plug experiment. Because of the difficulty of measuring precisely the extremely small temperature changes in a free expansion, Joule and Thomson (who later became Lord Kelvin) devised another experiment in which the temperature change of an expanding gas would not be masked by the relatively large heat capacity of its surroundings. Many gases have been carefully investigated in this way. Not only do the results provide information about intermolecular forces, but they can be used to reduce gas thermometer temperatures to the Kelvin scale, and the temperature drop produced in the process is used in the liquefaction of hydrogen and helium.

The apparatus used by Joule and Kelvin is shown schematically in Fig. 5-5. A continuous stream of gas at a pressure p_1 and temperature T_1 is forced through a porous plug in a tube, from which it emerges at a lower pressure p_2 and at a temperature T_2. The device is thermally insulated, and after it has operated for a long enough time for the steady state to become established, the only heat lost or gained by the gas stream is the small amount flowing through the insulation. That is, in the steady state, no heat flows from the gas to *change* the temperature of the walls and the large heat capacity of the walls does not mask the temperature change of the gas, which is practically what it would be were the system truly an isolated one.

Let us imagine that at some instant pistons are inserted in the tube at each side of the plug, as in Fig. 5-5(b), trapping a certain mass of gas between them. Let the gas outside the pistons be removed and forces F_1 and F_2 exerted on the pistons equal respectively to p_1A and p_2A, where A is the piston area. If the pistons are now moved to the right with velocities equal to those with which the gas is flowing, the conditions at the plug will be unaltered.

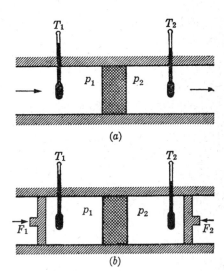

(a)

(b)

Fig. 5-5. Flow through a porous plug.

In a time interval during which a mass m of gas is forced through the plug, the volume of gas on the left decreases by an amount $V_1 = mv_1$, and that on the right increases by $V_2 = mv_2$, where v_1 and v_2 are the specific volumes of the gas on the left and the right. The net work done by the system, i.e., the gas between the pistons, is

$$W = p_2V_2 - p_1V_1 = m(p_2v_2 - p_1v_1).$$

The change in internal energy of the system equals the change in internal energy of the mass m that has passed through the plug, or

$$U_2 - U_1 = m(u_2 - u_1).$$

Because of the thermal insulation, the net heat Q flowing into the system is essentially zero. Hence from the first law,

$$U_2 - U_1 = Q - W,$$

$$m(u_2 - u_1) = 0 - m(p_2v_2 - p_1v_1),$$

or

$$u_2 - u_1 = p_1v_1 - p_2v_2,$$

$$u_1 + p_1v_1 = u_2 + p_2v_2. \tag{5-44}$$

The change in internal energy is therefore not zero, as it is in a free expansion, but is equal to the change in the pv product. Hence the results of the experiment cannot be interpreted as simply as those of the Joule experiment. On the other hand, the temperature difference between the entering and emerging gas is, in general, very much greater.

If we assume that the gas obeys van der Waals equation, that c_v can be considered constant, and that $c_v + R = c_p$, Eq. (5-44) reduces to

$$c_p(T_2 - T_1) \approx \frac{2a - RT_2b}{v_2} - \frac{2a - RT_1b}{v_1}, \tag{5-45}$$

which should be compared with Eq. (5-43) for the temperature change in a free expansion. We see that the constant b as well as a occurs in the equation, that is, molecular diameters as well as molecular forces determine the temperature change.

Eq. (5-45) cannot be solved simply for $T_2 - T_1$. However, let us estimate the magnitude of the term RTb compared to $2a$, for carbon dioxide at 300° K.

$$RTb = 8.31 \times 10^3 \times 300 \times 4.29 \times 10^{-2}$$

$$= 1.08 \times 10^5,$$

$$2a = 2 \times 3.66 \times 10^5$$

$$= 7.32 \times 10^5.$$

Thus RTb is only about 10% of $2a$, and since T_2 is not very different from T_1, we can without too great an error (since the van der Waals equation is only a second approximation to the true equation of state) let

$$RT_1b = RT_2b = RTb,$$

where T can be set equal to T_1 or T_2 or some mean temperature between them. Then

$$T_2 - T_1 \approx \frac{2a - RTb}{c_p}\left(\frac{1}{v_2} - \frac{1}{v_1}\right). \tag{5-46}$$

For the same increase in specific volume used in the example of a free expansion in the preceding section, we find for $T = 300°$ K,

$$T_2 - T_1 \approx \frac{(7.32 - 1.08)10^5}{4.40 \times 8.31 \times 10^3}\left(\frac{1}{4} - \frac{1}{2}\right)$$

$$\approx -4.3 \text{ deg.}$$

As explained above, the observed temperature drop would be very nearly equal to that in a truly isolated system.

For an ideal gas, $a = b = 0$, and the temperature change of such a gas, forced through a porous plug, is therefore zero.

5-10 Enthalpy. The combination of quantities

$$u + pv,$$

or

$$U + pV,$$

occurs frequently in thermodynamic equations. Thus we have seen in the preceding section that $u + pv$ does not change when a gas is forced through a porous plug. The sum $U + pV$ is called the *enthalpy* (accent on the second syllable) and is represented by H. The specific enthalpy, per unit mass or per mole, is represented by h.

$$H = U + pV, \quad h = u + pv.$$

Since u and pv are functions of the state of a system only, the same is true of the enthalpy, and hence dH and dh are exact differentials. In terms of enthalpy, Eq. (5-44) becomes simply

$$h_1 = h_2.$$

Suppose that a series of Joule-Kelvin experiments are performed on the same gas, keeping the initial pressure p_1 and temperature T_1 the same in each experiment, but varying the pumping rate so that the pressure on the downstream side of the plug is made to take on a series of values p_2, p_3, etc. Let the temperatures T_2, T_3, etc., be measured in each experiment. (Note that once the pressure on the downstream side is fixed, nothing can be done about the temperature. The properties of the gas determine what the temperature will be.) The corresponding pairs of values of p_2 and T_2, p_3 and T_3, etc., determine a number of points in a pressure-temperature diagram as in Fig. 5-6(a), and since $h_1 = h_2 = h_3$, etc., the enthalpy is the same at all of these points and a smooth curve drawn through the points is a curve of constant enthalpy. Note carefully that this curve does *not* represent the *process* executed by the gas in passing through the plug, since the process is irreversible and the gas does not pass through a series of equilibrium states. The final pressure and temperature must be measured at a sufficient distance from the plug for local non-uniformities in the stream to die out, and the gas passes by an irreversible process from one point on the curve to another.

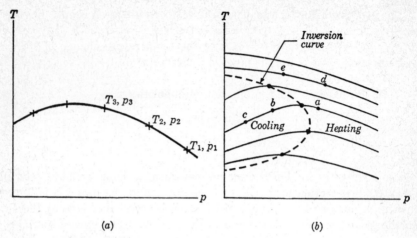

(a)   (b)

FIG. 5-6. (a) Points of equal enthalpy. (b) Isenthalpic curves and the inversion curve.

By performing other series of experiments, again keeping the initial pressure and temperature the same in each series but varying them from one series to another, a family of curves corresponding to different values of h can be obtained. Such a family is shown in Fig. 5-6(b), which is typical of all real gases. If the temperature is not too great the curves pass through a maximum called the *inversion point*. The locus of the inversion points is the *inversion curve*.

The slope of an isenthalpic curve at any point is $(\partial T/\partial p)_h$, and at the maximum of the curve, or the inversion point,

$$\left(\frac{\partial T}{\partial p}\right)_h = 0.$$

Again we anticipate a result that will be derived in Sec. 9-9 with the help of the second law, and which states that

$$\left(\frac{\partial T}{\partial p}\right)_h = -\frac{1}{c_p}\left[v - T\left(\frac{\partial v}{\partial T}\right)_p\right] = -\frac{v}{c_p}(1 - \beta T).$$

At an inversion point, therefore,

$$1 - \beta T_i = 0,$$

$$T_i = \frac{1}{\beta}.$$

Hence for a van der Waals gas,

$$T_i = \frac{RT_i v^3 - 2a(v - b)^2}{Rv^2(v - b)}$$

$$= \frac{2a(v - b)^2}{Rbv^2}.$$

The equation connecting T_i and the corresponding pressure p_i is obtained by eliminating v between the equation above and the equation of state. The derivation is left as a problem. The curve is shown by the dotted line in Fig. 5-6(b).

When the Joule-Kelvin effect is to be used in the liquefaction of gases it is evident that the initial temperature and pressure, and the final pressure, must be so chosen that the temperature decreases. This is possible only if the initial pressure and temperature lie on a curve having a maximum. Thus a drop in temperature would be produced by an expansion from point a or point b to point c, but a temperature rise would result in an expansion from d to e.

We conclude this section by deriving some other important properties of the enthalpy function. We can write for any infinitesimal reversible process,

$$h = u + pv,$$

$$dh = du + pdv + vdp.$$

But from the first law,

$$du + pdv = d'q,$$

so

$$dh = d'q + vdp.$$

In a process at constant pressure, $d'q = c_p dT_p$ and $dp = 0$, so

$$dh_p = c_p dT_p,$$

and

$$\left(\frac{\partial h}{\partial T}\right)_p = c_p. \tag{5-47}$$

For a finite process at constant pressure,

$$(h_2 - h_1)_p = (u_2 - u_1)_p + p(v_2 - v_1)_p.$$

If the process is reversible, the right side of this equation, from the first law, equals the heat q_p absorbed by the system, so

$$(h_2 - h_1)_p = q_p. \tag{5-48}$$

The heat absorbed in any reversible isobaric process is therefore equal to the difference between the enthalpies of the system in the end states of the process. We have seen that "heat" is not a property of a system and one cannot draw up a table listing the "heat in a system" as a function of the state of the system and use such a table to find the heat absorbed by the system in any given process. Enthalpy, however, is a property of a system and can be tabulated. Given such a table, one can look up the values of the enthalpy at the end states of any reversible *isobaric* process and by subtraction find the heat absorbed in such a process.

It is seen that enthalpy plays the same role in isobaric processes that internal energy does in isometric processes. That is,

$$c_p = \left(\frac{\partial h}{\partial T}\right)_p, \quad q_p = h_2 - h_1.$$

$$c_v = \left(\frac{\partial u}{\partial T}\right)_v, \quad q_v = u_2 - u_1.$$

5-11 Energy equation of steady flow. The large rectangle in Fig. 5-7 represents a device through which there is a flow of fluid. Heat is supplied to the device and mechanical work is done by it, as represented schematically in the diagram. The device might be a steam engine, a turbine, or a refrigerator. We shall assume that a *steady state* exists. That is, the rate of absorption of heat and the rate of doing work are constant,

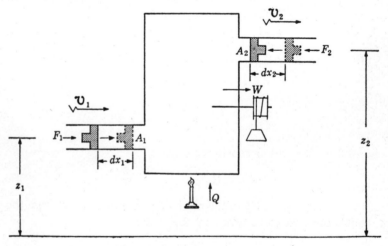

FIG. 5-7. Steady flow process.

the mass of fluid entering per unit time is constant and is equal to that leaving, and the state of the fluid at any point does not change with time (or it returns periodically to the same state). The fluid enters at an elevation z_1, with a velocity $\mathcal{V}_1$ and under a pressure p_1, and it leaves at an elevation z_2 with a velocity $\mathcal{V}_2$ and at a pressure p_2.

Let us imagine that at a certain instant, pistons are inserted in the pipes through which the fluid enters and leaves and that these are moved along the pipes with the appropriate velocities $\mathcal{V}_1$ and $\mathcal{V}_2$, for a time interval such that a mass m of fluid passes into and out of the device. The distances moved by the pistons during this time are respectively x_1 and x_2. The arrows F_1 and F_2 represent the forces exerted on the fluid between the pistons by the adjacent fluid. Let Q represent the heat absorbed and W the work output (the so-called "shaft work").

The net work done by the system, while a mass m flows into and out of the device, is

$$\text{Net work} = W + F_2x_2 - F_1x_1.$$

If A_1 and A_2 are the piston areas, then

$$F_1x_1 = p_1A_1x_1 = p_1V_1, \quad F_2x_2 = p_2A_2x_2 = p_2V_2,$$

and

$$\text{Net work} = W + p_2V_2 - p_1V_1,$$

where V_1 and V_2 are the volumes occupied by a mass m on entering and on leaving.

The state of the fluid at all points *within* the device does not change with time, so that in effect a mass m of fluid has been brought from its state at the entrance of the device to its state at the exit. The increase in internal energy of this mass is

$$m(u_2 - u_1),$$

where u_1 and u_2 are the specific internal energies at entrance and exit. In addition to the change in internal energy, the kinetic energy of the fluid has increased by

$$\tfrac{1}{2}m(\mathcal{V}_2^2 - \mathcal{V}_1^2),$$

and its potential energy by

$$mg(z_2 - z_1),$$

where g is the local acceleration of gravity. Equating the net energy supplied to the increase in the total energy of the fluid, we get

$$Q - (W + p_2V_2 - p_1V_1) = m[(u_2 - u_1) + \tfrac{1}{2}(\mathcal{V}_2^2 - \mathcal{V}_1^2) + g(z_2 - z_1)],$$

or, dividing through by m and rearranging terms,

$$(u_1 + p_1v_1 + \tfrac{1}{2}\mathcal{V}_1^2 + gz_1) - (u_2 + p_2v_2 + \tfrac{1}{2}\mathcal{V}_2^2 + gz_2) - w + q = 0.$$

But $(u_1 + p_1v_1)$ and $(u_2 + p_2v_2)$ are respectively the enthalpies h_1 and h_2 at the entrance and exit, so finally

$$(h_1 + \tfrac{1}{2}\mathcal{V}_1^2 + gz_1) - (h_2 + \tfrac{1}{2}\mathcal{V}_2^2 + gz_2) - w + q = 0. \qquad (5\text{-}49)$$

$$q = w + (h_2 - h_1) + \tfrac{1}{2}(\mathcal{V}_2^2 - \mathcal{V}_1^2) + g(z_2 - z_1)$$

This relation is the *energy equation for steady flow.* We now apply it to some special cases.

The Joule-Kelvin experiment. In this experiment the system is thermally insulated so that the heat flow in or out is negligible, no shaft work is done, there is no change in elevation, and the velocities are small enough for the difference in their squares to be negligible. Then Eq. (5-49) reduces to

$$h_1 = h_2,$$

as previously derived.

The turbine. The temperature in a steam turbine is higher than that of its surroundings but the flow of fluid through it is, in general, so rapid that only a small quantity of heat is lost per unit mass of steam. The shaft work is, of course, not zero in this device but differences in elevation between inlet and outlet can usually be neglected. Hence for a turbine the energy equation becomes

$$w = h_1 - h_2 + \frac{\mathcal{V}_1^2 - \mathcal{V}_2^2}{2}. \qquad (5\text{-}50)$$

The shaft work obtained from the turbine, per unit mass of steam, therefore depends on the enthalpy difference between inlet and outlet, and on the difference between the squares of the inlet and exhaust velocities.

Flow through a nozzle. The steam entering a turbine comes from a boiler where its velocity is small, and before it impinges on the turbine blades it is given a high velocity by flowing through a nozzle. Fig. 5-8 shows a nozzle in which steam enters at a velocity $\mathcal{V}_1$ and leaves at a higher velocity $\mathcal{V}_2$. The shaft work is zero, the heat flow is small and can be assumed zero, and differences in elevation are small. Hence for a nozzle,

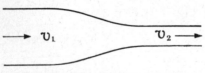

Fig. 5-8. Flow through a nozzle.

$$\mathcal{V}_2^2 = \mathcal{V}_1^2 + 2(h_1 - h_2). \qquad (5\text{-}51)$$

Bernoulli's equation. As a final example, we consider the flow of an incompressible fluid along a pipe of varying cross section and elevation. No shaft work is done and we assume the flow to be adiabatic. Then

$$h_1 + \tfrac{1}{2}\mathcal{V}_1^2 + gz_1 = h_2 + \tfrac{1}{2}\mathcal{V}_2^2 + gz_2 = \text{const},$$

or, writing out the expression for the enthalpy,

$$u + pv + \tfrac{1}{2}\mathcal{V}^2 + gz = \text{const.} \tag{5-52}$$

From the first law,

$$du = dq - p\,dv.$$

We have assumed no heat flow, so $dq = 0$, and if the fluid is incompressible $dv = 0$. Hence u is constant, and Eq. (5-52) reduces to

$$pv + \tfrac{1}{2}\mathcal{V}^2 + gz = \text{const},$$

or, replacing v by $1/\rho$,

$$p + \tfrac{1}{2}\rho\mathcal{V}^2 + \rho gz = \text{const},$$

which will be recognized as Bernoulli's equation for the steady flow of an incompressible fluid of zero viscosity. Bernoulli's equation is thus a special case of the general energy equation for steady flow.

5-12 The Carnot cycle. A simple cyclic process, first discussed by Carnot, is one in which a working substance takes in heat reversibly from a reservoir at a constant temperature T_2, expands adiabatically and reversibly to a lower temperature T_1, gives up heat reversibly to a reservoir at this temperature, and is then compressed reversibly and adiabatically to its original state. The working substance may be a solid, liquid, or gas (ideal or not), and it may even change from one phase to another during the cycle. The diagram of a Carnot cycle in the p-V plane is an area bounded by two isothermals and two adiabatics. If the working substance is a gas, the cycle has the general appearance of Fig. 5-9.

As a concrete example of a Carnot cycle, consider the *Carnot engine* illustrated in Fig. 5-10. The working substance is a fluid enclosed in a cylinder provided with a tightly fitting frictionless piston. The cylinder walls and

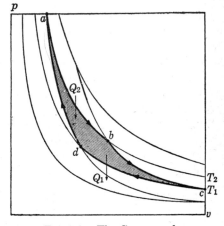

Fig. 5-9. The Carnot cycle.

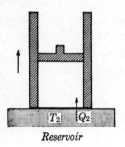 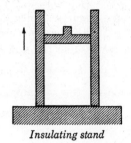 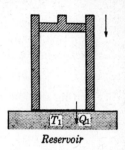

Reservoir   *Insulating stand*   *Reservoir*

FIG. 5-10.   A Carnot engine.

the piston are perfect heat insulators and the base is a heat conductor. Two heat reservoirs at temperatures T_2 and T_1 are provided, together with a heat insulating stand and a work reservoir. Let the cycle be started with the fluid at temperature T_2, corresponding to point a in Fig. 5-9. The cylinder is placed on the reservoir at temperature T_2 and the fluid is allowed to expand slowly. In this process some work is delivered to the work reservoir (not shown in the figure) and a quantity of heat Q_2 is absorbed from the heat reservoir. The amount of expansion in this stage is arbitrary. The cylinder is next placed on the insulating stand, so that it is completely thermally insulated. The fluid is allowed to expand still further adiabatically until its temperature drops to T_1. More work is done by the fluid in this stage but no heat is absorbed. The cylinder is then placed on the reservoir at temperature T_1 and the fluid is slowly compressed. Work must be provided by the work reservoir and heat Q_1 is delivered to the heat reservoir. This process is carried to such a state that if the cylinder is placed on the insulating stand and the fluid is compressed adiabatically, the system returns to its original state.

It will be seen from the diagram in Fig. 5-9 that the work done by the system in the two expansion stages, a to b to c, is greater than the work done on the system in the two compression stages, c to d to a. Let W represent the net work done by the system.

The system absorbs heat Q_2 from the reservoir at temperature T_2 and rejects heat Q_1 to the reservoir at temperature T_1. The net heat absorbed by the system is therefore $Q_2 + Q_1$ (we must write $Q_2 + Q_1$ and not $Q_2 - Q_1$, since Q_1 by our convention of sign is a negative quantity).

Since the system is carried through a cycle there is no change in its internal energy. We can therefore write from the first law,

$$Q_2 + Q_1 - W = 0,$$

or

$$W = Q_1 + Q_2, \tag{5-53}$$

and the net work W done by the system equals the sum (or the difference between the absolute magnitudes) of the heat absorbed from the high temperature reservoir and the heat rejected to the low temperature reservoir. These processes are common to all heat engines; heat is absorbed from a high temperature source, a part is converted to mechanical work, and the remainder is rejected as heat at a lower temperature.

It is helpful to represent the operation of any heat engine by a schematic flow diagram like that in Fig. 5-11. The width of the "pipe line" from the high temperature reservoir is proportional to the heat Q_2, the width of the line to the low temperature reservoir is proportional to Q_1, and the width of the line leading out from the side of the engine is proportional to the mechanical work output W. The circle is merely a schematic way of indicating the engine.

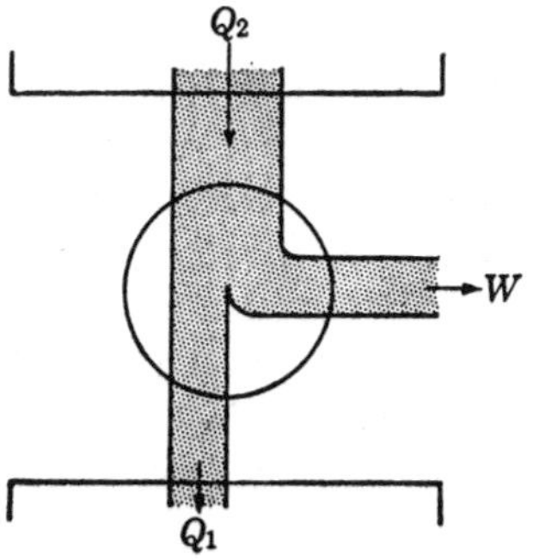

The efficiency of a heat engine, η, is defined as the ratio of the *work output*, W, to the *heat input*, Q_2. Making use of Eq. (5-53) we can write

$$\eta = \frac{W}{Q_2} = \frac{Q_2 + Q_1}{Q_2}. \qquad (5\text{-}54)$$

Fig. 5-11.   Schematic flow diagram of a heat engine.

The work output is what you get, the heat input is what you pay for. Of course, the heat Q_1 is in a sense a part of the "output" of the engine but ordinarily this is wasted (as in the hot exhaust gases of an automobile engine) and has no economic value. If the rejected heat were included as a part of its output, the efficiency of every engine would be 100%.

The definition of efficiency as work output divided by heat input applies to every type of heat engine and is not restricted to a Carnot engine.

If the Carnot cycle is traversed in a counterclockwise rather than a clockwise direction, the directions of all arrows in Figs. 5-10 and 5-11 are reversed, but there is no change in the magnitudes of Q_2, Q_1, and W. (The sequence of operations in Fig. 5-10 should be evident and will not be described.) Heat Q_1 is removed from the low temperature source, work W is given up by the work reservoir, and heat Q_2 equal to $W - Q_1$ is delivered to the high temperature reservoir. We now have a Carnot *refrigerator*, rather than a Carnot engine. That is, heat is pumped out of a system at low temperature (the interior of a household refrigerator, for example), mechanical work is done (by the motor), and heat equal to the sum of the mechanical work and the heat removed from the low temperature reservoir is liberated at a high temperature (and is absorbed by the air in the room).

The useful result of operating a refrigerator is the heat Q_1 removed from the low temperature reservoir; this is "what you get." What you have to pay for is the work input, $(-W)$. The greater the ratio of what you get to what you pay for, the better the refrigerator. A refrigerator is therefore rated by its *coefficient of performance*, E, defined as the ratio of Q_1 to $(-W)$. Again making use of Eq. (5-53), we can write

$$E = -\frac{Q_1}{W} = -\frac{Q_1}{Q_2 + Q_1}. \tag{5-55}$$

The coefficient of performance of a refrigerator, unlike the efficiency of a heat engine, can be much larger than 100%.

In order to calculate the efficiency of a Carnot engine (or coefficient of performance of a Carnot refrigerator) the equation of state of the working substance must be known. At least, it must be known at this stage of our development of the principles of thermodynamics. We shall show later that as a matter of fact the efficiencies of all Carnot engines operating between the same two temperatures are the same, whatever the working substance. Let us assume that the working substance is an ideal gas. The work done by the system in the isothermal expansion from a to b in Fig. 5-9 is then

$$W_{ab} = nRT_2 \ln \frac{V_b}{V_a}.$$

The work done in the adiabatic expansion from b to c is

$$W_{bc} = nc_v(T_2 - T_1).$$

The work done on the system in the isothermal compression from c to d is

$$W_{cd} = nRT_1 \ln \frac{V_d}{V_c},$$

and the work in the final adiabatic compression from d to a is

$$W_{da} = nc_v(T_1 - T_2).$$

If the working substance is an ideal gas, there is no change in internal energy in the isothermal processes and the heat absorbed is equal to the work done. That is,

$$W_{ab} = Q_2,$$
$$W_{cd} = Q_1.$$

The efficiency of the cycle is

$$\eta = \frac{W}{Q_2} = \frac{W_{ab} + W_{bc} + W_{cd} + W_{da}}{Q_2}$$

$$= \frac{nR\left(T_2 \ln \frac{V_b}{V_a} + T_1 \ln \frac{V_d}{V_c}\right)}{nRT_2 \ln \frac{V_b}{V_a}}. \tag{5-56}$$

But points b and c lie on the same adiabatic, as do points d and a. Hence

$$T_2^{\frac{1}{\gamma - 1}} V_b = T_1^{\frac{1}{\gamma - 1}} V_c,$$

$$T_2^{\frac{1}{\gamma - 1}} V_a = T_1^{\frac{1}{\gamma - 1}} V_d.$$

When one of these equations is divided by the other, we obtain

$$\frac{V_b}{V_a} = \frac{V_c}{V_d}.$$

Eq. (5-56) therefore reduces to

$$\boxed{\eta = \frac{T_2 - T_1}{T_2}.} \tag{5-57}$$

If the cycle is operated in the reverse direction, so that we have a Carnot refrigerator, the coefficient of performance is

$$\boxed{E = \frac{T_1}{T_2 - T_1}.} \tag{5-58}$$

Combining the equations above with the definitions of efficiency and coefficient of performance in terms of Q_1 and Q_2, we obtain for either cycle,

$$\frac{Q_2}{T_2} + \frac{Q_1}{T_1} = 0. \tag{5-59}$$

The (absolute magnitudes of the) quantities of heat absorbed and rejected are therefore proportional to the temperatures of the heat reservoirs in either cycle.

Problems

1. Complete the derivations of Eqs. (5-23) to (5-26).

2. Derive for a van der Waals gas the equations corresponding to (5-36) to (5-38) for an ideal gas.

3. The internal energy of a certain gas may be represented by the empirical equation

$$U = aT - bp,$$

where a and b are constants. The coefficients of thermal expansion and compressibility are respectively $1/T$ and $1/p$. Find the heat capacity at constant volume C_v in terms of a, b, p, and T.

4. An ideal gas for which $c_v = 5R/2$ is taken from point a to point b in Fig. 5-12 along the three paths acb, adb, and ab. Let $p_2 = 2p_1$, $v_2 = 2v_1$. (a) Compute the heat supplied to the gas, per mole, in each of the three processes. Express the answer in terms of R and T_1. (b) Compute the molar specific heat capacity of the gas, in terms of R, for the process ab.

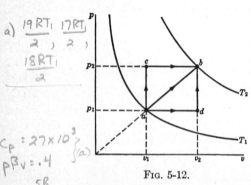

Fig. 5-12.

5. Compare the magnitudes of the terms c_p and $p\beta v$, in Eq. (5-19), (a) for copper at 600° K and 1 atm, and (b) for an ideal gas for which $c_p = 5R/2$. (c) When heat is supplied to an ideal gas in a process at constant pressure, what fraction goes into an increase in internal energy? (d) When heat is supplied to copper in a process at constant pressure, what fraction goes into an increase in internal energy?

6. Fig. 5-13 represents a cylinder with thermally insulated walls, containing a movable frictionless thermally insulated piston. On each side of the piston are n moles of an ideal gas. The initial pressure p_0, volume V_0, and temperature T_0 are the same on both sides of the piston. The value of γ for the gas is 1.50, and c_v is independent of temperature.

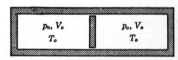

Fig. 5-13.

By means of a heating coil in the gas on the left side of the piston, heat is slowly supplied to the gas on this side. It expands and compresses the gas on the right side until its pressure has increased to $27p_0/8$. In terms of n, c_v, and T_0,

(a) How much work is done on the gas on the right side?
(b) What is the final temperature of the gas on the right?
(c) What is the final temperature of the gas on the left?
(d) How much heat flows into the gas on the left?

7. In the compression stroke of a Diesel engine, air is compressed from atmospheric pressure and room temperature to about 1/15th of its original volume. Find the final temperature, assuming a reversible adiabatic compression. See Table 12-3.

$$W = C_v (T_1 - T_2) + a \left[\left(\frac{1}{v_2} \right) - \left(\frac{1}{v_1} \right) \right]$$

8. Compute the work done in a reversible adiabatic expansion of a van der Waals gas by direct evaluation of $\int p \, dv$, and compare with Eq. (5-42). *same*

9. Discuss the feasibility of operating an automobile by means of the energy stored in a tank of compressed air.

10. An ideal gas for which $c_v = 3R/2$ occupies a volume of 4 m³ at a pressure of 8 atm and a temperature of 400° K. The gas expands to a final pressure of 1 atm. Compute the final volume and temperature, the work done, the heat absorbed, and the change in internal energy, for each of the following processes: (a) the expansion is reversible and isothermal, (b) the expansion is reversible and adiabatic, (c) the expansion takes place into a vacuum. *see p 369 (table)*

11. Suppose one of the vessels in the Joule apparatus of Fig. 5-4 contains n_A moles of a van der Waals gas and the other contains n_B moles, both at an initial temperature T_1. The volume of each vessel is V. Find the expression for the change in temperature when the stopcock is opened and the system is allowed to come to a new equilibrium state. Neglect any flow of heat to the vessels. Verify your solution for the cases where $n_A = n_B$, and where $n_B = 0$.

12. In the numerical examples in Secs. 5-8 and 5-9, compute the drop in temperature if the gas were helium instead of carbon dioxide. *−.068° , .61°*

13. Complete the derivation of Eq. (5-45). Use the equation of state in virial form and retain only terms in $1/v$.

14. At temperatures above 300° K, the value of c_p for copper can be approximated by a linear relation of the form

$$c_p = a + bT.$$

(a) Find as accurately as you can from Fig. 4-3 the values of a and b. (b) Compute the change in the specific enthalpy of copper at a pressure of 1 atm when the temperature is increased from 300° K to 1200° K.

15. Table 3 in Fig. 10-1 lists values of the specific enthalpy h for superheated steam as a function of temperature, at a constant pressure of 250 lb/in². The table below, also taken from Keenan and Keyes, gives corresponding values at a constant pressure of 2500 lb/in². The units of h are Btu/lb.

$t(°F)$	700°	800°	1000°	1200°	1400°	1600°
h(Btu/lb)	1176.8	1303.6	1458.4	1585.3	1706.1	1826.2

Construct graphs of h vs t, at the constant pressures of 250 and 2500 lb/in², and in the temperature range from 700° F to 1600° F. Locate the origin of the graph at $t = 700°$ F, $h = 1100$ Btu/lb. From inspection of the graphs, complete the following statements:

(a) At a temperature of 800° F, c_p for superheated steam (increases) (decreases) (remains constant) as the pressure is increased.

(b) At a pressure of 250 lb/in², c_p (increases) (decreases) (remains constant) as the temperature is increased.

(c) Same as (b), but for a pressure of 2500 lb/in².

(d) How many Btu are required to increase the temperature of one pound of superheated steam from 700° F to 1600° F, at pressures of 250 lb/in² and 2500 lb/in²?

(e) From the graph, find the ratio c_p/R for superheated steam at 250 lb/in² and 1000° F, where c_p is the molar specific heat. Compare with values of the ratio c_p/R listed in Table 12-3.

16. The molar specific enthalpy of most substances, at temperatures that are not too low, can be expressed by the empirical equation

$$h = aT + bT^2 + cT^{-1} + d,$$

where a, b, c, and d are constants. (a) Find the molar specific heat capacity at constant pressure. (See Problem 3 in Chapter 4.)

17. A steam turbine receives a steam flow of 5000 kgm/hr and its power output is 500 kw. Neglect any heat loss from the turbine. Find the change in specific enthalpy of the steam flowing through the turbine, (a) if entrance and exit are at the same elevation, and entrance and exit velocities are negligible, (b) if the entrance velocity is 60 m/sec, the exit velocity is 360 m/sec, and the inlet pipe is 3 m above the exhaust.

18. Show that the efficiency of a Carnot cycle, using as the working substance a gas obeying the Clausius equation of state, $p(v - b) = RT$, is the same as that for an ideal gas.

19. One mole of air at standard conditions is compressed isothermally and reversibly to one-half its original volume, and then is expanded adiabatically and reversibly to its original pressure. Find (a) the net work done by the gas, (b) the net heat flowing into the gas, (c) the change in internal energy, and (d) the final temperature.

20. In the M.I.T. transonic wind tunnel, air is stored in a tank of volume 40,800 ft³ at an absolute pressure of 45 lb/in² and a temperature of 70° F. The air is released through a pressure regulating valve which maintains a constant pressure of 23 lb/in² in the test section where measurements are made. The Mach number (ratio of velocity of air stream to velocity of sound) at the test section is 1.3.

(a) Starting with air at a pressure of 15 lb/in², how much work is necessary to increase the pressure in the tank from 23 to 45 lb/in², the temperature being kept constant at 70° F? Express the answer in horsepower-hours. (b) How much heat, in Btu, must be removed? How many pounds of ice would this quantity of heat melt? (c) What would be the temperature, in degrees Fahrenheit, of the air in the tank if it expanded reversibly and adiabatically from a pressure of 45 lb/in² to 23 lb/in², the initial temperature being 70° F? (d) During blowdown, air flows out of the tank at the rate of 205 lb/sec. For how long a time can this flow be maintained?

CHAPTER 6

CHANGES OF PHASE

6-1 p-v-T surfaces for real substances. There exists for every real substance a relation between the pressure, specific volume (or density), and temperature, i.e., the equation of state of the substance. Therefore all possible equilibrium states of the substance lie on a p-v-T surface. That of an ideal gas, in Fig. 2-3, is a simple example. However, real substances can exist in the *gas phase* only at sufficiently high temperatures and low pressures. At low temperatures and high pressures transitions occur to the *liquid phase* and the *solid phase*. The p-v-T surface includes these phases as well as the gas phase.

Figs. 6-1 and 6-2 are schematic diagrams of portions of the p-v-T surface for a real substance. The former is for a substance like carbon dioxide that contracts on freezing, the latter for a substance like water that expands on freezing.

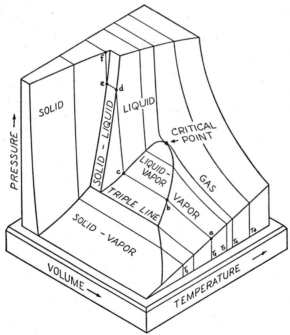

Fig. 6-1. p-v-T surface for a substance that contracts on freezing.

89

Study of the figures shows that there are certain regions (i.e., certain ranges of the variables) in which the substance can exist in a single phase only. These are the regions lettered solid, liquid, and gas or vapor. (The distinction between a gas and a vapor will be discussed shortly.) In other regions, labelled solid and liquid, solid and vapor, and liquid and vapor, both phases can exist simultaneously in equilibrium, and along a line called the triple line, all three phases can coexist. As with the p-v-T surface for an ideal gas, any line on the surface represents a possible reversible process, or a succession of equilibrium states. The lines in Figs. 6-1 and 6-2 are isothermal processes.

Those portions of the surfaces at which two phases can coexist are so-called *ruled surfaces*. That is, a straightedge parallel to the v-axis makes contact with the surface at all points. Hence, when the surfaces in Figs. 6-1 and 6-2 are projected onto the p-T plane these surfaces project as lines. The projection of the surface in Fig. 6-1 onto the p-T plane is shown in Fig. 6-3(a), and that of the surface in Fig. 6-2 is shown in Fig. 6-4(a). The lines corresponding to values of pressure and temperature

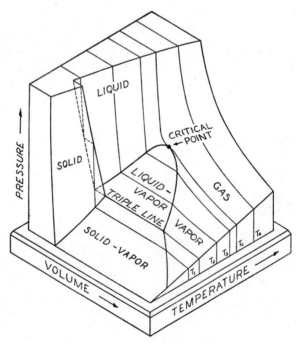

Fig. 6-2. p-v-T surface for a substance that expands on freezing.

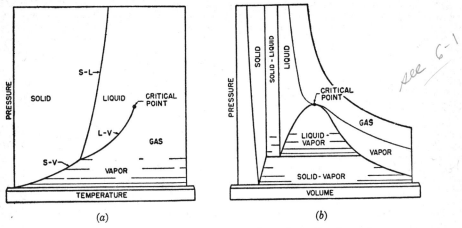

FIG. 6-3.   Projections of the surface in Fig. 6-1 on the p-T and p-v planes.

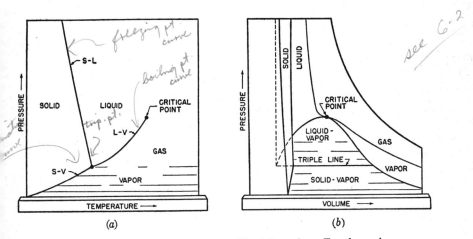

FIG. 6-4.   Projections of the surface in Fig. 6-2 on the p-T and p-v planes.

at which the solid and vapor phases, and the liquid and vapor phases, can coexist, always slope upward to the right.   The line representing the equilibrium between solid and liquid slopes upward to the right in Fig. 6-3, but upward to the left in Fig. 6-4.   We shall show in Sec. 7-5 that the former is characteristic of all substances that contract on freezing, the latter of substances (like water) that expand on freezing.

TABLE 6-1.

TRIPLE POINT DATA

Substance	t (°C)	p (mm of mercury)
O_2	-218	2.0
N_2	-210	96.4
A	-190	512
CO_2	-56.6	3880
H_2O	$+0.0098$	4.579

The triple line in Figs. 6-1 and 6-2 projects as a point in the p-T diagram, called the triple point. Triple point data for a few common substances are given in Table 6-1.

The projections of the surfaces in Figs. 6-1 and 6-2 onto the p-v plane are shown in Figs. 6-3(b) and 6-4(b). The surfaces can also be projected onto the v-T plane, but this projection is rarely used, since all the essential features of the surface can be shown in the first two projections.

Let us follow the changes in the state of the substance for which Fig. 6-1 is the p-v-T surface, in a process that takes us from point a to point f along the isothermal line at temperature T_2. To carry out this process, we imagine the substance to be enclosed in a cylinder with a movable piston. The cylinder is in contact with a heat reservoir at temperature T_2 and the piston is coupled to a work reservoir. Starting at the state represented by point a, where the substance is in the gas (or vapor) phase, we slowly increase the pressure on the piston. The volume decreases at first in a manner approximating that of an ideal gas. Work is done on the substance and heat is liberated. These two are not equal, however, so that there is an outstanding change in internal energy. When the state represented by point b is reached, drops of liquid appear in the cylinder. That is, the substance separates into two phases of very different densities, although both are at the same temperature and pressure. With further decrease in volume, along the line bc, the pressure does not increase but remains constant. More work is done on the substance and more heat is liberated. The work and heat are widely different in this part of the process and there is a substantial change in internal energy. The fraction

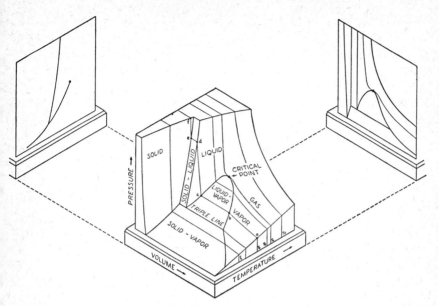

FIG. 6-5. Projection of p-v-T surface on the p-T and p-v planes.

of the substance in the vapor phase continuously decreases and the fraction in the liquid phase continuously increases.   In this part of the process,
where liquid and vapor can exist in equilibrium, the vapor is called a
saturated vapor and the liquid a *saturated liquid.* (The adjective "saturated" is an unfortunate one, for it brings to mind the concept of a
"saturated solution," that is, one in which the concentration of a dissolved
substance is a maximum.   There is nothing dissolved in a saturated vapor;
the substance that "precipitates" out with decreasing volume is not a
solute but the same substance as that of which the vapor is composed.)
The pressure exerted by a saturated vapor or liquid is called the *vapor
pressure.* The vapor pressure is evidently a function of temperature,
increasing as the temperature increases.   The curve lettered L-V in
Fig. 6-3(a), the projection of the liquid-vapor surface onto the p-T plane,
is the *vapor pressure curve.* The general shape of the vapor pressure curve
is the same for all substances, but the vapor pressure at a given temperature
varies widely from one substance to another.   Thus at a temperature of
20° C, the vapor pressure of mercury is 0.0012 mm of mercury; of water,
it is 17.535 mm of mercury; and of CO_2, 42959 mm of mercury.

Let us now return to the isothermal compression process.   At point c
the substance is entirely in the liquid phase.   To decrease the volume

from that at point c to that at point d, a very large increase in pressure is required, since the compressibilities of liquids are small. The work done on the substance is small because of the small change in volume, but it is not zero. Heat is liberated in an amount not equal to the work done, in general, and there is a change in internal energy.

At point d, the substance again separates into two phases. Crystals of the solid phase begin to develop, while the pressure remains constant as the volume diminishes. Work is done on the substance and heat is liberated. The work is much less than the heat, since the specific volumes of the liquid and solid are not very different, and there is a large change in internal energy.

The substance is entirely in the solid phase at point e and the volume decreases only slightly with further increase in pressure unless other forms of the solid can exist. Ice is an example of the latter case, where at least seven different forms have been observed at extremely high pressure, as

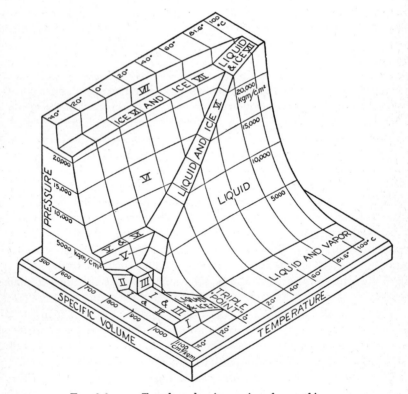

Fig. 6-6. p-v-T surface showing various forms of ice.

illustrated in Fig. 6-6.   Work is done when a solid is compressed, heat is liberated, and there is a change in internal energy.

If the volume of the system is now slowly increased, all of the changes described above proceed in the opposite direction and the quantities of heat absorbed by the system at each stage, and the work done by it, are numerically equal to the corresponding quantities in the compression process.

It will be seen from a study of Fig. 6-1 that if a compression process like that just described were carried out at a higher temperature, a higher pressure and a smaller specific volume would be required before a phase change from vapor to liquid commenced, and that when the substance was completely liquefied its specific volume would be somewhat larger than at the lower temperature.   At the particular temperature lettered T_c, called the *critical temperature*, the specific volumes of gas and liquid become equal. Above this temperature, no separation into two phases of different densities occurs in an isothermal compression from large volumes.   (That is, the liquid phase does not separate out.   Separation into a gas and a solid phase may occur at sufficiently high pressures.)   The common value of the specific volumes of gas and liquid at the critical temperature is called the *critical specific volume, v_c*, and the corresponding pressure the *critical pressure p_c*.   The point on the p-v-T surface whose coordinates are p_c, v_c, and T_c is the *critical point*.   The critical constants for a number of substances are given in Table 6-2.

TABLE 6-2

CRITICAL CONSTANTS

Substance	p_c n/m²	v_c m³/kgm-mole	T_c deg K
He	2.3×10^5	0.062	5.25
H₂	13	.065	33.2
N₂	34	.090	126
O₂	51	.075	154
CO₂	74	.095	304
H₂O	221	.057	647
Hg	3600	.040	1900

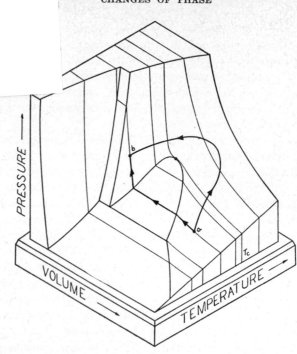

FIG. 6-7.

Suppose that a system originally in the state represented by point a in Fig. 6-7 is compressed isothermally. If the compression is carried out in a cylinder with transparent walls, we can observe the condensation to the liquid phase commence at the point where the isotherm meets the liquid-vapor surface, can see the liquid phase grow in amount while the vapor phase decreases, and at the state represented by point b we would be sure that the substance in the cylinder was wholly in the liquid phase. On the other hand, we could start with the substance in the same state (point a) and carry out the process represented by the line from a to b that curves around the critical point. (This process is of course not isothermal.) The end state of the system is the same in both processes but at no time in the second process did the substance separate into two phases. Nevertheless, it would certainly be described as a liquid at the end of the second process as well as at the end of the first. It has all the properties of a liquid, i.e., it is a fluid of high density (small specific volume) and small compressibility (the pressure increases rapidly for small decreases in volume) but its properties changed *continuously* from those associated with a vapor, at point a, to those associated with a liquid, at point b.

It is therefore possible to convert a vapor to a liquid without going through the process of "condensation," but no sharp dividing line can be drawn separating the portion of the p-v-T surface labelled "liquid" from that labelled "gas."

So far we have used the terms "gas" and "vapor" without distinguishing between them, and the distinction is in fact an artificial and unnecessary one. The term "vapor" is usually applied to a gas in equilibrium with its liquid (i.e., a saturated vapor) or to a gas at a temperature below the critical temperature, but the properties of a "vapor" differ in no essential respect from those of a "gas."

One may wonder whether or not the edges of the solid-liquid surface approach one another as do those of the liquid-vapor surface, and if there is another critical point for the solid-liquid transition. No such point has ever been observed, that is, there is always a finite difference in specific volume or density between the liquid and solid phases of a substance at the same temperature and pressure. This does not exclude the possibility of such critical points existing at extremely high pressures.

Suppose we have a vessel of liquid open to the atmosphere at a pressure p_1, in the state represented by point a in Fig. 6-8. As heat is supplied to the liquid its temperature increases at constant pressure p_1 and the representative point moves along an isobaric line to point b. When point b is reached, and if the supply of heat is maintained, the system separates into two phases, one represented by point b and the other by point c. The specific volume of the vapor phase is much greater than that of the liquid, and the volume of the system increases greatly. This is the familiar phenomenon of *boiling*. If the vessel is open, the vapor diffuses into the atmosphere. Thus the temperature T_b at which a liquid boils is merely that temperature at which its vapor pressure is equal to the external pressure, and the vapor pressure curve in Fig. 6-3(a) can also be considered as the *boiling point curve*. If the substance diagrammed in Fig. 6-8 is water (actually the solid-liquid line for water slopes in the opposite direction) and the pressure p_1 is 1 atmosphere, the corresponding temperature T_b is 373° K or 100° C. The vapor pressure curve always slopes upward to the right, so that an increase in external pressure always results in an elevation of the boiling temperature, and vice versa.

If, starting with the liquid at point a, heat is *removed* from it while the pressure is kept constant, the representative point moves along the isobaric line to point d. At this point, if one continues to withdraw heat, the system again separates into two phases, one represented by point d and the other by point e. For a substance like that represented in Fig. 6-8, the specific volume of the solid is less than that of the liquid, and the

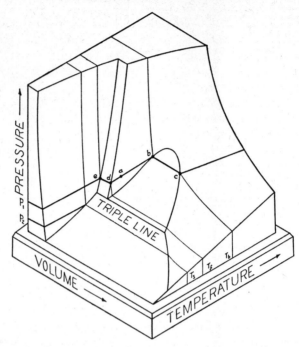

FIG. 6-8.   Phase changes in an isobaric process.

volume decreases. The process is that of *freezing* and evidently the solid-liquid equilibrium line in a p-T diagram like Fig. 6-3(a) is the *freezing point curve,* and at the pressure p_1 the freezing temperature is T_f. If the solid-liquid equilibrium line slopes upward to the right as in Fig. 6-8, an increase in pressure raises the freezing point and vice versa.

It is evident from a study of Fig. 6-8 that the liquid phase cannot exist at a temperature lower than that of the triple point, or at a pressure less than that at the triple point. If the pressure is less than that at the triple point, say the value p_2, the substance can exist in the solid and vapor phases only, or both can exist in equilibrium. The transition from one to the other takes place at the temperature of *sublimation* T_s, the direction of transfer depending upon whether heat is being absorbed or liberated (or whether the surroundings are at a slightly higher or lower temperature than T_s). Thus the solid-vapor equilibrium curve is also the *sublimation point curve.*

For example, the triple-point temperature of CO_2 is $-56.6°$ C and the corresponding pressure is 5.1 atm. Liquid CO_2 therefore cannot exist at atmospheric pressure, and no one has ever seen liquid CO_2 in an open

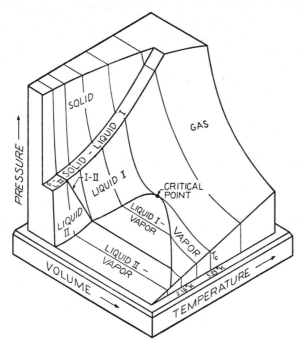

Fig. 6-9. *p-v-T* surface of helium.

vessel. When heat is supplied to solid CO_2 (dry ice) at atmospheric pressure, it sublimes and changes directly to the vapor phase. Liquid CO_2 can, of course, exist at room temperature, provided the pressure is sufficiently high. This material is commonly stored in steel tanks which when "full" contain mostly liquid and a small amount of vapor (both, of course, saturated). The temperature is room temperature if the tank has been standing in the room and the pressure is that of the ordinate of the vapor pressure curve at room temperature.

Fig. 6-9 is a schematic diagram of the *p-v-T* surface of helium. This substance exhibits a unique behavior at low temperatures, in the neighborhood of 4° K. The critical temperature and pressure are 5.25° K and 2.26 atm respectively. When helium in the vapor phase is compressed isothermally at temperatures between 5.25° K and 2.18° K, it condenses to a liquid phase called Helium I. When the vapor is compressed at temperatures below 2.18° K, a liquid phase called Helium II results. As is evident from the diagram, He I and He II can coexist in equilibrium over a range of temperatures and pressures, and He I can be converted to He II either by lowering the temperature, provided the pressure is not too great, or by reducing the pressure, provided the temperature is below 2.18° K. He II remains a liquid down to the lowest temperatures that have thus far been attained, and presumably does so all the way down to absolute zero.

Solid helium cannot exist at pressures lower than about 25 atm, nor can it exist in equilibrium with its vapor at any temperature or pressure. Helium has two triple points. An examination of Fig. 6-9 shows that at one of these the two forms of the liquid are in equilibrium with the vapor, while at the other they are in equilibrium with the solid. It is interesting to note also that the solid phase can exist at temperatures greater than the critical temperature.

Strictly speaking, the state of a system consisting of two phases in equilibrium is not represented on a p-v-T surface by a single point such as b in Fig. 6-10 but rather by the *two*

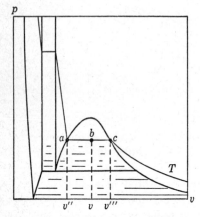

FIG. 6-10.   Liquid-vapor equilibrium.

points a and c. Whatever the relative masses of the two phases, the *state* of the liquid phase is represented by point a and the *state* of the vapor phase by point c. In a condensation process, starting with the system wholly in the vapor phase, the mass of the substance in state c decreases while the mass of that in state a increases, but the points representing the *states* (i.e., the pressure, density, and temperature) of the phases remain fixed.

Let us represent by v', v'', and v''' the specific volumes of the saturated solid, liquid, and vapor respectively. In Fig. 6-10, the abscissa of point c is the specific volume v''' of saturated vapor at the temperature T, and the abscissa of point a is the specific volume v'' of saturated liquid. When the state of the system is represented by point b, the system is partly in the liquid and partly in the vapor phase. We wish to compute the fraction of the mass of the system in each phase. If the specific volumes are per unit mass, then v''' and v'' are respectively the reciprocals of the densities of saturated vapor and liquid and v is the reciprocal of the *mean* density of the system, or the total volume V divided by the total mass m. Let V''' and V'' represent the actual volumes of the vapor and liquid phases, and m_3 and m_2 the masses of these phases. We then have the following relations:

$$V = V''' + V'', \quad m = m_3 + m_2,$$

$$v''' = \frac{V'''}{m_3}, \quad v'' = \frac{V''}{m_2}, \quad v = \frac{V}{m}.$$

It will be left as a problem to show that

$$\frac{m_3}{m} = \frac{v - v''}{v''' - v''}, \quad \frac{m_2}{m} = \frac{v''' - v}{v''' - v''}. \tag{6-1}$$

The differences $v - v''$, $v''' - v$, and $v''' - v''$, are respectively the lengths of the segments ab, bc, and ac, while the ratios m_3/m and m_2/m are the fractional masses of the substance in the vapor and liquid phases respectively.

The great distortion in scale of the p-v-T surface as drawn in Figs. 6-1 and 6-2 is evident from the fact that, for example, the specific volume of liquid water at 20° C and atmospheric pressure is 10^{-3} m³/kgm, while that of saturated water vapor at 20° C is 58 m³/kgm.

6-2 Critical constants of a van der Waals gas.

The point of coincidence of the three real roots of van der Waals equation is the critical point of a van der Waals gas (see Fig. 2-5). The critical isotherm at this point not only has a horizontal tangent but a point of inflection as well. That is, at this point,

$$\left(\frac{\partial p}{\partial v}\right)_T = \left(\frac{\partial^2 p}{\partial v^2}\right)_T = 0.$$

One of the useful features of the van der Waals equation is that it may be solved for p, and hence partial derivatives of p are easily calculated. We find

$$p = \frac{RT}{v - b} - \frac{a}{v^2}.$$

Hence

$$\left(\frac{\partial p}{\partial v}\right)_T = -\frac{RT}{(v - b)^2} + \frac{2a}{v^3},$$

$$\left(\frac{\partial^2 p}{\partial v^2}\right)_T = \frac{2RT}{(v - b)^3} - \frac{6a}{v^4}.$$

When $T = T_c$, the critical temperature, and $v = v_c$, the critical volume, each of the expressions above is zero. Solving the two equations simultaneously for v_c and T_c, and inserting these values in the original equation, we get

$$p_c = \frac{a}{27b^2}, \quad v_c = 3b, \quad T_c = \frac{8a}{27Rb}. \tag{6-2}$$

These equations are commonly used to determine the values of a and b for a particular gas, in terms of measured values of the critical constants. However, there are three equations for the two unknowns a and b and hence these are overdetermined. That is, we find from the second of the equations above that

$$b = \frac{v_c}{3},$$

while from simultaneous solution of the first and third equations,

$$b = \frac{RT_c}{8p_c}.$$

When experimental values of p_c, v_c, and T_c are inserted in the two preceding equations, we do not obtain the same value for b. In other words, it is not possible to fit a van der Waals p-v-T surface to that of a real substance at the critical point. Any two of the variables may be made to coincide but not all three. Since the critical volume is more difficult to measure accurately than the critical pressure and temperature, the latter two are used to determine the values of a and b in Table 2-1.

Another way of comparing the van der Waals equation with the equation of state of a real substance is to compare the values of the quantity RT/pv at the critical point. For a van der Waals gas,

$$\frac{RT_c}{p_c v_c} = \frac{8}{3} = 2.67,$$

and according to the van der Waals equation this ratio should have the value 8/3 for *all* substances at the critical point. (For an ideal gas, of course, the ratio equals unity.) Actual values are given in Table 6-3. The two are not equal, although the discrepancies are not large.

The van der Waals equation can be put in a form that is applicable to any substance by introducing the so-called *reduced* pressure, volume, and temperature, i.e., the ratios of the pressure, volume, and temperature to the critical pressure, volume, and temperature.

$$p_r = \frac{p}{p_c}, \quad v_r = \frac{v}{v_c}, \quad T_r = \frac{T}{T_c}.$$

TABLE 6-3.

EXPERIMENTAL VALUES OF $RT_c/p_c v_c$

Substance	$RT_c/p_c v_c$
He	3.06
H_2	3.27
O_2	3.42
CO_2	3.61
H_2O	4.30
Hg	1.10

Combining these equations with Eqs. (6-2) and the van der Waals equation, we get

$$\left(p_r + \frac{3}{v_r^2}\right)(3v_r - 1) = 8T_r. \tag{6-3}$$

The quantities a and b have disappeared and the same equation applies to any substance. The critical point has the coordinates 1, 1, 1, in a p_r-v_r-T_r diagram.

Eq. (6-3) is sometimes called the "law of corresponding states." It is a "law," of course, only to the extent that real gases obey the van der Waals equation. Two different substances are considered in "corresponding states" if their pressures, volumes, and temperatures are the same fraction (or multiple) of the critical pressure, volume, and temperature of the two substances.

6-3 Heats of transformation. Let us now return to the question of the heat absorbed or liberated during a change of phase. Consider a portion of an isothermal process in either the solid-liquid, the liquid-vapor, or the solid-vapor region, and let the process proceed in such a direction that a mass m is converted from solid to liquid, from liquid to vapor, or from solid to vapor. The system then absorbs heat, and the *latent heat of transformation*, l, is defined as the ratio of the heat absorbed, Q, to the mass m undergoing a change of phase. (One can also define the molar latent heat of transformation as the ratio of the heat absorbed to the number of moles, n, undergoing a change.)

$$l = \frac{Q}{m} = q,$$

$$l = \frac{Q}{n} = q. \tag{6-4}$$

Latent heats of transformation are expressed in joules per kilogram or joules per mole.

We shall use the notation l_{12}, l_{23}, l_{13}, to represent the latent heats of transformation from solid to liquid, liquid to vapor, and solid to vapor. These are called respectively the *latent heats of fusion*, of *vaporization*, and of *sublimation*. If the phase changes proceed in the opposite direction, the same quantity of heat is liberated.

The adjective "latent" is a carryover from the caloric theory, since in phase changes "caloric" was absorbed or liberated with no change in temperature and was said to become "latent." Today this term is often omitted and we speak merely of the heat of fusion, etc. Even this term is not well chosen, because a "heat of transformation" is not heat, but heat per unit mass or per mole.

Changes of phase are always associated with changes in volume, so that work is always done on or by a system in a phase change (except at the critical point, where the specific volumes of liquid and vapor are equal). If the change takes place at constant temperature, the pressure is constant also and the specific work done by the system is therefore

$$w = p(v_2 - v_1), \tag{6-5}$$

where v_2 and v_1 are the final and initial specific volumes. Then from the first law, the change in specific internal energy is

$$u_2 - u_1 = q - w$$

$$= l - p(v_2 - v_1). \tag{6-6}$$

As an example, consider the change in phase from liquid water to water vapor at a temperature of 100° C. The vapor pressure at this temperature is 1 atmosphere or 1.01×10^5 newtons/m² (by definition of 100° C), the heat of vaporization is 22.6×10^5 joules/kgm, the specific volume v''' of the vapor is 1.8 m³/kgm, and the specific volume v'' of the liquid is 10^{-3} m³/kgm. Then

$$u''' - u'' = l_{23} - p(v''' - v'')$$

$$= 22.6 \times 10^5 - 1.01 \times 10^5 (1.8 - 10^{-3})$$

$$= 20.8 \times 10^5 \text{ joules/kgm.}$$

Eq. (6-6) can be written

$$l = (u_2 + pv_2) - (u_1 + pv_1),$$

or, from the definition of enthalpy,

$$l = h_2 - h_1. \qquad (6\text{-}7)$$

The heat of transformation in any change of phase is therefore equal to the difference between the enthalpies of the system in the two phases. This is a special case of a general property of enthalpy discussed in Sec. 5-3, where we showed that in any reversible isobaric process the heat absorbed was equal to the change in enthalpy.

There is a simple relation between the three heats of transformation at the triple point. Consider two processes in which a solid at the triple-point temperature is transformed to a vapor, the first at a pressure slightly below the triple-point pressure and the second at a pressure slightly above. The initial and final states of the system are essentially the same in both processes, the total change in volume is the same, and the pressure is the same. The changes in internal energy and the work are therefore the same also, and hence the heat supplied is the same. In the first process the transformation is from solid to vapor and the heat supplied, per unit mass or per mole, is l_{13}. In the second process the substance first melts and then vaporizes and the heat is $l_{12} + l_{23}$. It follows that at the triple point,

$$l_{13} = l_{12} + l_{23}, \qquad (6\text{-}8)$$

and the heat of sublimation equals the sum of the heat of fusion and the heat of vaporization.

6-4 Specific heat capacity of saturated vapor. Fig. 6-11 is a projection on the p-v plane of a portion of the p-v-T surface. Consider the two cyclic processes lettered $abcd$. Starting at point a in either cycle, with the substance just at the left of the saturation line, we raise the temperature from T to $T + dT$, then carry out a change of phase bc at temperature $T + dT$, cool the substance just to the right of the saturation line to temperature T, and return to the original state along da. Since there has been no change of internal energy, the net heat flowing into the system equals the net work done by it.

The processes ab and cd are neither at constant pressure nor constant volume, but are characterized by the fact that the substance remains saturated. We therefore define the specific heat capacity c_s of a saturated solid, liquid, or vapor, as the heat absorbed per unit mass or per mole, per degree rise in temperature, in a process in which the substance remains

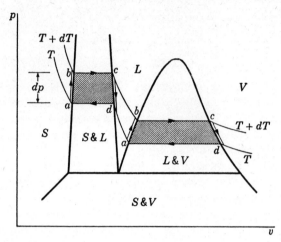

Fig. 6-11. Cyclic processes involving a change of phase.

saturated. For solids and liquids, c_s is not very different from c_p, although for a vapor this is not the case.

Let us consider the liquid-vapor cycle in Fig. 6-11. Let $l(T)$ and $l(T + dT)$ represent the latent heats at T and $T + dT$. The net heat supplied to the system, per unit mass or per mole, is

$$q = c_s'' dT + l(T + dT) - c_s''' dT - l(T).$$

The net work done is, very nearly,

$$w = dp(v''' - v'').$$

Since

$$l(T + dT) = l(T) + \frac{dl}{dT} dT,$$

we obtain, after equating q and w and dividing by dT,

$$c_s''' - c_s'' = \frac{dl}{dT} - \frac{dp}{dT}(v''' - v'').$$

But from the Clapeyron equation (see Sec. 7-5),

$$\frac{dp}{dT}(v''' - v'') = \frac{l}{T},$$

$$c_s''' - c_s'' = \frac{dl}{dT} - \frac{l}{T},$$

or

$$c_s''' - c_s'' = T \frac{d}{dT}\left(\frac{l}{T}\right). \tag{6-9}$$

The same reasoning can of course be applied to the liquid-solid or solid-vapor transformation, or to a chemical reaction. In the latter case, the specific heat capacities refer to the products and components of the reaction, and l is replaced by the heat absorbed in the reaction. If the volume change is negligible, which will be the case if no gases are involved, then $w = 0$ and we have

$$c_2 - c_1 = \frac{dq}{dT}, \tag{6-10}$$

where c_1 and c_2 are the heat capacities before and after the reaction and q is the heat absorbed in the reaction. (In chemistry, q is considered positive if heat is liberated.) Thus the temperature coefficient of the heat of a chemical reaction at constant volume equals the difference between the heat capacities of the products and components of the reaction.

Problems

1. A cylinder provided with a piston contains water vapor at a temperature of $-10°$ C. From a study of Fig. 6-6, describe the changes that take place as the volume of the system is decreased isothermally. Make a graph of the process in the p-v plane, approximately to scale.

2. Refer to the data in problem 6-9. A cylinder of volume 2 ft^3 contains saturated water and water vapor at a temperature of 600° F. (a) If the masses of liquid and vapor are equal, find the volume occupied by each. (b) If the volumes are equal, find the mass in each phase. (c) Make a sketch like Fig. 6-10, showing approximately the position of point b for each case above.

3. A cylinder with a tightly fitting frictionless piston makes thermal contact with a heat reservoir at a temperature of 300° K. The initial volume of the cylinder is 8 m^3, and it contains 8 moles of a substance having the following properties, all at a temperature of 300° K.

$$v''' = 0.5 \text{ m}^3/\text{mole}, \qquad h''' = 1800 \text{ joules/mole},$$
$$v'' = 0.1 \text{ m}^3/\text{mole}, \qquad h'' = 600 \text{ joules/mole}.$$

Assume that the vapor phase is an ideal gas.

The piston is slowly forced into the cylinder until the volume is reduced to 1.6 m^3.

(a) At what pressure and volume does condensation begin?

(b) Draw a diagram of the process in the p-V plane.

(c) At the end of the process, how many moles have condensed to the liquid phase?

(d) How much heat was given to the heat reservoir during the condensation stage of the process?

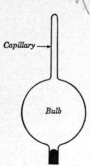

FIG. 6-12.

Capillary

Bulb

4. The volume of the bulb in Fig. 6-12 is 250 cm³. The capillary is 10 cm long and its diameter is 1 mm. Mercury is forced into the bottom of the bulb and compresses the gas until it occupies a volume 1 cm in length in the capillary. What will be the pressure of the gas in the capillary if the temperature is 20° C, the initial pressure was 10^{-3} mm of mercury, and the gas is (a) nitrogen, (b) water vapor? In case (b), how many grams of water vapor condense? The vapor pressure of water at 20° C is 17.5 mm of mercury.

5. Show that for a system consisting of two phases in equilibrium, the specific heat capacity at constant pressure, the coefficient of volume expansion, and the isothermal compressibility, are all infinite.

6. Using the critical constants listed in Table 6-2, compute the value of b in the van der Waals equation for CO_2, (a) from v_c, and (b) from T_c and p_c.

7. The critical constants of CO_2 are $p_c = 74 \times 10^5$ n/m², $v_c = .095$ m³/mole, $T_c = 304°$ K. At 299° K the vapor pressure is 66×10^5 n/m² and the specific volume of the liquid is .063 m³/mole. At the triple point, $T = 216°$ K, $p = 5.1 \times 10^5$ n/m², and the specific volumes of the solid and liquid are respectively .029 and .037 m³/mole.

(a) Construct as much as you can of the p-v diagram for CO_2 corresponding to Fig. 6-3 (b).

(b) One mole of solid CO_2 is introduced into a vessel whose volume varies with pressure according to the relation

$$p = 7 \times 10^7 V,$$

where V is in m³ and p in n/m². Describe the change in the contents of the vessel as the temperature is slowly increased to 310° K.

8. (a) Show that the critical constants of a substance obeying the Dieterici equation of state,

$$p(v - b) \exp (a/v\,RT) = RT,$$

are:

$$p_c = a/4\epsilon^2 b^2, \qquad v_c = 2b, \qquad T_c = a/4Rb.$$

(b) Compare the ratio $RT_c/p_c v_c$ for a Dieterici gas with the experimental values in Table 6-3.

9. The following table is taken from Keenan and Keyes, *Thermodynamic Properties of Steam*. The critical temperature is 705.4° F.

(a) Compute the external work and the increase in internal energy, in Btu, of one pound of water when converted to steam at 100° F, at 212° F, at 600° F.

(b) Make a graph of the latent heat of vaporization as a function of temperature. (Use the same units as in the table below.)

(c) Make a graph of the vapor pressure as a function of temperature. (Use the units in the table.)

(d) At a temperature of 200° F, compare the specific volume of the vapor with that computed from the ideal gas law.

t (°F)	p (lb/in²)	v'' (ft³/lb)	v''' (ft³/lb)	l_{23} (Btu/lb)
100	.949	.0161	350.4	1037
200	11.53	.0166	33.64	977.9
212	14.70	.0167	26.80	970.3
300	67.01	.0175	6.466	910.1
400	247.3	.0186	1.863	826.0
500	680.8	.0204	.6749	713.9
600	1543	.0236	.2668	548.5
700	3094	.0369	.0761	172.1
705.4	3206	.0503	.0503	0

10. The following data, taken from the Keenan and Keyes steam tables, give the specific enthalpies and specific volumes of saturated liquid and vapor at a number of temperatures. h is expressed in Btu/lb, v in ft³/lb, and p in lb/in².

t (°F)	h''	h'''	v''	v'''	p
200	167.99	1145.9	.01663	33.64	11.526
400	374.97	1201.0	.01864	1.8633	247.31
600	617.0	1165.5	.0236	.2668	1542.9
705.4	902.7	902.7	.0503	.0503	3206.2

(a) Compute the heat of vaporization l at each temperature, and make a graph of l vs t. The data need not be converted to mks units.

(b) Compute the change in specific internal energy, in Btu/lb, when saturated liquid is converted to saturated vapor at a temperature of 400° F. (The steam tables give 741.5 Btu/lb.)

11. Using the reduced form of a van der Waals equation, compute enough values of p_r to plot four isotherms of a van der Waals gas at temperatures 0.7 T_c, 0.9 T_c, 1.0 T_c, and 1.2 T_c, over a range of reduced specific volumes v_r from 0.5 to 1.5, and of reduced pressure p_r between 0 and 1.5. The computations are simplest if arbitrary values are assigned to v_r, at each value of T_r, and the equation is solved for p_r.

12. From the data in Problem 9, find c_s''' for water vapor between 200° F and 212° F. Let $c_s'' = c_p'' = 1$ Btu/lb-deg F.

CHAPTER 7

THE SECOND LAW OF THERMODYNAMICS

7-1 The second law of thermodynamics. Consider the following three processes. (1) Two blocks at different temperatures are brought in contact with each other but are thermally insulated from their surroundings. The two blocks eventually come to the same temperature and the heat flowing out of the warmer block equals that flowing into the colder. (2) A rotating flywheel is brought to rest by friction in its bearings. The temperature of the wheel and bearings rises and the increase in their internal energy is equal to the original kinetic energy of the flywheel. (3) An ideal gas performs a free expansion through a stopcock into an evacuated vessel. The temperature remains constant but the final pressure is less than the original pressure and the final volume is greater. In each of these processes, according to the first law or the principle of conservation of energy, the total energy of the system involved remains constant. Also, given the initial conditions, we know that the processes will take place as described above.

Now suppose we start with the three systems in the end states of the above processes, and imagine the processes to take place in reversed order. In the first example, one of the blocks would spontaneously become cooler and the other warmer until their original temperatures were restored. In the second, the wheel and bearings would cool down and the flywheel would start rotating with its original kinetic energy. In the third, the gas would rush back through the stopcock and compress itself into its original container. Everyone realizes that these reversed processes do not happen. But why not? The total energy of each system would remain constant in the reversed process as it did in the original, and there would be no violation of the first law. There must therefore be some other natural principle, in addition to the first law and not derivable from it, which determines the *direction* in which a process can take place in an isolated system. This principle is the second law of thermodynamics. Like the first, it is a generalization from experience and is a statement that certain processes such as those above, which would be entirely consistent with the first law, nevertheless do not happen.

These three impossible processes were selected as illustrations because they appear at first sight to differ widely from one another. The first is characterized by a spontaneous flow of heat from one body to another at a higher temperature. In the second, heat flows out of an object and an equivalent amount of kinetic energy appears. In the third, the volume of an isolated sample of gas decreases and its pressure increases while its

110

temperature remains constant.   Many other illustrations could be given. In the field of chemistry, for example, oxygen and hydrogen gas in the proper proportions can be enclosed in a vessel and a chemical reaction can be initiated by a spark.   If the enclosure has rigid nonheat-conducting walls the internal energy of the system remains constant.   After the reaction has taken place the system consists of water vapor at a high temperature and pressure, but the water vapor will not spontaneously dissociate into hydrogen and oxygen at a lower temperature and pressure.

Can we find some feature which all of these dissimilar impossible processes have in common?   Given two states of an isolated system, in both of which the internal energy is the same, can we find a criterion that determines which is a possible initial state and which a possible final state of a process taking place in the system?   What are the conditions under which no process at all can occur, i.e., when a system is in equilibrium? These questions could be answered if there existed some property of the system, that is, some function of the state of the system, which had a different value at the beginning and at the end of a possible process.   This function cannot be the internal energy, since this is constant in an isolated system.   A function having the desired property can be found, however. It was first devised by Clausius and is called the *entropy* of the system. Like the internal energy, it is a function of the state of the system only and, as we shall prove, it either increases or remains constant in any possible process taking place in an isolated system.   In terms of entropy, the second law may be stated:

Processes in which the entropy of an isolated system would decrease do not occur, or, in every process taking place in an isolated system the entropy of the system either increases or remains constant.

Furthermore, if an isolated system is in such a state that its entropy is a maximum, any change from that state would necessarily involve a decrease in entropy and hence will not happen.   Therefore the necessary condition for the equilibrium of an isolated system is that its entropy shall be a maximum.

Notice carefully that the statements above apply to isolated systems only.   It is quite possible for the entropy of a nonisolated system to decrease in an actual process but it will always be found that the entropy of other systems with which the first interacts increases by at least an equal amount.

To understand why the entropy function exists and what its properties are, we first state the second law in more familiar terms.   Many different statements can be made, all of them to the effect that some specified process is impossible.   All such statements can be shown to be equivalent.   Two useful formulations are the following:

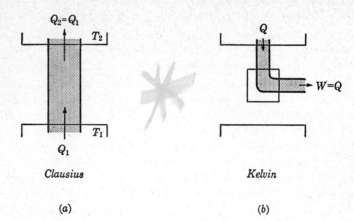

FIG. 7-1.   Schematic diagrams of the impossible processes referred to in (a) the Clausius and (b) the Kelvin statement of the Second Law.

    I. *No process is possible whose sole result is the removal of heat from a reservoir at one temperature and the absorption of an equal quantity of heat by a reservoir at a higher temperature.*

    II. *No process is possible whose sole result is the abstraction of heat from a single reservoir and the performance of an equivalent amount of work.*

The former is known as the Clausius statement of the second law, and the latter as the Kelvin (or Kelvin-Planck) statement.

The impossible processes are shown diagrammatically in Fig. 7-1(a) and (b).

That the Kelvin and Clausius statements of the second law are equivalent may be shown as follows. The proof consists of showing that if it were possible to violate one statement of the law, the other would or could be violated also. Suppose we have a cyclic heat engine that violates the Kelvin statement, that is, it takes in heat from a single reservoir at constant temperature and converts it completely to mechanical work. We could use the work output of this engine, represented by the rectangle in Fig. 7-2(a), to drive a refrigerator (not necessarily a Carnot refrigerator) as illustrated in the figure. The latter, if it is a refrigerator at all, takes in less heat from its low temperature reservoir than it delivers to its high temperature reservoir. A part of the heat it delivers to the high temperature reservoir can be diverted as shown to furnish the heat input to the engine, while there remains an outstanding flow of heat from a low to a high temperature reservoir. The device would operate continuously, with the engine providing just enough work to run the refrigerator, but would violate the Clausius statement of the second law.

On the other hand, suppose we had a continuous flow of heat from a low to a high temperature reservoir, in violation of the Clausius statement, as illustrated by the left pipe line in Fig. 7-2(b). We could then operate an engine (any heat engine) between the two heat reservoirs. Whatever its efficiency, this engine takes in more heat than it rejects. Let it reject heat at the same rate at which heat flows upward from the low to the high temperature reservoir, and take in enough additional heat from the high temperature reservoir to provide for its output of mechanical work. This system will also operate continuously, and it will be seen that its sole outstanding result is to withdraw heat from a single reservoir and convert it completely into mechanical work, in violation of the Kelvin statement. Therefore the two statements are equivalent.

A cyclic device which *would* continuously abstract heat from a single reservoir and convert the heat completely to mechanical work is called a *perpetual motion machine of the second kind*. Such a machine would not violate the first law (the principle of conservation of energy) since it would not *create* energy, but economically it would be just as valuable as if it did so, because of the existence of heat reservoirs, such as the oceans or the earth's atmosphere, from which heat could be abstracted continuously at no cost. Hence the second law is sometimes stated: "A perpetual motion machine of the second kind is impossible."

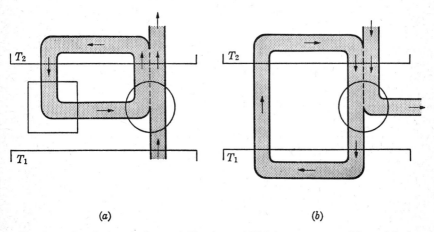

(a)   (b)

FIG. 7-2.   Proof of equivalence of Clausius and Kelvin statements of Second Law.

7-2 Efficiencies of reversible engines. We next derive two important consequences of the second law:

(a) No heat engine operating in cycles between two reservoirs at constant temperatures can have a greater efficiency than a reversible engine operating between the same two reservoirs.

(b) All reversible engines operating between two reservoirs at constant temperatures have the same efficiency.

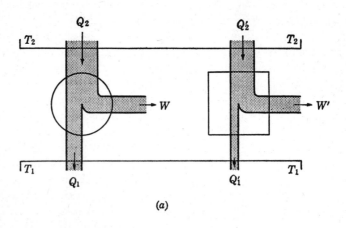

(a)

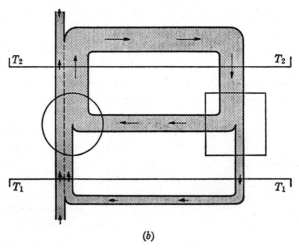

(b)

FIG. 7-3. No engine can be more efficient than a reversible engine operating between the same two temperatures.

Note that a reversible engine which absorbs heat at a single temperature and rejects heat at a single (different) temperature is necessarily a Carnot engine and its cycle is bounded by two isothermals and two adiabatics.

The method of proving the statements above is to show that if they were *not* true, either the Kelvin or the Clausius statement of the second law would be violated.

In Fig. 7-3(a), the circle represents a reversible engine operating between two reservoirs at temperatures T_2 and T_1, taking in heat Q_2 from the reservoir at temperature T_2, rejecting heat Q_1 to the reservoir at temperature T_1, and doing work $W = Q_2 - Q_1$. (We are considering both Q_2 and Q_1 as positive quantities.) The efficiency of this engine as shown is about 50%. The rectangle at the right of the diagram represents an assumed engine having a higher efficiency than the reversible engine (about 75%). We assume that the engines are built or operated so that each delivers the same mechanical work. (This could be the work per cycle or the work in some whole number of cycles.) Since the engine at the right is assumed to have a higher efficiency than the reversible engine, it takes in less heat from the high temperature reservoir and rejects less to the low temperature reservoir.

Now since the reversible engine is reversible, it can be reversed in the thermodynamic as well as the mechanical sense. That is, *it can be operated as a refrigerator with no changes in the magnitudes of* Q_2, Q_1, *and* W. Let us therefore couple the assumed high efficiency engine to the other engine operated in reverse as a refrigerator, as in Fig. 7-3(b). It should be evident from the diagram that the device will run itself and will result in a transfer of heat from a lower to a higher temperature, in violation of the Clausius statement of the second law. Therefore the efficiency of the assumed engine cannot be greater than that of the reversible engine.

Now suppose that two engines, both reversible, have different efficiencies when operated between two given temperatures. Let the one with the higher efficiency, operated as an engine, drive the one with lower efficiency as a refrigerator. The diagram is the same as Fig. 7-3(b) and the second law is violated. Hence neither engine can have a higher efficiency than the other, which means that their efficiencies are equal.

Notice carefully that we have *not* proved that the efficiency of an *irreversible* engine is *lower* than that of a reversible engine but only that no engine, reversible or not, can have a *higher* efficiency than a reversible engine. We shall show, however, that the efficiency of an irreversible engine actually *is* lower than that of a reversible one operating between the same two temperatures.

7-3 The Kelvin temperature scale. The conclusions drawn in the preceding section regarding the efficiencies of reversible engines were used by Kelvin to define a temperature scale that is independent of the properties of any particular thermometric material.

We showed in Sec. 5-12 that when a Carnot engine *using an ideal gas as the working substance* is operated between two reservoirs at different temperatures, and when the temperatures of these reservoirs are measured *by a gas thermometer using an ideal gas*, the ratio of the heat absorbed to the heat rejected is equal to the ratios of the temperatures.

$$\frac{Q_2}{Q_1} = \frac{T_2}{T_1}. \tag{7-1}$$

We have shown in Sec. 7-2 that even if the working substance is *not* an ideal gas, the efficiencies of all Carnot engines operating between the same two temperatures are the same. That is, whatever the nature of the fluid in the cylinder in Fig. 5-10, if heat Q_2 is taken in at the higher temperature, the same amount of heat Q_1 will be rejected at the lower temperature. *The ratio Q_2/Q_1 is therefore independent of the nature of the working substance.* The same is *not* true of the temperature ratio T_2/T_1, if temperatures are measured by thermometers utilizing different materials. A constant volume helium thermometer, for example, filled to a finite pressure p_i at the ice point, will give a different value for the ratio T_2/T_1 than will a constant volume hydrogen thermometer and neither ratio will equal the ratio of the heat absorbed to the heat liberated by a Carnot engine.

Kelvin proposed that we use a Carnot engine as a thermometer and *define* the ratio of two temperatures as the ratio of the heat absorbed by the engine to the heat rejected, when the engine is operated between reservoirs at these temperatures. Then the equality

$$\frac{Q_2}{Q_1} = \frac{T_2}{T_1} \tag{7-2}$$

becomes a matter of definition, and the fundamental problem of thermometry, that of establishing a temperature scale, reduces to a problem in calorimetry. That is, the experimental quantities that are measured in determining an unknown temperature are quantities of heat rather than pressures, volumes, lengths, etc. Temperatures defined in this way are called Kelvin temperatures. Since Eq. (7-2) has been shown to be satisfied if temperatures are measured by an ideal gas thermometer, it follows that the ideal gas temperature scale and the Kelvin scale are identical.

A definition of the *ratio* of two temperatures alone does not completely define the temperatures. They can be completely defined by assigning an arbitrary value to the *difference* between any two temperatures. We therefore say arbitrarily that the difference between the Kelvin temperatures of the steam and ice points shall be exactly 100 degrees, and the Kelvin scale, as the term is ordinarily used, should properly be called the Kelvin centigrade scale. In engineering work, a difference of 180° is assigned to the steam point-ice point interval, with the same definition of the ratio of two temperatures, and the scale is called the Rankine scale. The size of the Rankine degree is the same as on the Fahrenheit scale.

As an example, suppose we wish to determine the temperature of a tank of water, using a Carnot engine as the only thermometer. As auxiliary equipment we require a heat reservoir at the steam point (of course, no thermometer is needed to ensure that it is at the steam point), a heat reservoir at the ice point (again no thermometer is required), and a calorimeter for measuring heats absorbed and liberated by the Carnot engine. Even the calorimeter does not require the use of a thermometer. For example, the heat withdrawn from the reservoir at the steam point can be measured by measuring the input of electrical energy to a heating coil that keeps the reservoir at the steam point as heat is withdrawn. Let T_s, T_i, and T represent, on the Kelvin scale, the steam point temperature, ice point temperature, and the temperature of the tank of water. All of these, including steam point and ice point, are unknown at the start of the experiment.

We first carry out a Carnot cycle between the reservoirs at the steam point and the ice point. Let Q_s and Q_i represent the quantities of heat absorbed and rejected. Then carry out a second cycle between the reservoir at the steam point and the tank of water (we could equally well use the tank of water and the reservoir at the ice point) and for simplicity let us take in the same amount of heat Q_s at the steam point. Let Q be the heat rejected at the unknown temperature T. We then have the following equations:

$$\frac{Q_s}{Q_i} = \frac{T_s}{T_i},$$

$$\frac{Q_s}{Q} = \frac{T_s}{T},$$

$$T_s - T_i = 100 \text{ degrees.}$$

The quantities Q_s, Q_i, and Q are known from experiment and we have three equations from which to determine the three unknowns T_s, T_i, and T.

No one has ever measured a temperature in the manner described above. The Kelvin temperature scale is established by correcting the readings of a gas thermometer to what they would be if the gas were ideal, or by equivalent procedures for temperatures above and below the range accessible to gas thermometry. (By "establishing" the scale is meant that a large number of fixed temperatures such as the steam point, ice point, freezing point of gold, etc., are carefully measured once and for all.) This correction can be made from certain equations derived from the second law, and the experiments involved in ascertaining the magnitudes of the corrections require the measurement of quantities of heat. Hence the measurements reduce essentially to problems in calorimetry, as stated above, although the calorimetry is less direct than in our idealized experiment.

A Carnot engine operated in reverse becomes a Carnot refrigerator. Since all processes are reversible, the ratio of the heat Q_1 absorbed from the reservoir at the lower temperature T_1, to the heat Q_2 rejected to the reservoir at the higher temperature T_2, is equal to the ratio of the temperatures,

$$\frac{Q_1}{T_1} = \frac{Q_2}{T_2}.$$

The work W required to operate the refrigerator, from the first law, is

$$W = Q_2 - Q_1,$$

and the coefficient of performance is

$$E = \frac{Q_1}{W} = \frac{Q_1}{Q_2 - Q_1} = \frac{T_1}{T_2 - T_1}.$$

The coefficient of performance is independent of the nature of the working substance.

It is left as a problem to show by the method used in Sec. 7-2 that no refrigerator operating between two given temperatures can have a greater coefficient of performance than a Carnot refrigerator.

7-4 Absolute zero. It follows from the definition of temperature on the Kelvin scale that Kelvin temperatures of zero degrees or less cannot exist. Consider a Carnot engine operated between a reservoir at a fixed temperature T_2 and a second reservoir at a lower temperature T_1. Let the engine take in heat Q_2 from the reservoir at temperature T_2. The mechanical work W done by the engine, from the first law, is

$$W = Q_2 - Q_1,$$

and from the definition of Kelvin temperature,

$$Q_1 = Q_2 \frac{T_1}{T_2}.$$

Hence

$$W = Q_2 - Q_2 \frac{T_1}{T_2},$$

and

$$T_1 = T_2 \left(1 - \frac{W}{Q_2}\right). \tag{7-3}$$

The larger the work W, the lower the temperature T_1. But from the second law,

$$W < Q_2,$$

since the engine cannot convert to work all of the heat supplied to it. Therefore the term in parentheses in Eq. (7-3) is always greater than zero, and hence the lowest attainable temperature is greater than zero. In other words, a temperature of absolute zero or less is unattainable.

7-5 The Clausius-Clapeyron equation. To state the fact that all Carnot engines operated between two given temperatures have the same efficiency is one way of stating the second law of thermodynamics. We shall put this law in a more useful analytical form in a later section, but many of its consequences can be deduced directly from the statement above.

A Carnot cycle is any reversible cycle bounded by two isotherms and two adiabatics. The working substance need not be an ideal gas. It may be a real gas, a liquid, a solid, or changes in phase may take place during the cycle. By considering a Carnot engine operated between two reservoirs differing infinitesimally in temperature, and by letting the

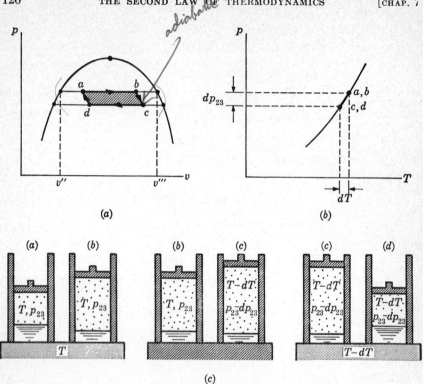

FIG. 7-4. Infinitesimal reversible cycle used to derive Clausius-Clapeyron equation.

working substance undergo a change in phase, we can derive an important relation known as the Clausius-Clapeyron equation, giving the slope of the equilibrium lines in a pressure-temperature diagram.

We shall describe a cycle in which the phases in equilibrium are liquid and vapor, but the same argument can be applied to the solid-vapor or solid-liquid equilibrium. The cycle is indicated by shading in Fig. 7-4(a) and the Carnot engine is shown in Fig. 7-4(c). The initial state of the system is represented by point a in Fig. 7-4(a) and by part (a) of Fig. 7-4(c). The cylinder of the Carnot engine contains a liquid and vapor in equilibrium at temperature T and pressure p_{23}. The specific volumes of the liquid and vapor phases are respectively v'' and v'''. We first carry out an isothermal expansion at temperature T until an arbitrary mass m has been vaporized, at which time the state of the system is represented by point b in Fig. 7-4(a) and by part (b) of Fig. 7-4(c). The pressure remains constant in this part of the cycle. The mass m, while in the liquid phase, occupied a volume mv'' and in the vapor phase it occupies a volume mv'''. The increase in volume of the system is therefore $m(v''' - v'')$. The heat Q absorbed by the system in this part of the cycle is the product of the mass m and the latent heat of vaporization l_{23}.

In the next stage of the cycle, the cylinder at temperature T and pressure p_{23} is transferred to an insulating stand, and a very small adiabatic expansion is carried out. The work done is negligible and, of course, no heat is absorbed, but the temperature drops to $T - dT$ and the pressure to $p_{23} - dp_{23}$. The state of the system is now represented by point c in Fig. 7-4(a).

The cylinder is next moved to a heat reservoir at temperature $T - dT$ and an isothermal and isobaric compression is carried out, taking the system to point d in Fig. 7-4(a). A final adiabatic compression returns the system to point a.

We have shown that the efficiency of any Carnot cycle is

$$\frac{W}{Q_2} = \frac{Q_2 - Q_1}{Q_2} = \frac{T_2 - T_1}{T_2}.$$

In the present infinitesimal cycle, this becomes

$$\frac{d'W}{Q} = \frac{dT}{T},$$

where Q is the heat absorbed at the higher temperature and is given by

$$Q = ml_{23}.$$

If the small volume changes in the adiabatic processes are neglected, the net work $d'W$ done in the cycle is the area of the shaded "rectangle" in Fig. 7-4(a), whose base is $m(v''' - v'')$ and whose height is dp_{23}.

$$d'W = m(v''' - v'')dp_{23}.$$

Then

$$\frac{d'W}{Q} = \frac{m(v''' - v'')dp_{23}}{ml_{23}} = \frac{dT}{T},$$

and

$$\boxed{\frac{dp_{23}}{dT} = \frac{l_{23}}{T(v''' - v'')}.} \qquad (7\text{-}4)$$

This is one form of the Clausius-Clapeyron equation. It expresses the *slope* of the vapor pressure curve at any temperature in terms of the temperature, the latent heat of vaporization at that temperature, and the specific volumes of vapor and liquid. When the same reasoning is applied to the solid and vapor or solid and liquid phases, one obtains the corresponding equations

$$\frac{dp_{13}}{dT} = \frac{l_{13}}{T(v''' - v')}, \quad \frac{dp_{12}}{dT} = \frac{l_{12}}{T(v'' - v')}.$$

Although the latent heat of any transformation varies with temperature, it is always positive, as is the temperature T. Also, the specific volume of the vapor phase is always greater than that of either the liquid or solid phase and the quantities $(v''' - v'')$ and $(v''' - v')$ are always positive. The slopes of the vapor pressure curves and sublimation pressure curves are therefore always positive. The specific volume of the solid phase, however, may be greater or less than that of the liquid phase, and so the slope of the solid-liquid equilibrium line may be either positive or negative. We can now understand more fully why the p-v-T surface for a substance like water, which expands on freezing, differs from that for a substance which contracts on freezing. (See Figs. 6-1 and 6-2.) The term $(v'' - v')$ is negative for a substance that expands on freezing and is positive for a substance that contracts on freezing. Therefore the solid-liquid equilibrium surface, or its projection as a line in the p-T plane, slopes upward to the left for a substance like water that expands and upward to the right for a substance that contracts. Projections of the liquid-vapor and solid-vapor surfaces always have positive slopes.

An examination of Fig. 6-6 will show that Ice I (ordinary ice) is the only form of the solid phase with a specific volume greater than that of the liquid phase. Hence the equilibrium line between Ice I and liquid water is the only one that slopes upward to the left in a p-T diagram; all others slope upward to the right. ·

For changes in temperature and pressure that are not too great, the latent heats of transformation and the specific volumes can be considered constant, and the slope of an equilibrium line can be approximated by the ratio of the finite pressure and temperature changes, $\Delta p/\Delta T$. Thus the latent heat at any temperature can be found approximately from measurements of equilibrium pressures at two nearby temperatures, if the corresponding specific volumes are known. Conversely, if the equilibrium pressure and the latent heat are known at any one temperature, the pressure at a nearby temperature can be calculated. In calculations of this sort we usually assume that the vapor behaves like an ideal gas.

To integrate the Clausius-Clapeyron equation and obtain an expression for the pressure itself as a function of temperature, the heats of transformation and the specific volumes must be known as functions of temperature. This is an important problem in physical chemistry but we shall not pursue it further here except to mention that if variations in latent heat can be neglected, and if one of the phases is a vapor, and if the vapor is assumed to be an ideal gas, and if the specific volume of the liquid or solid is neglected in comparison with that of the vapor, the integration can be readily carried out. The resulting expression is

$$\frac{dp}{dT} = \frac{l}{T\,\dfrac{RT}{p}} ,$$

$$\frac{dp}{p} = \frac{l}{R}\frac{dT}{T^2} ,$$

$$\ln p = -\frac{l}{RT} + \ln C \qquad\qquad (7\text{-}5)$$

$$p = Ce^{-\frac{l}{RT}} .$$

In Sec. 9-7 we shall give a more formal derivation of the Clausius-Clapeyron equation. The derivation above was given at this point to show how an important consequence of the second (and first) law can be deduced in a very simple way.

7-6 Derivation of Stefan's law. As another example of the second law, we use it to derive Stefan's law for an ideal radiator. This law as usually given in elementary texts states that the total rate of emission of radiant energy by an ideal radiator or blackbody is proportional to the 4th power of the Kelvin temperature. It can be shown from this that the radiant energy density, or radiant energy per unit volume, within an enclosure whose walls are at a uniform temperature, is also proportional to the 4th power of the Kelvin temperature, provided there is in the enclosure at least a speck of perfectly absorbing material, so that the frequency distribution of the radiant energy is always that given by Planck's law. Under these conditions the energy density is a function of the temperature only, and the internal energy can be identified with the radiant energy.

Both the classical and quantum theories of radiation predict that when homogeneous isotropic radiant energy falls on a perfectly reflecting surface it exerts on the surface a pressure equal to $\frac{1}{3}$ of the energy density. Imagine an evacuated cylinder whose walls are perfectly reflecting thermal insulators, containing a "batch" of radiant energy which can be expanded or compressed like a gas. Provision is made for a flow of heat into or out of the cylinder, and a speck of perfectly absorbing material is included.

Let the radiant energy in the cylinder be carried through the Carnot cycle in Fig. 7-5. Process ab is an isothermal expansion at the temperature T, bc is an infinitesimal adiabatic expansion in which the temperature drops to $T - dT$, cd is an isothermal compression, and da is an adiabatic compression. Let e represent the energy density, so that

$$p = \tfrac{1}{3}e. \tag{7-6}$$

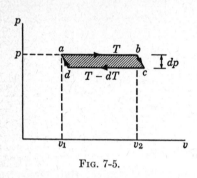

FIG. 7-5.

The work W done by the system in the isothermal process ab is

$$W = p(V_2 - V_1) = \tfrac{1}{3}e(V_2 - V_1).$$

Since the energy density is a function of the temperature only, it remains constant in this process and the change in internal energy is

$$U_2 - U_1 = e(V_2 - V_1).$$

From the first law, the heat Q flowing into the system is

$$Q = (U_2 - U_1) + W = \tfrac{4}{3}e(V_2 - V_1).$$

The net work $d'W$ done in the cycle is the shaded area in Fig. 7-5, or

$$d'W = dp(V_2 - V_1).$$

From Eq. (7-6),

$$dp = \tfrac{1}{3}de,$$

$$d'W = \tfrac{1}{3}de(V_2 - V_1).$$

From the second law, the efficiency of the cycle, $d'W/Q$, is equal to dT/T, or

$$\frac{\tfrac{1}{3}de(V_2 - V_1)}{\tfrac{4}{3}e(V_2 - V_1)} = \frac{dT}{T}.$$

Hence

$$\frac{de}{e} = 4\frac{dT}{T},$$

$$\ln e = 4 \ln T + \text{const},$$

$$e = \text{const} \times T^4.$$

The energy density is therefore proportional to the 4th power of the Kelvin temperature.

Problems

1. An inventor claims to have developed an engine that takes in 100,000 Btu at a temperature of 400° K, rejects 40,000 Btu at a temperature of 200° K, and delivers 15 kwh of mechanical work. Would you advise investing money to put this engine on the market?

2. A Carnot engine absorbs heat from a reservoir at a temperature of 100° C and rejects heat to a reservoir at a temperature of 0° C. If the engine absorbs 1000 joules from the high temperature reservoir, find the work done, the heat rejected, and the efficiency.

3. Which is the more effective way to increase the efficiency of a Carnot engine, to increase the temperature T_2, keeping T_1 fixed, or to decrease the temperature T_1, keeping T_2 fixed?

4. Prove by the method used in Sec. 7-2 that no refrigerator operating in cycles between two reservoirs at constant temperatures can have a greater coefficient of performance than a reversible refrigerator operating between the same two reservoirs. Draw diagrams corresponding to Fig. 7-3(a) and (b).

5. A refrigerator having a coefficient of performance one-half as great as that of a Carnot refrigerator is operated between reservoirs at temperatures of 200° K and 400° K, and it absorbs 600 joules from the low temperature reservoir. How much heat is rejected to the high temperature reservoir?

6. A Carnot refrigerator or heat pump is operated between reservoirs at 0° C *a)* 1370 J and 100° C. (a) If 1000 joules are absorbed from the low temperature reservoir, *b)* 2.7 how many joules are rejected to the high temperature reservoir? (b) What is the coefficient of performance?

7. Refrigeration cycles have been developed for heating buildings. Heat is absorbed from the earth by a fluid circulating in buried pipes and heat is delivered at a higher temperature to the interior of the building. If a Carnot refrigerator *11.9 Kwh* were available for use in this way, operating between an outside temperature of 0° C and an interior temperature of 25° C, how many kilowatt-hours of heat would be supplied to the building for every kilowatt-hour of electrical energy needed to operate the refrigerator?

8. The temperature in a household refrigerator is 0° C and the temperature of the room in which it is located is 25° C. The heat flowing into the refrigerator from the warmer room every 24 hours is 8×10^6 joules (enough to melt about *8.5 watts,* 50 lb of ice) and this heat must be pumped out again if the refrigerator is to be *.4¢* kept cold. If a Carnot refrigerator were available, operating between the temperatures of 0° C and 25° C, how much mechanical power in watts would be required to operate it? Compare the daily cost, at 2 cents per kwh, with the cost of 50 lb of ice (about 40 cents in Cambridge).

9. In Fig. 7-6, *abcd* represents a Carnot cycle, bounded by two adiabatics and by two isotherms at the temperatures T_1 and T_2, where $T_2 > T_1$. The oval figure is a reversible cycle for which T_2 and T_1 are respectively the maximum and minimum temperatures. In this cycle, heat is absorbed at temperatures less than or equal to T_2, and is rejected at temperatures greater than or equal to T_1. Prove

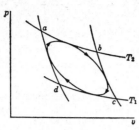

FIG. 7-6.

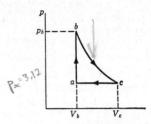

FIG. 7-7.

that the efficiency of the second cycle is less than that of the Carnot cycle.   Hint: Approximate the second cycle by a large number of small Carnot cycles.

10. One mole of a monatomic ideal gas ($c_v = \frac{3}{2}R$) is carried around the closed cycle abc in Fig. 7-7.   Process bc is a reversible adiabatic expansion.   Given that $p_b = 10$ atm, $V_b = 2$ m³, and $V_c = 4$ m³, (a) compute the heat input to the gas, the heat output, and the efficiency of the cycle.   (b) What is the maximum efficiency of an engine operating between the extremes of temperature of the cycle?

11. (a) Calculate the slope of the fusion curve of ice, in (newtons/m²)/°K, at the normal melting point.   The heat of fusion at this temperature is 3.34×10^5 joules/kgm and the change in specific volume on melting is -9.05×10^{-5} m³/kgm.
(b) Ice at $-2°$ C and atmospheric pressure is compressed isothermally. Find the pressure at which the ice starts to melt.
(c) Calculate $(\partial p/\partial T)_v$ for ice at $-2°$ C.   The value of β is 15.7×10^{-5} deg⁻¹, and that of κ is 120×10^{-12} (newtons/m²)⁻¹.
(d) Ice at $-2°$ C and atmospheric pressure is kept in a container at constant volume, and the temperature is gradually increased.   Find the temperature and pressure at which the ice starts to melt.   Show this process and that in part (b) in a p-T diagram like that in Fig. 6-4(a), and on a p-v-T surface like that in Fig. 6-2. Assume that the fusion curve and the rate of change of pressure with temperature, at constant volume, are both linear.

12. Calculate the heat of sublimation of ice at $-20°$ C from the following vapor pressure data:

$t(°C)$	-19.5	-20.0	-20.5
p (mm of mercury)	.808	.770	.734

13. Prove that the slope of the sublimation curve at the triple point is greater than that of the vaporization curve at the same point.

14. The vapor pressure of water at a temperature of 70° F is 0.3631 lb/in², and the heat of vaporization at this temperature is 1054 Btu/lb.   (a) Find the value of the constant in Eq. (7-5) in mks units.   (b) Calculate the vapor pressure at 80° F from Eq. (7-5) and compare with the experimental value of 0.5069 lb/in².

CHAPTER 8

ENTROPY

8-1 The Clausius inequality. The Clausius inequality is a relation between the temperatures of an arbitrary number of heat reservoirs and the quantities of heat given up or absorbed by them, when some working substance is carried through an arbitrary cyclic process in the course of which it interchanges heat with the reservoirs. For simplicity we shall consider only the three reservoirs at temperatures T_0, T_1 and T_2, shown schematically in Fig. 8-1, but the argument is readily extended to any number. The rectangle lettered "system" refers to any device (such as a gas in a cylinder) which is capable of absorbing and liberating heat with accompanying changes in volume. The processes taking place in the system are not necessarily reversible and of course the pipe lines are schematic only.

We consider any arbitrary process in which the system is carried through a closed cycle, so that its end state is the same as its initial state. Let Q_0, Q_1, Q_2, represent respectively the quantities of heat interchanged between the system and the heat reservoirs, and W the net amount of work done by the system. In the diagram, the system is shown absorbing heat from the reservoirs at temperatures T_2 and T_1, rejecting heat to the reservoir at temperature T_0, and performing mechanical work, but in the

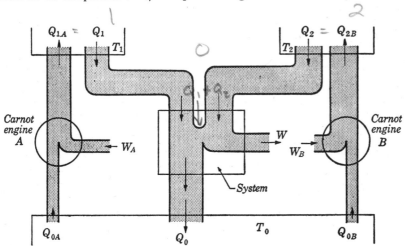

Fig. 8-1. Schematic diagram to illustrate the Clausius inequality.

127

general argument that follows we shall make no restriction on the directions of these interchanges except that they shall be consistent with the first and second laws.

To determine whether they are consistent, it is necessary to reduce the general problem to a process that can be compared either with the Kelvin or Clausius statements of the second law. Let us introduce as auxiliary equipment two Carnot engines, operating between pairs of heat reservoirs as shown. (In the diagram, the engines are actually refrigerators. We shall use the generic term, "engine," since in the general case some might be operated as engines and others as refrigerators.) Engine A supplies to the reservoir at temperature T_1 a quantity of heat Q_{1A} equal to that given up by this reservoir in the original cyclic process. This engine withdraws heat Q_{0A} from the reservoir at temperature T_0 and work W_A is supplied to it. By this process we eliminate any outstanding change in the reservoir at temperature T_1.

Carnot engine B supplies heat Q_{2B} to the reservoir at temperature T_2, in amount just equal to that given up to the system. It also withdraws heat Q_{0B} from the reservoir at temperature T_0 and work W_B is supplied to it. Thus there has been no outstanding change in the reservoir at temperature T_2. Since the original process through which the system was carried was cyclic, everything is now as it was at the start, except for the reservoir at temperature T_0 and the mechanical system that supplied or absorbed work. Unless Q_0 happens to be equal to the sum of Q_{0A} and Q_{0B}, the reservoir at temperature T_0 will have gained or lost some heat and unless W and $(W_A + W_B)$ are equal, the mechanical system has gained or lost work. Of course, we know from the first law that the *net* flow of heat from or to the heat reservoir must equal the *net* work done on or by the mechanical system and, as far as the first law is concerned, it is a matter of indifference whether the heat reservoir loses or gains heat, as long as the mechanical system gains or loses the same quantity of work. It is not, however, a matter of indifference from the point of view of the second law, since the second law (Kelvin statement) obviously would be violated if the heat reservoir lost heat and the mechanical system gained an equal amount of work. Therefore the heat reservoir must have *gained* heat and the mechanical system given up work, except in the special case where both have neither lost nor gained. That is, the heat Q_0 must be greater than the heat $(Q_{0A} + Q_{0B})$ or, in the limiting case, just equal to it.

Before putting these conclusions in analytic form, it is necessary to adopt a convention of sign for the Q's. We shall write our equations from the point of view of the *system*. That is, a quantity of heat Q is considered positive if heat is given to the system and negative if the system gives up heat.   Since Q_2, for example, is at the same time heat given to the system and heat given up by a reservoir, it follows that heat given up by a reservoir is positive, heat given to a reservoir is negative.

We can now write the following equations:

$$\frac{Q_{1A}}{T_1} + \frac{Q_{0A}}{T_0} = 0, \quad Q_{1A} + Q_1 = 0, \tag{8-1}$$

$$\frac{Q_{2B}}{T_2} + \frac{Q_{0B}}{T_0} = 0, \quad Q_{2B} + Q_2 = 0. \tag{8-2}$$

In the diagram as drawn, Q_1 and Q_2 are positive, Q_0 is negative, Q_{1A} is negative, Q_{0A} is positive, Q_{2B} is negative, Q_{0B} is positive.   However, in setting up the *general* equations, we write these all as positive quantities just as one writes $\Sigma F_x = 0$, $\Sigma F_y = 0$ for forces in equilibrium at a point, or $\Sigma i = 0$ in Kirchhoff's point rule.

From Eqs. (8-1) we have

$$Q_{0A} = T_0 \left(\frac{Q_1}{T_1} \right), \tag{8-3}$$

and from Eqs. (8-2),

$$Q_{0B} = T_0 \left(\frac{Q_2}{T_2} \right). \tag{8-4}$$

The *net* quantity of heat given up by the reservoir at temperature T_0 is $Q_0 + Q_{0A} + Q_{0B}$.   But the second law requires that the reservoir can only receive heat, not give it up.   Therefore the sum $Q_0 + Q_{0A} + Q_{0B}$ must be a negative quantity or, in the limiting case, zero.

$$Q_0 + Q_{0A} + Q_{0B} \leqq 0.$$

Inserting the expressions for Q_{0A} and Q_{0B} from the preceding equations, we get

$$Q_0 + T_0 \left(\frac{Q_1}{T_1} \right) + T_0 \left(\frac{Q_2}{T_2} \right) \leqq 0.$$

After dividing both sides of the inequality by T_0, this reduces to the symmetrical form

$$\frac{Q_0}{T_0} + \frac{Q_1}{T_1} + \frac{Q_2}{T_2} \leqq 0.$$

It should be evident that by making use of a sufficiently large number of Carnot engines, a process in which the system in Fig. 8-1 interchanged heat with any number of reservoirs could be reduced to an energy interchange between a single heat reservoir and a work reservoir. We would then find

$$\sum \frac{Q}{T} \leqq 0. \tag{8-5}$$

By extension, when the number of reservoirs becomes infinitely large and the system may exchange only infinitesimal amounts of heat with each, the finite sum becomes an integral and

$$\int \frac{d'Q}{T} \leqq 0. \tag{8-6}$$

Either Eq. (8-5) or (8-6) expresses the *Clausius inequality*, a relation between the quantities of heat absorbed or liberated by a number of heat reservoirs and *the temperatures of those reservoirs* when a working substance is carried through a cyclic process of any sort, reversible or irreversible. The quantities Q or $d'Q$ are considered positive when heat is given up by a reservoir. The inequality makes no statements about the *system* that was carried through the original process, which it obviously cannot do, since at no point did the temperature *of the system* enter the argument. The only temperatures considered are those of the reservoirs.

We give three examples of the Clausius inequality. First, consider the flow of heat by conduction from a reservoir at a temperature T_2 to a reservoir at a lower temperature T_1. This is a very simple case in which no "system" at all is involved, other than the material which conducts heat from one reservoir to the other. The quantities of heat Q_2 and Q_1 are necessarily equal in magnitude, but Q_2 is positive while Q_1 is negative. As a numerical example, let $T_2 = 400°$ K, $T_1 = 200°$ K, $Q_2 = 800$ joules, $Q_1 = -800$ joules. Then

$$\sum \frac{Q}{T} = \frac{800}{400} + \frac{-800}{200}$$

$$= 2 - 4$$

$$= -2 \text{ joules/deg,}$$

and we see that $\Sigma(Q/T)$ is actually less than zero.

As a second example, consider a heat engine operating between reservoirs at 400° K and 200° K.   The efficiency of a Carnot engine operating between these temperatures would be 50%.   Let us assume that our engine is less efficient than a Carnot engine, with an efficiency of only 25% (we have shown that it cannot be *more* efficient).   Assume that the engine takes in 800 joules from the high temperature reservoir.   It then converts 25% of this, or 200 joules, into work and rejects 600 joules to the low temperature reservoir.   The engine then becomes the system in our general argument.   We have

$$\sum \frac{Q}{T} = \frac{800}{400} + \frac{-600}{200}$$

$$= 2 - 3$$

$$= -1 \text{ joule/deg,}$$

and again $\Sigma(Q/T)$ is less than zero.

Finally, consider a Carnot engine operating between reservoirs at 400° K and 200 °K.   Its efficiency is 50% and if it takes in 800 joules it rejects 400 joules.   Hence

$$\sum \frac{Q}{T} = \frac{800}{400} - \frac{400}{200}$$

$$= 2 - 2,$$

$$= 0,$$

and in this case the equality sign holds, rather than the inequality.

8-2 Entropy.   In deriving the Clausius inequality, no restrictions were placed on the reversibility or irreversibility of the cycle through which the system was carried.   Let us now assume the cycle to be reversible, and let the system traverse it first in one direction and then in the opposite direction.   Let $d'Q_1$ represent the heat flowing into the *system* at any point in the first cycle, and $d'Q_2$ the heat flowing into it at the same point in the second cycle.   Since all processes in the second cycle are the reverse of those in the first, then

$$d'Q_1 = -d'Q_2. \tag{8-7}$$

If the cycle is reversible, the temperature of the *system* while it is exchanging heat with any reservoir is the same as the temperature of that reservoir. We can therefore write the Clausius inequality for the two cycles as

$$\oint \frac{(d'Q)_1}{T} \leqq 0, \quad \oint \frac{(d'Q)_2}{T} \leqq 0. \tag{8-8}$$

The symbol $\oint$ means that the integration is carried around a cyclic path. We could not use this symbol in Eq. (8-6) because this equation applied to the reservoirs which were not carried through cyclic processes. Combining Eqs. (8-7) and (8-8), we get

$$\oint \frac{(d'Q)_1}{T} \leqq 0, \quad - \oint \frac{(d'Q)_1}{T} \leqq 0.$$

But the only way in which both of these relations can be true is if the equality sign holds, and not the inequality. We therefore have the very important result that *when a system is carried around a reversible cycle and the heat d'Q added to it at every point is divided by its temperature at that point, the sum of all such quotients is zero.*

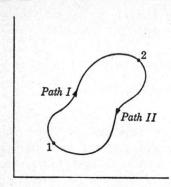

FIG. 8-2.

$$\oint \frac{d'Q}{T} = 0. \tag{8-9}$$
$$\text{Rev}$$

Consider now an arbitrary reversible cycle such as that represented by the closed curve in Fig. 8-2. Points 1 and 2 are any two points on the curve. The integral around the closed curve can be written as the sum of two integrals, one along path I from 1 to 2, the second along path II from 2 back to 1.

$$\oint \frac{d'Q}{T} = (I) \int_1^2 \frac{d'Q}{T} + (II) \int_2^1 \frac{d'Q}{T} = 0. \tag{8-10}$$

If the path II from 2 to 1 were traversed in the opposite direction, we would have, since the cycle is reversible,

from mech. —> thermo
(x, y, z) —> (p, v, T)   must
scalar field —> state func.   have exact
closed path —> cycle   differentia

$$(\text{II}) \int_2^1 \frac{d'Q}{T} = - (\text{II}) \int_1^2 \frac{d'Q}{T}. \qquad (8\text{-}11)$$

Combining this result with Eq. (8-10), we get

$$(\text{I}) \int_1^2 \frac{d'Q}{T} = (\text{II}) \int_1^2 \frac{d'Q}{T}. \qquad (8\text{-}12)$$

That is, the integral is the same along the two reversible paths. Also, since the original cycle was entirely arbitrary, it follows that *the integral is the same along all reversible* paths from 1 to 2. In mathematical terms, the quantity $d'Q/T$ is an *exact differential* of some function S of the state of the system, and may be represented by dS. Then

$$\int_1^2 \frac{d'Q}{T} = \int_1^2 dS = S_2 - S_1, \qquad (8\text{-}13)$$

since the integral of an exact differential along any path is equal to the difference between the values of the function at the end points of the path. The quantity S is called the *entropy* of the system, and Eq. (8-13) states that *the change in entropy of a system between any two equilibrium states is found by taking the system along any reversible path connecting the states, dividing the heat added to the system at each point of the path by the temperature of the system, and summing the quotients thus obtained.*

Thus we see that while $d'Q$ is not an exact differential, there are two ways in which an exact differential involving $d'Q$ can be obtained. One is to subtract from $d'Q$ the inexact differential $d'W$. The sum is the exact differential dU and the statement of this fact constitutes the first law of thermodynamics.

$$d'Q - d'W = dU. \qquad (8\text{-}14)$$

The second method is to divide $d'Q$ by the temperature T. The quotient is the exact differential dS and the statement of this fact constitutes the second law of thermodynamics.

$$\frac{d'Q}{T} = dS. \qquad (8\text{-}15)$$

In the mks system, entropy is expressed in *joules per degree Kelvin*. In engineering, the Btu per degree Rankine is used. Another common unit is the calorie per degree Kelvin.

The following points should be noted.

(a) The entropy of a system is defined for equilibrium states only.

(b) Only *changes* in entropy or entropy *differences* can be computed from Eq. (8-13). In many practical problems, such as the design of steam engines, we are concerned only with differences in entropy. For convenience, the entropy of a substance may be assumed zero in some convenient reference state and a numerical value can then be assigned to the entropy in any other state. Thus in computing steam tables, the entropy of water is assumed zero when it is in the liquid phase at 0° C and 1 atmosphere pressure, and a value is listed for the entropy over a wide range of temperatures and pressures, in the vapor as well as in the liquid phase.

(c) The entropy of a system in an equilibrium state is a function of the state of the system only and is independent of its past history. The entropy can therefore be expressed as a function of the thermodynamic coordinates of the system, such as the pressure and temperature or pressure and volume.

(d) Changes in entropy can be computed from Eq. (8-13) for *reversible* processes only. However, *any* reversible process between the same two end states can be used, since the change in entropy is the same for *all* reversible processes between the same two end states.

(e) To compute the change in entropy of a system when it goes from one equilibrium state to another equilibrium state by an *irreversible* process, several methods can be used:

(1) We can devise a reversible process connecting the same two end states and use Eq. (8-13).

(2) If a table such as a steam table has already been prepared, tabulating the entropy in a large number of states, we can read the entropies at the end states from the table and subtract one from the other.

(3) If the equation for the entropy as a function of the thermodynamic coordinates of the system is known, the entropies at the end states can be calculated from this equation and one subtracted from the other.

Methods (2) and (3) can also be applied to reversible processes.

Entropy is an extensive property of a system, proportional to the mass of the system or to the number of moles. We shall make frequent use of the specific entropy, represented by s and defined by

$$s = \frac{S}{m},$$

or by

$$s = \frac{S}{n}.$$

8-3 Calculation of changes in entropy. We now give a few examples of the methods used to compute changes in entropy. To begin with, it is obvious that when a system undergoes a *reversible adiabatic* process there is *no change* in its entropy, since by definition the heat absorbed in such a process is zero. *A reversible adiabatic process therefore proceeds at constant entropy* and may be described as *isentropic*. The entropy is *not* constant in an *irreversible* adiabatic process and we shall return to this point later.

The simplest process involving a *change* in entropy is a reversible process at constant temperature. For such a process the constant temperature T may be taken outside the integral sign and the general equation,

$$s_2 - s_1 = \int \frac{d'q}{T},$$

reduces to

$$(s_2 - s_1)_T = \frac{1}{T} \int d'q_T = \frac{q_T}{T}. \tag{8-16}$$

That is, the change in (specific) entropy of a system in a reversible isothermal process equals the heat absorbed by the system, per unit mass or per mole, divided by the Kelvin temperature of the system.

A common example of a reversible isothermal process is a change in phase at constant pressure, during which, as we have seen, the temperature remains constant also. To carry out the change reversibly, the system is brought into contact with a heat reservoir at a temperature infinitesimally greater than the equilibrium temperature at the given pressure. The change in phase then proceeds very slowly, and at all stages of the process the system is essentially at the equilibrium temperature T. The heat q_T absorbed by the system, per mole or per unit mass, equals the heat of transformation l and the change in (specific) entropy is merely

$$s_2 - s_1 = \frac{l}{T}. \tag{8-17}$$

In most processes, a reversible absorption of heat is accompanied by a change in temperature, and calculation of the corresponding entropy change requires an evaluation of the integral of $d'q/T$. It is therefore necessary to express $d'q$ in terms of T or vice versa, or to express both in terms of a single variable. If the process takes place at constant volume, for example, and if changes in phase are excluded, then

$$d'q = c_v dT$$

and

$$(s_2 - s_1)_v = \int_{T_1}^{T_2} c_v \frac{dT_v}{T}. \qquad (8\text{-}18)$$

If the process is at constant pressure,

$$d'q = c_p dT_p,$$

$$(s_2 - s_1)_p = \int_{T_1}^{T_2} c_p \frac{dT_p}{T}. \qquad (8\text{-}19)$$

A system originally at the temperature T_1 *could* be raised to the temperature T_2 by bringing it in contact with a heat reservoir at temperature T_2. Such a process would be highly irreversible, since there would be large temperature differences between parts of the system, and between the system and the reservoir. The same end result can be attained reversibly with the help of a large number of heat reservoirs, as described in Sec. 1-4. During each stage of a process carried out in this way, the temperature of the system increases by dT and each stage is essentially reversible and isothermal. The increase in entropy of the system is the same whether the process is reversible or not, since the change in entropy depends only on the end points. Where, then, is there any essential difference between the reversible and irreversible processes? We shall answer this question in Sec. 8-4.

As a numerical example of the processes just described, let us compute the increase in the specific entropy of water when it is heated at constant atmospheric pressure from a temperature of 200° K (ice) to a temperature of 400° K (superheated steam). The process is represented by the line *abcdef* in Fig. 8-3(a). For simplicity, we shall ignore variations in specific heat capacity with temperature and assume that

c_p (ice) = 2.09 × 10³ joules/kgm-deg (= 0.50 cal/gm-deg),
c_p (water) = 4.18 × 10³ joules/kgm-deg (= 1.00 cal/gm-deg),
c_p (steam) = 2.09 × 10³ joules/kgm-deg (= 0.50 cal/gm-deg).
l_{12} (273° K) = 3.34 × 10⁵ joules/kgm (= 80 cal/gm),
l_{23} (373° K) = 22.6 × 10⁵ joules/kgm (= 540 cal/gm).

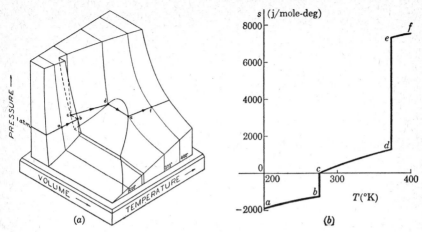

FIG. 8-3.　Entropy changes in an isobaric process.

The first stage of the process consists of heating the ice from 200° K to its melting temperature of 273° K. During this process the increase in entropy is

$$s_b - s_a = \int_{T_a}^{T_b} c_p \frac{dT}{T}$$

$$= c_p \ln \frac{T_b}{T_a}$$

$$= 2.09 \times 10^3 \times \ln \frac{273}{200}$$

$$= 651 \text{ joules/kgm-deg.}$$

The increase in entropy when the ice is melted is

$$s_c - s_b = \frac{l_{12}}{T}$$

$$= \frac{3.34 \times 10^5}{273}$$

$$= 1230 \text{ joules/kgm-deg.}$$

The increase in entropy of the liquid water when heated from 273° K to 373° K is

$$s_d - s_c = c_p \ln \frac{T_d}{T_c}$$

$$= 4.18 \times 10^3 \times \ln \frac{373}{273}$$

$$= 1310 \text{ joules/kgm-deg.}$$

In the process of vaporizing the water at 373° K the entropy increase is

$$s_e - s_d = \frac{l_{23}}{T}$$

$$= \frac{22.6 \times 10^5}{373}$$

$$= 6060 \text{ joules/kgm-deg.}$$

Finally, the increase in entropy on heating the vapor to 400° K is

$$s_f - s_e = c_p \ln \frac{T_f}{T_e}$$

$$= 2.09 \times 10^3 \times \ln \frac{400}{373}$$

$$= 146 \text{ joules/kgm-deg.}$$

In engineering work, the entropy of water is arbitrarily set equal to zero in the liquid phase at 273° K and atmospheric pressure. Relative to this reference state, then, the specific entropy of the saturated liquid at 373° K and 1 atm is 1310 joules/kgm-deg, that of saturated vapor at the same temperature and pressure is 1310 + 6060 = 7370 joules/kgm-deg, and that of superheated steam at 400° K and 1 atm is 7370 + 146 = 7520 joules/kgm-deg. The entropy of the saturated solid at 273° K and 1 atm is −1230 joules/kgm-deg, and that of the solid at 200° K and 1 atm is −1230 − 651 = −1880 joules/kgm-deg. The figures above are only approximate, since we have neglected variations in the specific heat capacity with temperature.

The entropy changes in the process are shown in the graph of Fig. 8-3(b), where the points lettered a, b, c, d, e, f correspond to those in Fig. 8-3(a).

8-4 Entropy changes in irreversible processes. We next compute the change in entropy of a system in an *irreversible* process. Suppose two bodies at different temperatures are brought into contact within a rigid adiabatic enclosure and allowed to come to thermal equilibrium. The equilibrium state will be attained spontaneously without the help of heat or work reservoirs. If we consider the two bodies together to constitute a system, no heat is absorbed or given up by the system and $\int (d'Q/T)$ is zero. It does *not* follow that the change in entropy of the system is zero, however, because the change in entropy of a system is given by $\int (d'Q/T)$ for reversible processes only and the flow of heat through a finite temperature difference is an irreversible process.

Let us use method (e) (1) in Sec. 8-2 to find the change in entropy. That is, we devise a reversible process leading from the same initial to the same final state. To be specific, consider the process of mixing 1 kgm of water at 373° K (100° C) with 1 kgm of water at 273° K (0° C). If small variations in specific heat capacity are neglected, elementary calorimetry shows that the final equilibrium temperature is 323° K (50° C). Physical mixing of the hot and cold water is, of course, not essential. The same end state of 2 kgm of water at 323° K will be reached if the hot and cold water are allowed to exchange heat by conduction or radiation.

To reach this end state reversibly, we can make use of an infinite series of heat reservoirs at temperatures ranging from 273° K to 373° K. Heat the water originally at 273° K reversibly, using the reservoirs between 273° K and 323° K, and cool the water originally at 373° K in a similar manner. We then have 2 kgm of water at 323° K and the entire process has been reversible.

The increase in entropy of 1 kgm of water when heated from 273° K to 323° K is

$$S_2 - S_1 = 1 \times 4.18 \times 10^3 \times \ln \frac{323}{273}$$

$$= 704 \text{ joules/deg.}$$

The increase in entropy of 1 kgm of water when cooled from 373° K to 323° K is

$$S_2' - S_1' = 1 \times 4.18 \times 10^3 \times \ln \frac{323}{373}$$

$$= -603 \text{ joules/deg.}$$

The negative sign means that the entropy has *decreased*.
The net change in entropy of the water is

$$704 - 603 = 101 \text{ joules/deg,}$$

and the entropy of the water has *increased* by 101 joules/deg in the reversible process. But the change in entropy of the water is the same in the irreversible process of mixing, since the end states are the same in both processes, and the problem is solved.

We must note carefully an important difference between the process in which the hot and cold water are mixed directly and that in which they are brought to their final temperature by reversible heat exchange with a series of reservoirs. In the first process, no bodies other than the two masses of water are involved, and the net increase in entropy of the water is also the net increase in entropy of the universe. In the second process the heat reservoirs are involved as well as the water, and the change in entropy of the reservoirs at each stage is equal and opposite to that of the water. Hence, although the entropy of the water increases in the reversible process, the entropy of the reservoirs decreases by exactly the same amount and the net change in entropy of the universe is zero.

We can now gain a further insight into the significance of the terms *reversible* and *irreversible*. According to the definition previously given, that a reversible process is a succession of equilibrium states, the mixing of the hot and cold water is an irreversible process. The fact that it is irreversible in the thermodynamic sense does not imply, of course, that the 2 kgm of water at 323° K cannot be restored to its original state of 1 kgm at 373° K and 1 kgm at 273° K. But let us see what happens when we do restore the original state. Let us heat 1 kgm from 323° K to 373° K, using the heat reservoirs between 323° K and 373° K, and cool 1 kgm from 323° K to 273° K, using the reservoirs between 323° K and 273° K. By the same methods as used in Sec. 8-3, we find that the entropy of the water heated from 323° K to 373° K has increased by 603 joules/deg, while that of the reservoirs from which it absorbed heat has decreased by the same amount. The entropy of the water cooled from 323° K to 273° K has decreased by 704 joules/deg and that of the reservoirs has increased by 704 joules/deg. Therefore the net decrease in entropy of the *water* has been 101 joules/deg and the net increase in entropy of the *reservoirs* has been 101 joules/deg.

The entropy of the water has decreased by the same amount that it increased in the mixing process, so that its entropy is the same as it was originally. However, the entropy of the reservoirs has *increased*, and by an amount just equal to the increase in the entropy of the water in the mixing process. Thus while any outstanding change in the entropy of the *water* has been eliminated, the entropy increase in the original irreversible mixing process has been passed along to the *reservoirs*. Any other process we may devise to restore the reservoirs to their initial condition will be found to end with an entropy increase of some other system or systems, at least as great as that in the original irreversible process. Hence, while a finite *system* can always be restored to its original state after an irreversible process, *the increase in entropy associated with the process can never be wiped out.* At most, it can be passed on from one system to another. This is the true significance of the term irreversible. We shall give in Sec. 8-5 a general proof of the fact that the entropy of an isolated system increases in any irreversible process.

Fig. 8-4, which should be studied carefully, illustrates the processes described above.

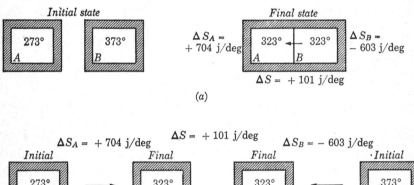

(a)

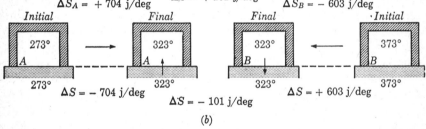

(b)

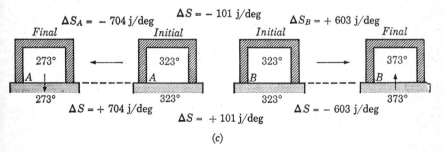

(c)

FIG. 8-4.

The reader may well ask at this point, "Who cares whether a process is reversible or not? Suppose the entropy of the universe *has* been irretrievably increased in an irreversible process? What of it? There has been no loss of *energy* in the process. In what significant way have things been changed?"

One answer to the question above is that the entropy change in a process is the criterion we sought at the beginning of the chapter, namely, it determines the direction in which a given process, consistent with the first law, will go. The physical chemist is chiefly concerned with this aspect of entropy. Will two substances react chemically or will they not? If the reaction would result in a decrease in entropy, the reaction is impossible. However, while the entropy might decrease if the reaction were to take place at one temperature and pressure, it is possible that it could increase at other values of temperature and pressure. Hence a knowledge of the entropies of substances as functions of temperature and pressure is all-important in determining the possibilities of chemical reactions.

The mechanical engineer is interested in reversibility and entropy changes for a somewhat different reason. From his point of view, something has been "lost" when an irreversible process takes place in a steam engine or turbine. What is lost, however, is not energy, but opportunity— the opportunity to convert internal energy to mechanical energy. Since the internal energy of the working substance in a heat engine is usually replenished by a flow of heat into it, we often say that what is lost is an opportunity to convert heat to mechanical work. Let us illustrate by the example of mixing hot and cold water. The internal energy of the system is the same before and after mixing, but at the end of the process we have a single reservoir (considering the water now as a reservoir) all at one temperature, whereas at the beginning we had two reservoirs at different temperatures. It is impossible to withdraw heat from a single reservoir and operate a cyclic engine, whereas we *could* have operated an engine between the original hot and cold reservoirs, withdrawing heat from one, rejecting heat to the other, and diverting a part of the heat to produce mechanical work. Once the reservoirs have come to the same temperature, this opportunity is irretrievably lost. Thus any irreversible process in a heat engine reduces its efficiency, that is, it reduces the amount of mechanical work that can be abstracted from a given amount of heat absorbed by the working substance.

8-5 The principle of the increase of entropy. All actual processes are irreversible. They take place at a finite rate, with finite differences of temperature and pressure between parts of a system or between a system and its surroundings. We now show that it is a necessary consequence of the second law that the entropy of an isolated system increase in every natural (i.e., irreversible) process.

In mechanics, one of the reasons that justifies the introduction of the concepts of energy, momentum, and angular momentum is that they obey a conservation principle. Entropy is *not* conserved, however, except in reversible processes, and this unfamiliar property, or lack of property, of the entropy function is one reason why such an aura of mystery usually surrounds the concept of entropy. When a beaker of hot water is mixed with a beaker of cold water, the heat lost by the hot water equals the heat gained by the cold water. "Heat" is conserved in this process or, more generally, energy is conserved. On the other hand, while the entropy of the hot water decreases in the mixing process and the entropy of the cold water increases, the decrease in entropy is not equal to the increase, and the total entropy of the system is greater at the end of the process than it was at the beginning. Where did this additional entropy come from? The answer is that the additional entropy was created in the process of mixing the hot and the cold water. Furthermore, once entropy has been created, it can never be destroyed. The universe must forever bear this additional burden of entropy. "Energy can neither be created nor destroyed," says the first law of thermodynamics. "Entropy cannot be destroyed," says the second law, "but it can be created."

In Fig. 8-5, the crosshatching represents a natural (and hence irreversible) process taking place in an isolated system. As a result of this process, the system moves from an equilibrium state represented by point 1 to another equilibrium state represented by point 2. The continuous line represents a reversible process, involving interchanges of energy with heat and work reservoirs, by which the system is returned from state 2 to state 1. Taken together, processes I and II constitute a cycle. The cycle as a whole is irreversible, since part I is irreversible. Hence, from the Clausius inequality,

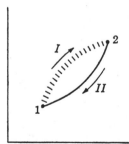

$$\oint \frac{d'Q}{T} < 0,$$

FIG. 8-5. A system undergoes an irreversible process from state (1) to state (2), and is returned by a reversible process from state (2) to state (1).

or, writing the integral as the sum of two integrals,

$$\text{(I)} \int_1^2 \frac{d'Q}{T} + \text{(II)} \int_2^1 \frac{d'Q}{T} < 0.$$

But the first integral is zero, since the system was isolated in the irreversible process and could not receive or give out heat. This integral, however, is *not* equal to $S_2 - S_1$, since only for *reversible* processes is $dS = d'Q/T$. The second integral, since path II is reversible, is $S_1 - S_2$. It follows that

$$S_1 - S_2 < 0,$$

or

$$S_2 > S_1.$$

That is, the entropy of the system in state 2 is greater than in state 1. Since the original process was arbitrary, we conclude that *the entropy of an isolated system increases in every natural (i.e., irreversible) process.*

Note that the statement above is restricted to isolated systems and that the entropy refers to the *total* entropy of the system. When natural processes take place in an isolated system, the entropy of parts of the system may decrease and that of other parts may increase. The increases, however, are always greater than the decreases. The entropy of a non-isolated system may either increase or decrease, depending on whether heat is added to or removed from it or whether irreversible processes take place within it. Hence, in discussing increases and decreases in entropy, it is very important that the system under consideration shall be clearly defined.

Problems

1. A 20-ohm resistor carrying a constant current of 10 amp is kept at a constant temperature of 27° C by a stream of cooling water. In a time interval of 1 second, (a) What is the change in entropy of the resistor? (b) What is the change in entropy of the universe? *a)0 b) 6.7 j/deg*

2. A thermally insulated 20-ohm resistor carries a current of 10 amp for 1 sec. The initial temperature of the resistor is 10° C, its mass is 5 gm, and its specific heat capacity is 850 joules/kgm-deg. (a) What is the change in entropy of the resistor? (b) What is the change in entropy of the universe? *a+b) 4.2 j/deg*

3. One kilogram of water is heated by an electric heating coil from 20° C to 80° C. Compute the change in entropy of (a) the water, (b) the universe. *a+b) 780 j/deg*

4. 1 kgm of water at a temperature of 280° K is mixed with 2 kgm of water at a temperature of 310° K in a thermally insulated vessel. Find the change in entropy of the universe. *15 j/deg*

5. A mass m of a liquid at a temperature T_1 is mixed with an equal mass of the same liquid at a temperature T_2. The system is thermally insulated. Show that the entropy change of the universe is

$$2\,mc_p \ln \frac{(T_1 + T_2)/2}{\sqrt{T_1 T_2}},$$

and prove that this is necessarily positive.

6. Suppose bodies A and B in Fig. 8-4, after the irreversible process in part (a), were restored to their original state by bringing A in contact with a single reservoir at 273° K, and bringing B in contact with a single reservoir at 373° K. What would be the net change in entropy of the universe as a result of this process and process (a) combined?

7. (a) One kilogram of water at 0° C is brought into contact with a large heat reservoir at 100° C. When the water has reached 100° C, what has been the change in entropy of the water? of the heat reservoir? of the universe? *a) 1300, -1120, 180 j/deg*

(b) If the water had been heated from 0° C to 100° C by first bringing it in contact with a reservoir at 50° C and then with a reservoir at 100° C, what would have been the change in entropy of the universe? *92 j/deg*

(c) Explain how the water might be heated from 0° C to 100° C with no change in the entropy of the universe.

8. The value of c_p for a certain substance can be represented by

$$c_p = a + bT.$$

(a) Find the heat absorbed and the increase in entropy of a mass m of the substance when its temperature is increased at constant pressure from T_1 to T_2.

(b) Find the increase in the molar specific entropy of copper, when the temperature is increased at constant pressure from 300° K to 1200° K. (See Problem 14 in Chapter 5.) *a) $a \ln(T_2/T_1) + b(T_2 - T_1)$ b) 38×10^3 j/kmole-deg*

9. 10 kgm of water at a temperature of 20° C is converted to superheated steam at 250° C and at constant atmospheric pressure. Compute the change in entropy of the water.

c_p (liquid) = 4180 joules/kgm-deg,

c_p (vapor) = $1670 + 0.494\,T + 1.86 \times 10^6\,T^{-2}$ joules/kgm-deg.

l_{23} (at 100° C) = 22.6×10^5 joules/kgm.

10. 10 kgm of water at 20° C is converted to ice at -10° C and at constant atmospheric pressure. Assume that the specific heat capacities of water and of ice at constant pressure are constant and equal to 4180 joules/kgm-deg and 2090 joules/kgm-deg respectively. The heat of fusion of ice at atmospheric pressure is 3.34×10^5 joules/kgm. Find the change in entropy of the system.

11. A body of finite mass is originally at a temperature T_2, which is higher than that of a heat reservoir at a temperature T_1. An engine operates in infinitesimal cycles between the body and the reservoir until it lowers the temperature of the body from T_2 to T_1. In this process heat Q is abstracted from the body. Prove that the maximum work obtainable from the engine is

$$Q - T_1(S_1 - S_2),$$

where $S_1 - S_2$ is the decrease in entropy of the body.

12. Two identical bodies of constant heat capacity, originally at the temperatures T_1 and T_2 respectively, are used as reservoirs for a heat engine operating in infinitesimal reversible cycles. If the bodies remain at constant pressure and undergo no change of phase, show that (a) the final temperature T_f is

$$T_f = \sqrt{T_1 T_2},$$

(b) the work obtained is

$$C_p(T_1 + T_2 - 2\, T_f).$$

13. The circle in Fig. 8-6 represents a reversible engine. The engine is first operated between the reservoirs at temperatures T_1 and T_2, and then between the reservoirs at temperatures T_1 and T_3. During some integral number of complete cycles the engine absorbs 1200 joules from the reservoir at 400° K and performs 200 joules of mechanical work. (a) Find the quantities of heat exchanged with the other reservoirs, and state whether the reservoir gives up or absorbs heat. (b) Find the change in entropy of each reservoir. (c) What is the change in entropy of the universe?

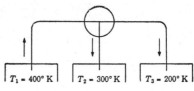

FIG. 8-6.

CHAPTER 9

COMBINED FIRST AND SECOND LAWS

9-1 Combined first and second laws. The analytical formulation of the first law of thermodynamics is

$$du = d'q - d'w.$$

The second law states that for a reversible process,

$$d'q = Tds.$$

The two laws may therefore be combined to give

$$du = Tds - d'w. \tag{9-1}$$

This is the fundamental equation of thermodynamics and the whole of this science grows out of its consequences, just as the whole science of mechanics is based on Newton's laws of motion.

If we consider pdv work only, then

$$du = Tds - pdv. \tag{9-2}$$

A very large number of thermodynamic relations can now be derived by considering, as we did in Chapter 5, that T and v, T and p, or p and v are independent variables, and expressing ds in terms of the differentials of these variables and the partial derivatives of s. Also, since the internal energy u, the enthalpy h, and other quantities also are functions of the state of the system, the state (of a homogeneous system) is completely defined by *any* pair of these variables such as s and v or h and p. The partial derivative of any one variable with respect to any other, with any one of those remaining held constant, thus has a physical meaning and it is obviously out of the question to attempt to tabulate all possible relations between all of these derivatives. However, every partial derivative can be expressed in terms of $\beta \left(= \frac{1}{v}\left(\frac{\partial v}{\partial T}\right)_p \right)$, $\kappa \left(= -\frac{1}{v}\left(\frac{\partial v}{\partial p}\right)_T \right)$, and c_p, together with the state variables p, v, and T themselves, so that no physical properties of a substance other than those already discussed need be measured. A derivative is said to be in "standard form" when it is expressed in terms of the quantities above. We next demonstrate the

147

general method by which the derivatives are evaluated, and work out a few relations that will be needed later on.

Let us first consider T and v as independent. Then

$$du = \left(\frac{\partial u}{\partial T}\right)_v dT + \left(\frac{\partial u}{\partial v}\right)_T dv,$$

and from the combined first and second laws,

$$ds = \frac{1}{T}(du + pdv). \tag{9-3}$$

Combining these equations, we get

$$ds = \frac{1}{T}\left(\frac{\partial u}{\partial T}\right)_v dT + \frac{1}{T}\left[p + \left(\frac{\partial u}{\partial v}\right)_T\right] dv.$$

But we can also write

$$ds = \left(\frac{\partial s}{\partial T}\right)_v dT + \left(\frac{\partial s}{\partial v}\right)_T dv. \tag{9-4}$$

Since dT and dv are independent, their coefficients in the two preceding equations must be equal. Therefore

$$\left(\frac{\partial s}{\partial T}\right)_v = \frac{1}{T}\left(\frac{\partial u}{\partial T}\right)_v, \tag{9-5}$$

$$\left(\frac{\partial s}{\partial v}\right)_T = \frac{1}{T}\left[p + \left(\frac{\partial u}{\partial v}\right)_T\right]. \tag{9-6}$$

We now take advantage of the useful fact that the *second* derivative of s with respect to T and v is independent of the order of differentiation. That is,

$$\left[\frac{\partial}{\partial v}\left(\frac{\partial s}{\partial T}\right)_v\right]_T = \left[\frac{\partial}{\partial T}\left(\frac{\partial s}{\partial v}\right)_T\right]_v = \frac{\partial^2 s}{\partial v \partial T} = \frac{\partial^2 s}{\partial T \partial v}.$$

Hence from Eqs. (9-5) and (9-6), differentiating the first partially with respect to T and the second with respect to v, we obtain

$$\frac{1}{T}\frac{\partial^2 u}{\partial v \partial T} = \frac{1}{T}\left[\frac{\partial^2 u}{\partial T \partial v} + \left(\frac{\partial p}{\partial T}\right)_v\right] - \frac{1}{T^2}\left[\left(\frac{\partial u}{\partial v}\right)_T + p\right].$$

Hence

$$\left[\left(\frac{\partial u}{\partial v}\right)_T + p\right] = T\left(\frac{\partial p}{\partial T}\right)_v, \tag{9-7}$$

or in standard form,

$$\left(\frac{\partial u}{\partial v}\right)_T = \frac{T\beta}{\kappa} - p. \tag{9-8}$$

This is the equation we made use of in Chapter 5, to evaluate $(\partial u/\partial v)_T$ for an ideal gas and for a van der Waals gas.

In Chapter 5, using the first law alone, we derived the relation (Eq. (5-5)),

$$c_p - c_v = \left[\left(\frac{\partial u}{\partial v}\right)_T + p\right]\left(\frac{\partial v}{\partial T}\right)_p.$$

Making use of Eq. (9-7), we see that

$$c_p - c_v = T\left(\frac{\partial p}{\partial T}\right)_v\left(\frac{\partial v}{\partial T}\right)_p. \tag{9-9}$$

But

$$\left(\frac{\partial p}{\partial T}\right)_v = \frac{\beta}{\kappa}, \quad \left(\frac{\partial v}{\partial T}\right)_p = \beta v,$$

so

$$c_p - c_v = \frac{\beta^2 T v}{\kappa}. \tag{9-10}$$

Thus the difference $c_p - c_v$ can be computed for any substance for which β and κ are known, even if the complete equation of state is not known, and c_v can be expressed in standard form, i.e., in terms of β, κ, c_p, T, and v. The quantities T, v, and κ are always positive, and while β may be positive, negative, or zero (for water, it is zero at 4° C and is negative between 0° C and 4° C), β^2 is always positive or zero. It follows that c_p is never smaller than c_v. When the expressions for β and κ for an ideal gas and a van der Waals gas are inserted in Eq. (9-10), it reduces to Eqs. (5-29) and (5-30) previously derived. For copper, at a temperature of 300° K,

$$c_p - c_v = \frac{(4.9 \times 10^{-5})^2 \times 300 \times (7.15 \times 10^{-3})}{7.7 \times 10^{-12}} = 667 \text{ joules/mole-deg.}$$

This difference is much smaller than that for a gas, where $c_p - c_v = R = 8315$ joules/mole-deg.

Let us now return to the expressions for $(\partial s/\partial T)_v$ and $(\partial s/\partial v)_T$ in Eqs. (9-5) and (9-6). Using Eqs. (9-7) and (9-10), and the fact that $c_v = (\partial u/\partial T)_v$, the partial derivatives of s with respect to T and v become

$$\left(\frac{\partial s}{\partial T}\right)_v = \frac{c_v}{T} = \frac{c_p}{T} - \frac{\beta^2 v}{\kappa}, \tag{9-11}$$

$$\left(\frac{\partial s}{\partial v}\right)_T = \left(\frac{\partial p}{\partial T}\right)_v = \frac{\beta}{\kappa}. \tag{9-12}$$

Next, inserting the expressions for the partial derivatives in Eq. (9-4), we get

$$ds = \frac{c_v}{T} dT + \frac{\beta}{\kappa} dv,\tag{9-13}$$

or

$$Tds = c_v dT + \frac{\beta T}{\kappa} dv.\tag{9-14}$$

If c_v is known as a function of T, and β and κ are known as functions of v, Eq. (9-13) can be integrated to find the change in entropy of any substance in terms of T and v. From Eq. (9-14) we can compute the heat dq ($= Tds$) absorbed by any homogeneous substance in a reversible process.

Finally, equating the second derivatives of s with respect to v and T from Eqs. (9-11) and (9-12), we get

$$\left(\frac{\partial c_v}{\partial v}\right)_T = T\left(\frac{\partial^2 p}{\partial T^2}\right)_v.\tag{9-15}$$

For any substance for which the pressure is a linear function of the temperature at constant volume, $\left(\dfrac{\partial^2 p}{\partial T^2}\right)_v = 0$ and the specific heat capacity at constant volume is independent of the volume, although it may depend on the temperature. For an ideal gas,

$$\left(\frac{\partial p}{\partial T}\right)_v = \frac{R}{v},$$

and for a van der Waals gas,

$$\left(\frac{\partial p}{\partial T}\right)_v = \frac{R}{v - b}.$$

Hence for both of these substances

$$\left(\frac{\partial c_v}{\partial v}\right)_T = T\left(\frac{\partial^2 p}{\partial T^2}\right)_v = 0,$$

and c_v is independent of v. It is independent of p also, since

$$\left(\frac{\partial c_v}{\partial p}\right)_T = \left(\frac{\partial c_v}{\partial v}\right)_T \left(\frac{\partial v}{\partial p}\right)_T = 0.$$

Equations corresponding to the above can be derived by considering T and p, and p and v, as independent. The derivation is left for a problem. The results are,

$$\left(\frac{\partial u}{\partial p}\right)_T = p\kappa v - T\beta v,\tag{9-16}$$

$$\left(\frac{\partial s}{\partial T}\right)_p = \frac{c_p}{T}, \quad \left(\frac{\partial s}{\partial p}\right)_T = -\beta v, \tag{9-17}$$

$$\left(\frac{\partial s}{\partial p}\right)_v = \frac{\kappa c_v}{\beta T}, \quad \left(\frac{\partial s}{\partial v}\right)_p = \frac{c_p}{\beta v T}, \tag{9-18}$$

$$\left(\frac{\partial c_p}{\partial p}\right)_T = -T\left(\frac{\partial^2 v}{\partial T^2}\right)_p; \tag{9-19}$$

Inserting the expressions for the partial derivatives of s in the two expressions for ds in terms of dT and dp, and dp and dv, and including Eq. (9-14) for completeness, we get

$$\left. \begin{array}{l} Tds = c_v dT + \dfrac{\beta T}{\kappa}\, dv, \\[2mm] Tds = c_p dT - \beta v T dp, \\[2mm] Tds = \dfrac{\kappa c_v}{\beta}\, dp + \dfrac{c_p}{\beta v}\, dv. \end{array} \right\} \tag{9-20}$$

The three equations above are called the Tds equations. They enable one to compute the heat Tds absorbed by any homogeneous substance in a reversible process or, when divided through by T, give expressions for ds in terms of the differentials of each pair of state variables. The six partial derivatives of s with respect to the state variables are then the coefficients of the six differentials on the right side of the equations.

9-2 Entropy of an ideal gas. We now show how the three Tds equations are used to compute entropy differences. When each of these is divided through by T, we obtain an expression for ds and integration then gives the entropy difference between two equilibrium states. The integration can be performed only if the coefficients of the differentials are known in terms of the respective variables and, in general, graphical or machine methods of integration must be used, or the coefficients must be expressed empirically as a power series.

We consider first an ideal gas, for which c_p and c_v are functions of temperature only and for which $\beta = 1/T$, $\kappa = 1/p$. The three equations then reduce to

$$ds = c_v \frac{dT}{T} + R\frac{dv}{v}, \tag{9-21}$$

$$ds = c_p \frac{dT}{T} - R\frac{dp}{p}, \tag{9-22}$$

$$ds = c_p \frac{dv}{v} + c_v \frac{dp}{p} \,. \tag{9-23}$$

Let us select some arbitrary reference state at temperature T_0, pressure p_0, and specific volume v_0, in which the specific entropy is s_0. Then integration of the equations above gives

$$s = s_0 + \int_{T_0}^{T} c_v \frac{dT}{T} + R \ln \frac{v}{v_0} \,, \tag{9-24}$$

$$s = s_0 + \int_{T_0}^{T} c_p \frac{dT}{T} - R \ln \frac{p}{p_0} \,, \tag{9-25}$$

$$s = s_0 + \int_{v_0}^{v} c_p \frac{dv}{v} + \int_{p_0}^{p} c_v \frac{dp}{p} \,. \tag{9-26}$$

If c_p and c_v can be considered constant over the temperature range between T_0 and T, these equations simplify further to

$$s = s_0 + c_v \ln \frac{T}{T_0} + R \ln \frac{v}{v_0} \,, \tag{9-27}$$

$$s = s_0 + c_p \ln \frac{T}{T_0} - R \ln \frac{p}{p_0} \,, \tag{9-28}$$

$$s = s_0 + c_p \ln \frac{v}{v_0} + c_v \ln \frac{p}{p_0} \,. \tag{9-29}$$

It is left as a problem to show that the three equations are all equivalent. In fact, any two of them can be derived from the third with the help of the equation of state.

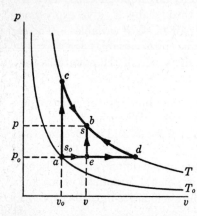

FIG. 9-1. The change in entropy is the same along all reversible paths between two given equilibrium states.

The physical meaning of the three derivations for the entropy change will be made more evident by a reference to Fig. 9-1. Point a is the arbitrary reference state at temperature T_0, pressure p_0, and volume v_0, and point b is any other state at temperature T, pressure p, and volume v. The three evaluations of the entropy difference $s - s_0$ are equivalent to integrating the entropy change along the three paths acb, adb, and aeb. That is, the first term on the right of Eq. (9-21), in which temperature and volume are independent variables, is integrated along the path ac at constant volume, while the second term is integrated along the path cb at constant temperature. The first term in Eq. (9-22) is integrated along path ad at constant pressure, and the second along path db at constant temperature. Eq. (9-23) is integrated first along ae at constant pressure and then along eb at constant volume. The fact that the integral of dq/T is the same along all three paths between points a and b serves as a specific example of the general discussion in Sec. 8-2.

Consider next a van der Waals gas. Taking the expressions for β and κ from Eqs. (3-14) and (3-17) and using the first $T ds$ equation, we get

$$ds = c_v \frac{dT}{T} + R \frac{dv}{v - b},$$

$$s = s_0 + \int_{T_0}^{T} c_v \frac{dT}{T} + R \ln \frac{v - b}{v_0 - b}. \tag{9-30}$$

This is the same as the corresponding expression for an ideal gas, with the volume reduced from v to $v - b$. The van der Waals constant a has no effect on the entropy. If c_v can be assumed constant, Eq. (9-30) becomes

$$s = s_0 + c_v \ln \frac{T}{T_0} + R \ln \frac{v - b}{v_0 - b}. \tag{9-31}$$

Expressions for the entropy in terms of T and p, or p and v, can readily be derived if desired from the other $T ds$ equations, or by combining the preceding equation with the equation of state.

9-3 Reversible adiabatic processes. Since the entropy of a system remains constant in a reversible adiabatic process, the relation between any two of the state variables in such a process can be found from the $T ds$ equations, setting $ds = 0$, or from any expression for the entropy, setting $s = $ const. Thus the differential adiabatic equations for an ideal gas follow at once from Eqs. (9-21) to (9-23), setting $ds = 0$, or the integrated forms from Eqs. (9-27) to (9-29), setting $s = $ const. For a van der Waals gas, we obtain from Eq. (9-31)

$$T(v - b)^{\frac{R}{c_v}} = \text{const.} \tag{9-32}$$

From the expression for the entropy in terms of p and v, or by combining Eq. (9-32) with the equation of state, we find

$$\left(p + \frac{a}{v^2}\right)\left(v - b\right)^{\frac{R + c_v}{c_v}} = \text{const.} \tag{9-33}$$

These are obviously generalizations of the corresponding equations for an ideal gas,

$$Tv^{\gamma - 1} = \text{const,}$$

$$pv^{\gamma} = \text{const.}$$

The increase in temperature in a solid or liquid when it is compressed adiabatically can be found from the first Tds equation. We have

$$Tds = 0 = c_v \, dT_s + \frac{\beta T}{\kappa} \, dv_s,$$

$$dT_s = - \frac{\beta T}{\kappa c_v} \, dv_s.$$

The temperature rise will be small enough so that T can be considered constant and, if variations in β, κ, and c_v are neglected,

$$(T_2 - T_1)_s = \frac{\beta T}{\kappa c_v} (v_1 - v_2)_s. \tag{9-34}$$

If $v_2 < v_1$, then $T_2 > T_1$ when β is positive, but $T_2 < T_1$ when β is negative. Thus while ordinarily the temperature of a solid or a liquid increases when the volume is decreased adiabatically, the temperature of water between $0°$ C and $4°$ C decreases in an adiabatic compression.

If the increase in pressure, rather than the decrease in volume, is specified, the temperature change can be found from the second Tds equation.

$$Tds = 0 = c_p dT_s - \beta v T dp_s,$$

$$dT_s = \frac{\beta v T}{c_p} \, dp_s, \tag{9-35}$$

and

$$(T_2 - T_1)_s = \frac{\beta v T}{c_p} (p_2 - p_1)_s, \tag{9-36}$$

if we neglect variations in β, v, T, and c_p. If β is positive, the temperature increases when pressure is applied. Hence if it is desired to keep the temperature constant during the application of pressure, heat must be removed. The amount removed can also be found from the second Tds equation, setting $dT = 0$ and $Tds = dq_T$.

$$dq_T = -\beta v T dp_T,$$

$$q_T = -\beta v T (p_2 - p_1)_T. \tag{9-37}$$

Comparison of Eqs. (9-36) and (9-37) shows that for a given change in pressure the heat evolved in an isothermal process equals the temperature rise in an adiabatic process, multiplied by the specific heat capacity at constant pressure.

The pressure needed to decrease the volume of a substance adiabatically is found from the third Tds equation.

$$Tds = 0 = \frac{\kappa c_v}{\beta} dp_s + \frac{c_p}{\beta v} dv_s$$

and hence

$$-\frac{1}{v}\left(\frac{\partial v}{\partial p}\right)_s = \kappa \frac{c_v}{c_p}. \tag{9-38}$$

It will be recalled that the compressibility κ is, strictly speaking, the *isothermal* compressibility, defined by the equation

$$\kappa = -\frac{1}{v}\left(\frac{\partial v}{\partial p}\right)_T.$$

The left side of Eq. (9-38) defines the *adiabatic* compressibility, which we shall write as κ_s. (To be consistent, the isothermal compressibility should be written κ_T.) Denoting the ratio c_p/c_v by γ, Eq. (9-38) becomes

$$\kappa_s = \frac{\kappa_T}{\gamma}. \tag{9-39}$$

Since c_p is always greater than c_v, γ is always greater than unity even for a solid or liquid, and the adiabatic compressibility is always less than the isothermal. This is natural, because an increase in pressure causes a rise in temperature, and the expansion resulting from this temperature rise offsets to some extent the contraction brought about by the pressure. Thus for a given pressure increase dp, the volume change dv is less in an adiabatic than in an isothermal compression, and the compressibility is therefore smaller.

In terms of the adiabatic compressibility κ_s, Eq. (9-38) becomes

$$dv_s = -\kappa_s v dp_s \tag{9-40}$$

and, assuming κ_s and v constant,

$$(v_2 - v_1)_s = \kappa_s v (p_1 - p_2).$$

When a sound wave passes through a substance, the compressions and rarefactions are adiabatic rather than isothermal. The velocity of a compressional wave in a solid or a liquid, it will be recalled, is the square root of the reciprocal of the product of density and compressibility, and the adiabatic rather than the isothermal compressibility should be used. Conversely, from a measurement of the velocity of compressional waves, the adiabatic compressibility can be determined. The natural frequencies of oscillation of a quartz crystal or a magnetostriction bar are directly related to the velocity of compressional waves in the crystal or the bar.

The work done in an adiabatic process can be found either from the change in internal energy or by evaluating $\int p\,dv_s$. Both methods lead to the same result. From the definition of the adiabatic compressibility κ_s,

$$dv_s = -\kappa_s v\,dp_s,$$

and

$$w_s = \int p\,dv_s \approx -\kappa_s v \int_{p_1}^{p_2} p\,dp_s \approx \frac{\kappa_s v}{2}\,(p_1^2 - p_2^2), \qquad (9\text{-}41)$$

since κ_s and v are nearly constant. Comparison with Eq. (3-20) shows that the work is given by the same expression as for an isothermal process, except that κ is replaced by κ_s.

9-4 Temperature-entropy diagrams. Since the specific entropy of a substance can be considered as a function of T and v, T and p, or p and v, the entropy can be represented by a surface, plotting s and any pair of the state variables along three mutually perpendicular axes. The most useful surface is that in which s, p, and T are selected as variables. Fig. 9-2 shows the surface obtained by plotting the entropy of an ideal gas vertically, and the pressure and temperature horizontally. The geometrical significance of the partial derivatives $(\partial s/\partial T)_p$ and $(\partial s/\partial p)_T$ is the slope of the tangent lines bc and ad, at any point. The entropy increases logarithmically with temperature and decreases logarithmically with pressure. The surface has the same general shape for all gases.

Fig. 9-3 is a diagram of the s-p-T surface for the liquid and vapor phases of water, drawn to scale. The surface resembles a p-v-T surface. It can be drawn to scale because the relative entropy increase between liquid and vapor phases is much smaller than the relative volume increase. Planes perpendicular to the s-axis intersect the surface in lines of constant s and therefore represent adiabatics.

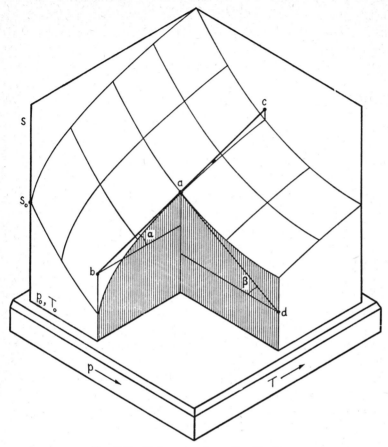

FIG. 9-2.   Entropy surface of an ideal gas.

It often suffices to consider only the projection of the surface onto the
T-s plane.   This projection has the following useful property.   The curve
in Fig. 9-4(a) represents an arbitrary reversible process.   The area of
the narrow vertical strip is $T ds$, which equals the heat absorbed, dq.   The
total heat q absorbed between states a and b is

$$q = \int dq = \int_{s_a}^{s_b} T ds,$$

and is represented by the area bounded by the curve, the s-axis, and vertical
lines at s_a and s_b.   Hence areas in a temperature-entropy diagram represent *heat*, just as areas in a pressure-volume diagram represent work.

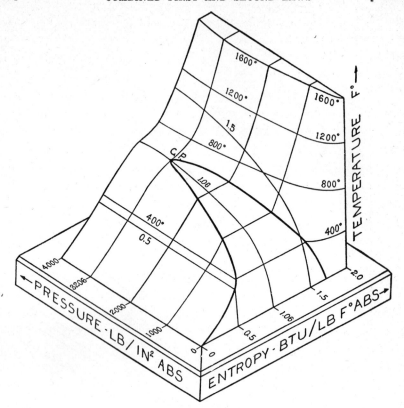

FIG. 9-3. s-p-T diagram for water.

The heat q is positive (i.e., heat is absorbed by a system) if the process proceeds in the direction shown.   If the process goes in the other direction, heat is given up by the system and q is negative.

Isothermal processes in the T-s diagram are represented by horizontal straight lines, adiabatics by vertical lines.   A Carnot cycle, bounded by two isothermals and two adiabatics, projects as a rectangle, as shown in Fig. 9-4(b).

The area bounded by a closed curve representing a cyclic process, such as the Carnot cycle in Fig. 9-4, represents the net heat absorbed by the system in the cycle and therefore, from the first law, represents the net work also.   (Note that this applies only to *closed* curves.   The area between a curve and the s-axis does *not* represent work.)

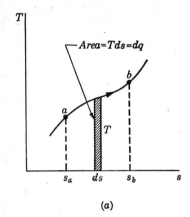

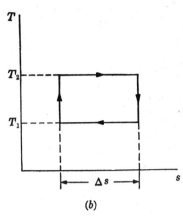

(a)   (b)

FIG. 9-4.   (a) The area under a curve in a T-s diagram represents heat absorbed.
(b) The Carnot cycle.

The efficiency of a Carnot cycle can be deduced at once from Fig. 9-4(b). The heat Q_2 absorbed at the higher temperature equals the area $T_2\Delta s$. The work w is the area $(T_2 - T_1)\Delta s$.   The efficiency is therefore

$$\eta = \frac{w}{q_2} = \frac{(T_2 - T_1)\Delta s}{T_2\Delta s}$$

$$= \frac{T_2 - T_1}{T_2}.$$

9-5 The Helmholtz function and the Gibbs function.   The Helmholtz function and the Gibbs function, like the enthalpy, are combinations of thermodynamic variables that occur frequently enough to justify giving them special names and symbols.   The Helmholtz function F is defined as

$$F = U - TS,$$

and the Gibbs function G as

$$G = U - TS + pV$$

$$= F + pV$$

$$= H - TS.$$

In any infinitesimal process,

$$dF = dU - TdS - SdT,$$

$$dG = dU - TdS - SdT + pdV + Vdp.$$

From the first and second laws, for a reversible process,

$$d'W = TdS - dU.$$

Therefore

$$d'W = -dF - SdT, \tag{9-42}$$

$$d'W = -dG - S'dT + pdV + Vdp. \tag{9-43}$$

One often wishes to know how much work is done in a process, over and above any "pdV" work. For example, when a voltaic cell discharges in the open it can do electrical work and, if there are any gaseous products of the reaction, it will also do pdV work in pushing back the atmosphere. Let us define a quantity $d'A$ as the work done, exclusive of any pdV work. That is,

$$d'A = d'W - pdV.$$

Equation (9-43) then becomes

$$d'A = -dG - SdT + Vdp. \tag{9-44}$$

If the temperature is constant, then from Eq. (9-42)

$$d'W_T = -dF_T,$$

and for a finite isothermal process

$$W_T = (F_1 - F_2)_T. \tag{9-45}$$

If both temperature and pressure are constant, Eq. (9-44) reduces to

$$d'A_{T,p} = -dG_{T,p},$$

and for a finite isothermal-isobaric process

$$A_{T,p} = (G_1 - G_2)_{T,p}. \tag{9-46}$$

Hence the total work done by a system in a reversible isothermal process is equal to the decrease in the Helmholtz function of the system, and the work done in a reversible isothermal-isobaric process, exclusive of any pdV work, is equal to the decrease in the Gibbs function of the system.

As an example, the Helmholtz function of an ideal gas for which c_v is constant is

$$F = U - TS$$

$$= U_0 + nc_v(T - T_0) - TS_0 - nc_v \ln \frac{T}{T_0} - nRT \ln \frac{V}{V_0}.$$

For two equilibrium states at the same temperature T and in which the volumes are V_1 and V_2,

$$F_1 - F_2 = nRT \ln \frac{V_2}{V_1}.$$

But this is the familiar expression for the work done in a reversible isothermal expansion of an ideal gas.

An ideal gas cannot, of course, undergo a process in which *both* T and p are constant. However, a change of phase, as from liquid to vapor, proceeds at constant pressure when the temperature is constant. Let g'' and g''' represent respectively the specific Gibbs functions of a liquid and its vapor in equilibrium at temperature T and pressure p. Then, going over to the specific form of the variables,

$$g'' - g''' = (u'' - Ts'' + pv'') - (u''' - Ts''' + pv''')$$

$$= -(u''' - u'') + T(s''' - s'') - p(v''' - v'').$$

But $T(s''' - s'')$ is the heat of transformation l_{23} and $p(v''' - v'')$ is the work done per mole in the change from liquid to vapor. Hence from the first law the right side of the preceding equation is zero and

$$g'' = g'''.$$

The specific Gibbs function therefore has the same value for the liquid and vapor phases of a substance in equilibrium. The same argument could evidently have been applied to any two phases in equilibrium, or, in fact, if all three were in equilibrium at the triple point.

It follows that in a reversible change of phase at constant temperature and pressure there is no change in the Gibbs function of a system and hence the work done, exclusive of pdV work, is zero. This is evidently correct, since in this case *all* the work is pdV work. In Section 9-10 we give an example of a process in which work other than pdV work is done by a system.

The function F was called by Helmholtz the *free energy* of a system, because its change in a reversible isothermal process equals the energy that can be "freed" in the process and converted to mechanical work. Note, however, that it is not necessarily internal energy of the system that is freed. In the reversible isothermal expansion of an ideal gas, for example, the change in internal energy of the gas is zero and the source of energy is the heat reservoir which maintains the temperature of the gas constant.

The same term, free energy, has also been used for the Gibbs function G because of its similar properties. To avoid confusion it seems preferable to abandon the term "free energy" altogether and to refer to F and G simply as the Helmholtz function and the Gibbs function.

We next derive some further important relations involving these functions. For a reversible process in a system whose state is completely defined by p, v, and T (going over to the specific form of the variables) $d'w = pdv$ and $d'a = 0$. Then Eqs. (9-42) and (9-44) become

$$df = -sdT - pdv,$$

$$dg = -sdT + vdp.$$

For completeness, we also have from the definition of enthalpy,

$$dh = Tds + vdp,$$

and from the combined first and second laws,

$$du = Tds - pdv.$$

But

$$du = \left(\frac{\partial u}{\partial s}\right)_v ds + \left(\frac{\partial u}{\partial v}\right)_s dv,$$

with corresponding expressions for df, dg, and dh. By comparing coefficients, we obtain the following equations:

$$\left(\frac{\partial u}{\partial s}\right)_v = T, \qquad \left(\frac{\partial u}{\partial v}\right)_s = -p, \qquad (9\text{-}47)$$

$$\left(\frac{\partial f}{\partial v}\right)_T = -p, \qquad \left(\frac{\partial f}{\partial T}\right)_v = -s, \qquad (9\text{-}48)$$

$$\left(\frac{\partial g}{\partial T}\right)_p = -s, \qquad \left(\frac{\partial g}{\partial p}\right)_T = v, \qquad (9\text{-}49)$$

$$\left(\frac{\partial h}{\partial s}\right)_p = T, \qquad \left(\frac{\partial h}{\partial p}\right)_s = v. \qquad (9\text{-}50)$$

Elementary courses in mechanics usually begin by discussing force, mass, and acceleration. Energy and momentum are introduced later as derived concepts. More advanced treatments introduce energy and momentum at the start as the fundamental quantities of mechanics. Similarly, in thermodynamics the concepts of internal energy and entropy may be introduced at the start as the fundamental quantities, instead of beginning, as we have done, with pressure, volume, and temperature. If this procedure is followed, the first of Eqs. (9-47) becomes the *definition* of temperature. That is, temperature is defined as the rate of change of internal energy with entropy at constant volume.

The methods of statistical mechanics, as we shall see later, enable us to derive expressions for the internal energy u and entropy s of a system. The temperature of the system is then given by the ratio of du to ds in a process at constant volume. The Helmholtz function $f = u - Ts$ can then be computed, and from the first of Eqs. (9-48) we can compute the pressure and thus obtain the equation of state.

9-6 The Maxwell equations. The second partial derivatives of u, f, g, and h, with respect to any pair of variables, are independent of the order of differentiation. Thus, for example,

$$\frac{\partial^2 u}{\partial s \partial v} = \frac{\partial^2 u}{\partial v \partial s},$$

with corresponding equations for f, g, and h. It follows therefore from Eqs. (9-47) to (9-50) that

$$\left(\frac{\partial s}{\partial p}\right)_v = -\left(\frac{\partial v}{\partial T}\right)_s, \qquad (9\text{-}51)$$

$$\left(\frac{\partial s}{\partial v}\right)_T = \left(\frac{\partial p}{\partial T}\right)_v, \qquad (9\text{-}52)$$

$$\left(\frac{\partial s}{\partial p}\right)_T = -\left(\frac{\partial v}{\partial T}\right)_p, \qquad (9\text{-}53)$$

$$\left(\frac{\partial s}{\partial v}\right)_p = \left(\frac{\partial p}{\partial T}\right)_s. \qquad (9\text{-}54)$$

These four relations are the *Maxwell equations*. The right side of each equation is readily reduced to standard form. The equations have already been derived by other methods in Eqs. (9-12), (9-17), and (9-18).

9-7 The Clausius-Clapeyron equation. We showed in Section 9-5 that when two phases are in equilibrium the specific Gibbs function g has the same value in both phases. Let us consider a liquid and its vapor in equilibrium at a pressure p and a temperature T, and let g'' and g''' represent the Gibbs functions of liquid and vapor respectively. Let the temperature be increased to $T + dT$. The vapor pressure changes to $p + dp$ and the Gibbs functions change to $g'' + dg''$ and $g''' + dg'''$. But since liquid and vapor are in equilibrium at the new temperature and pressure, it follows that the changes dg'' and dg''' are equal also.   We have shown that in a reversible process,

$$dg = -sdT + vdp.$$

Since dT and dp are the same for both phases,

$$-s''dT + v''dp = -s'''dT + v'''dp,$$

or

$$(v''' - v'')dp = (s''' - s'')dT.$$

But

$$s''' - s'' = \frac{l_{23}}{T},$$

and hence

$$\frac{dp}{dT} = \frac{l_{23}}{T(v''' - v'')},$$

which is the Clausius-Clapeyron equation for the liquid-vapor equilibrium, derived by another method in Section 7-5.

9-8 Dependence of vapor pressure on total pressure. As a second application of the Gibbs function, we consider the dependence of the vapor pressure of a liquid on the total pressure, and the distinction between the triple point of water and the ice point.   Phase diagrams such as Fig. 6-3 apply to a system consisting of a single substance only.   Thus correspond-ing values of pressure and tempera-ture at a point on the liquid-vapor equilibrium line in a p-T diagram refer to a system like Fig. 9-5(a), where the points represent mole-cules in the vapor phase.   The pressure in the system equals the vapor pressure.   If an indifferent gas (i.e., one that does not react chemically with the substance) is introduced into the space above the liquid, as represented by the open circles in Fig. 9-5(b), the total pres-sure on the system is the sum of the vapor pressure and partial pressure of the indifferent gas.   The question is, will the vapor pressure (i.e., partial pressure of the vapor) be changed when this is done, the temperature being kept constant?

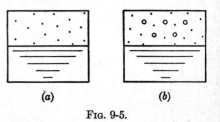

(a)   (b)

FIG. 9-5.

Let π_0 represent the vapor pressure of the substance at a temperature T in the absence of an indifferent gas, π_{23} the vapor pressure when the gas is present, and p the total pressure.   Then $p = \pi_0$ in the absence of an indifferent gas.   Keeping the temperature constant, let us force in a small additional quantity of the gas, increasing the total pressure by dp.   Let $(d\pi_{23})_T$ represent the corresponding increase in vapor pressure and dg'' and dg''' the changes in the Gibbs functions of liquid and vapor.   Then since we have equilibrium at the new pressure,

$$dg'' = dg'''.$$

But

$$dg = -sdT + vdp = vdp,$$

since the temperature is constant.

The change in the pressure of the vapor is $(d\pi_{23})_T$, but the change in the pressure on the liquid is dp.   Then if v'' and v''' are the specific volumes of liquid and vapor,

$$v''dp = v'''(d\pi_{23})_T,$$

or

$$(d\pi_{23})_T = \frac{v''}{v'''}\, dp. \tag{9-55}$$

Since v'' and v''' are always positive, an increase in the total pressure always increases the vapor pressure.   That is, as more of the indifferent gas is pumped in, more of the liquid evaporates, contrary to what might be expected.   However, since $v''' >> v''$, the change in vapor pressure is very small compared with the change in total pressure.

We consider next the distinction between the ice point, and the triple point of water.   Pure water at its triple point is represented in Fig. 9-6(a).   Water vapor, pure water, and pure ice are in equilibrium and the total pressure equals the vapor pressure, 4.58 mm of mercury.   Of course the vapor pressure of water and the sublimation pressure of ice

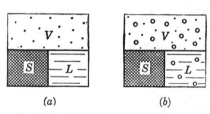

FIG. 9-6.   (a) Triple point of a pure substance.   (b) An indifferent gas changes the equilibrium temperature.

are equal at the triple point.   The ice point is represented in Fig. 9-6(b). There is air in the space above the solid and liquid, sufficient in amount to raise the total pressure to 1 atm or 760 mm of mercury, and air is also dissolved in the water.   For simplicity we shall at first neglect the effect of the dissolved air.   By definition, the temperature of system (b) is exactly 0° C, and we wish to compute the temperature of system (a).

Fig. 9-7 appears complicated but will repay careful study.   The full lines lettered π_{23} and π_{13} represent the vapor pressure of water and the

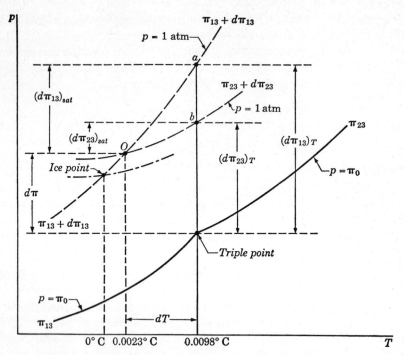

Fig. 9-7. Distinction between triple point of water and ice point.

sublimation pressure of ice, when the total pressure equals the vapor pressure π_0. These curves intersect, of course, at the triple point. The dashed line labelled $\pi_{23} + d\pi_{23}$ represents the vapor pressure of water when the total pressure is 1 atm, neglecting any effect of dissolved air. It lies everywhere above the curve of π_{23}, by an amount $(d\pi_{23})_T$ given by Eq. (9-55). The dashed line lettered $\pi_{13} + d\pi_{13}$ represents the sublimation pressure of ice when the total pressure is 1 atm. It also lies everywhere above the curve π_{13} and, by the same argument as above, the increase $(d\pi_{13})_T$ is

$$(d\pi_{13})_T = \frac{v'}{v'''}\, dp. \qquad (9\text{-}56)$$

Since $v' > v''$ for water, $d\pi_{13} > d\pi_{23}$ as indicated. Hence if the system is originally at the triple point and air is pumped in, the vapor pressure over the ice increases to point a, and that over the liquid to point b. The pressure in the left side of the vapor region in Fig. 9-6(b) is greater than that in the right, and vapor flows from left to right, increasing the pressure over the liquid and decreasing that over the vapor. As a result of the increased pressure over the liquid, some of the vapor condenses, giving up its heat of vaporization, while some of the ice vaporizes and the heat of sublimation is abstracted from it.   At the triple point, the heat of sublimation is greater than the heat of vaporization, and the result is a lowering of the temperature of the system, assuming it thermally insulated. (If it were kept at constant temperature, all the ice would eventually melt.)   As the temperature decreases, the vapor pressures over both liquid and solid decrease along the dashed curves, and a new equilibrium state is attained at O, the point of intersection of these curves.   The process just described illustrates the general principle that at a given temperature the phase of lower vapor pressure is the stable one.   That is, at temperatures greater than that at O the liquid phase is stable, while at lower temperatures the solid phase is the stable one.

In going from the triple point to point O, the net changes in vapor pressure of the liquid and solid are the same.   The vapor pressure of the liquid increases by an amount $(d\pi_{23})_T$ at the triple-point temperature T, as a result of the increased pressure, and decreases along the saturation line by an amount $(d\pi_{23})_{sat}$ as a result of the lowering of temperature. The net increase is

$$d\pi = (d\pi_{23})_T + (d\pi_{23})_{sat}. \qquad (9\text{-}57)$$

(We must pretend ignorance of the algebraic sign of $(d\pi_{23})_{sat}$ and assume it positive, if we wish the algebraic sign of dT in the answer to tell us whether the temperature goes up or down.)

In the same way, the net increase in the vapor pressure of the solid is

$$d\pi = (d\pi_{13})_T + (d\pi_{13})_{sat}. \qquad (9\text{-}58)$$

The change in pressure with temperature along a saturation line is given by the Clapeyron equation.   In our present notation, the equation states that

$$(d\pi_{23})_{sat} = \frac{l_{23}}{T(v''' - v'')} \, dT,$$

$$(d\pi_{13})_{sat} = \frac{l_{13}}{T(v''' - v')} \, dT.$$

Using these equations, taking the expressions for $(d\pi_{23})_T$ and $(d\pi_{13})_T$ from Eqs. (9-55) and (9-56), and equating the right sides of Eqs. (9-57) and (9-58), we get

$$\frac{v''}{v'''} \, dp + \frac{l_{23}}{T(v''' - v'')} \, dT = \frac{v'}{v'''} \, dp + \frac{l_{13}}{T(v''' - v')} \, dT.$$

Since v' and v'' are both negligible compared with v''', and since at the triple point $l_{13} = l_{12} + l_{23}$, this reduces to

$$dT = \frac{T(v'' - v')}{l_{12}} \, dp. \tag{9-59}$$

For water at the triple point,

$$T \approx 273° \text{ K}, \quad v'' = 1.00 \times 10^{-3} \text{ m}^3/\text{kgm},$$

$$v' = 1.09 \times 10^{-3} \text{ m}^3/\text{kgm}, \quad l_{12} = 3.3 \times 10^5 \text{ joules/kgm}.$$

The increase in pressure is from 4.58 to 760 mm of mercury, or approximately 10^5 newtons/m².

Hence

$$dT = \frac{273(1.00 \times 10^{-3} - 1.09 \times 10^{-3})}{3.3 \times 10^5} \times 10^5$$

$$= -0.0075 \text{ degree.}$$

The temperature at point O therefore lies 0.0075 degree below the triple point.

Now consider the effect of the dissolved air. It is a familiar fact that any substance dissolved in a liquid lowers the freezing point of the liquid. Although phenomena of this sort form a large part of the application of thermodynamics to chemistry, we shall not discuss them in this book. Suffice it to say that the "reason" for the lowering of the freezing point is that the dissolved substance lowers the vapor pressure of the liquid, as indicated by the dot-dash line in Fig. 9-7 lying slightly below the curve $\pi_{23} + d\pi_{23}$. Hence the actual equilibrium point of the system in Fig. 9-6(b) is below and to the left of point O in Fig. 9-7, the temperature difference between them being 0.0023° C. But this last point is, by definition, the ice point, and its temperature is exactly 0° C. The triple-point temperature is accordingly 0.0023 + 0.0075, or 0.0098 degree above the ice point.

9-9 The Joule-Kelvin inversion curve. We now derive two equations which were used in Sec. 5-10 in connection with the Joule-Kelvin effect. We have from the definition of enthalpy

$$dh = Tds + vdp,$$

which can be written

$$dh = T\left(\frac{\partial s}{\partial T}\right)_p dT + \left[T\left(\frac{\partial s}{\partial p}\right)_T + v\right] dp. \tag{9-60}$$

But we showed in Eq. (9-17) that

$$T\left(\frac{\partial s}{\partial T}\right)_p = c_p,$$

and from the Maxwell equation (9-53),

$$\left(\frac{\partial s}{\partial p}\right)_T = -\left(\frac{\partial v}{\partial T}\right)_p.$$

Therefore Eq. (9-60) becomes

$$dh = c_p dT + \left[v - T\left(\frac{\partial v}{\partial T}\right)_p\right] dp. \tag{9-61}$$

If h is constant and $dh = 0$, then

$$\left(\frac{\partial T}{\partial p}\right)_h = -\frac{1}{c_p}\left[v - T\left(\frac{\partial v}{\partial T}\right)_p\right]. \tag{9-62}$$

This is the equation used in Sec. 5-10 to derive the inversion curve for a van der Waals gas.

9-10 The Gibbs-Helmholtz equation. It was shown in Section 9-5 that the work (exclusive of "pdV" work) done by a system in a reversible iso-thermal-isobaric process is equal to the decrease in the Gibbs function of the system. In general, the source of the work is in part the system itself and in part the heat reservoir with which it is in contact.

A common process in which work other than pdV work is done by a system is the discharge of a voltaic cell, where electrical work EdC is done when a charge dC flows through a cell of terminal voltage E. (We use C rather than the standard electrical symbol Q to avoid confusion with the symbol for heat.) This is in addition to any pdV work which may be done in a volume change of the system, such as would result if there were some gaseous products of the reaction taking place in the cell. In the most general case, the total work will consist of a sum of terms, each being the product of an intensive variable (such as p or E) and the differential of an extensive variable (such as V or the electric charge C). Thus in addition to the term pdV, which we shall write separately, the work done by a system will be given by a sum of terms of the form $Y_1 dX_1$, $Y_2 dX_2$, etc., where Y_1, Y_2, etc., represent the intensive variables and X_1, X_2, etc., the associated extensive variables. To avoid too many complications we consider a system in which there is only one additional work term, YdX. For a voltaic cell, Y is the terminal voltage E and dX is the charge dC. The work is then

$$d'W = pdV + YdX.$$

From the definition of the Gibbs function, $G = U - TS + pV$, it follows that

$$dG = dU - TdS - SdT + pdV + Vdp.$$

From the first and second laws,

$$TdS = dU + d'W = dU + pdV + YdX.$$

Then

$$dG = -SdT + Vdp + YdX. \tag{9-63}$$

We see that G is a function of three independent variables, T, p, and X. The coefficient of each differential on the right side of Eq. (9-63) is therefore the partial derivative of G with respect to the corresponding variable, the other two being held constant. That is,

$$\left(\frac{\partial G}{\partial T}\right)_{p,X} = -S, \quad \left(\frac{\partial G}{\partial p}\right)_{T,X} = V, \quad \left(\frac{\partial G}{\partial X}\right)_{T,p} = Y.$$

These are evidently generalizations of Eqs. (9-49). Substituting the first of these in the defining equation for G, and recalling that $H = U + pV$, we get

$$G = H + T\left(\frac{\partial G}{\partial T}\right)_{p,X}. \tag{9-64}$$

To correlate G with the work done by the system, we need an expression for the difference $G_1 - G_2$, where the subscripts refer to two states at the same temperature and pressure, but at different values of X, say X_1 and X_2. Figure 9-8 shows two graphs of G as a function of T. (The curves are schematic only and do not represent any specific system.) Both are constructed at the same pressure p, but $X = X_1$ at all points of the upper curve and $X = X_2$ at all points of the lower. The process represented by the line ba is therefore a reversible isothermal-isobaric one, and the difference between G_1 and G_2 at points b and a is what we wish to find. From the preceding equation,

$$G_1 = H_1 + T\left(\frac{\partial G_1}{\partial T}\right)_{p,X},$$

$$G_2 = H_2 + T\left(\frac{\partial G_2}{\partial T}\right)_{p,X},$$

where the first equation is evaluated at point b and the second at point a. Subtraction gives

$$(G_1 - G_2) = (H_1 - H_2) + T\left[\left(\frac{\partial G_1}{\partial T}\right)_{p,X} - \left(\frac{\partial G_2}{\partial T}\right)_{p,X}\right]. \tag{9-65}$$

The second term on the right can be more conveniently written as follows. Points d and e in Fig. 9-8 represent values of G at pressure p and temperature $T + \Delta T$. The length of the line segment ab equals $(G_1 - G_2)$ at the temperature T, while that of ed equals $(G_1 - G_2)$ at the temperature $T + \Delta T$. Now approximately,

$$(G_1 - G_2)_{(T+\Delta T)} = (G_1 - G_2)_{(T)} + \left[\frac{\partial(G_1 - G_2)}{\partial T}\right]_p \Delta T.$$

Also, approximately,

$$fe = \left(\frac{\partial G_2}{\partial T}\right)_{p,z} \Delta T, \quad bc = \left(\frac{\partial G_1}{\partial T}\right)_{p,z} \Delta T,$$

and from inspection of the diagram,

$$ab + bc = fe + ed.$$

In the limit as ΔT approaches zero, the approximations become exact, and replacing ΔT by dT, we have from the preceding equations,

$$(G_1 - G_2)_{(T)} + \left(\frac{\partial G_1}{\partial T}\right)_{p,z} dT$$
$$= \left(\frac{\partial G_2}{\partial T}\right)_{p,z} dT + (G_1 - G_2)_{(T)} + \left[\frac{\partial(G_1 - G_2)}{\partial T}\right]_p dT.$$

After cancelling $(G_1 - G_2)_{(T)}$ and dividing by dT, we get

$$\left(\frac{\partial G_1}{\partial T}\right)_{p,z} - \left(\frac{\partial G_2}{\partial T}\right)_{p,z} = \left[\frac{\partial(G_1 - G_2)}{\partial T}\right]_p.$$

Finally, representing the work (exclusive of pdV work) by the symbol A, we get from Eq. (9-65),

$$A = (H_1 - H_2) + T\left(\frac{\partial A}{\partial T}\right)_p. \tag{9-66}$$

This is one form of the Gibbs-Helmholtz equation. It is important to note that A *is not a function of the state of the system,* but that it equals the *difference* between the values of the Gibbs function of the system for two specified values of X, at the same temperature T and pressure p. For these specified values of X, the work A depends only on the temperature and pressure at which the process is carried out. Thus A (for two specified values of X) is a function of two variables only, T and p. Graphically, $(\partial A/\partial T)_p$ means the rate at which the length of a vertical line between the curves in Fig. 9-8 varies as the temperature is varied. (Since these curves are different at different pressures, the length of a vertical line between them, at a constant temperature T, varies with pressure.

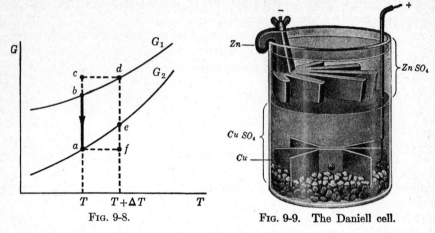

FIG. 9-8.   FIG. 9-9.   The Daniell cell.

The partial derivative $(\partial A/\partial p)_T$ describes the rate at which the length of this line varies with pressure.)

To illustrate the application of the Gibbs-Helmholtz equation to a specific problem, we consider the Daniell cell. It consists of a zinc electrode in a solution of zinc sulfate and a copper electrode in a saturated solution of copper sulfate. In the cell illustrated in Fig. 9-9, known as a gravity cell, the two solutions are kept separated (except for a slow interdiffusion on open circuit) by the difference in their densities. When the cell discharges, zinc goes into solution and copper is deposited on the copper electrode. The net chemical effect is the disappearance of Zn and Cu^{++} and the appearance of Zn^{++} and Cu, as represented by

$$Zn + Cu^{++} \rightarrow Zn^{++} + Cu. \qquad (9\text{-}67)$$

By forcing a current through the cell in the opposite direction the process can be reversed, that is, copper goes into solution and zinc is deposited.

Let the terminals of the cell be connected to a potentiometer. If the voltage across the potentiometer is made just equal to the emf of the cell the current in the cell is zero. By making the voltage slightly larger or smaller than the emf, the reaction in the cell can be made to go in either direction. Furthermore, since heat losses in the circuit are proportional to the square of the current while the electrical work done is proportional to the first power, the former can be made negligible by making the current very small. Hence the cell can be operated as a reversible system in the thermodynamic sense. Let the cell be placed in a thermostatically controlled bath which maintains it at a constant temperature T, and let p

be the constant external pressure. The terminal voltage of the cell, if the current is very small, will equal its emf $\mathcal{E}$. The electrical work done by the cell while a quantity of charge C flows through it is then $\mathcal{E}C$, and since the process is reversible, isothermal, and isobaric, this is equal to the work A.

$$A = \mathcal{E}C.$$

The same chemical reaction as in Eq. (9-67) can be made to take place in a purely chemical manner, quite apart from a Daniell cell. Thus if zinc powder is shaken in a solution of copper sulfate all the zinc will dissolve (i.e., become ions in solution) and all the copper ions will become metal atoms, provided the original amounts of the two substances are chosen properly. If the initial and final states are at the same temperature and pressure, heat is liberated. That is, the reaction is *exothermic*. The enthalpy difference $H_1 - H_2$ equals the heat liberated in this reaction, since $H_2 - H_1$ equals the heat *absorbed* in an isobaric process. The heat liberated, per mole of reacting substance, is called in chemistry the *heat of the reaction* and is represented by Q, with a positive sign. (This is opposite to the usual thermodynamic convention.) Therefore if n moles react,

$$H_1 - H_2 = nQ.$$

The Faraday constant F, equal to 9.65194×10^7 coul/kilomole, is the quantity of charge carried by one mole of singly charged ions. For ions of valence z the charge per mole is zF and the charge of n kilomoles is nzF. Therefore in a process in which n kilomoles react,

$$C = nzF.$$

Combining the three preceding equations with the Gibbs-Helmholtz equation, we get

$$\mathcal{E}C = nQ + TC\left(\frac{\partial \mathcal{E}}{\partial T}\right)_p,$$

$$\mathcal{E} = \frac{nQ}{C} + T\left(\frac{\partial \mathcal{E}}{\partial T}\right)_p,$$

$$\mathcal{E} = \frac{Q}{zF} + T\left(\frac{\partial \mathcal{E}}{\partial T}\right)_p. \tag{9-68}$$

For two equilibrium states of a system at the same temperature and pressure, the enthalpy change $H_1 - H_2$ is the same whatever the process connecting the states. If the process is carried out in a purely "chemical" manner, no work other than pdV work is done and the decrease in enthalpy equals the heat evolved. The general equation, Eq. (9-66), states that if a process can be devised between the same two end states, but in which work other than pdV work is done, the amount of this work may be equal to, greater than, or less than the heat evolved in the first process, depending on the magnitude and sign of $(\partial A/\partial T)_p$. The difference is accounted for by the heat absorbed from or given to the reservoir which maintains the system at constant temperature. Specifically, for an electrolytic cell, the electrical work $\mathcal{E}C$ done when the cell discharges at constant temperature and pressure may be equal to, greater than, or less than the heat nQ evolved in the corresponding chemical reaction, depending on the magnitude and sign of the temperature coefficient of the emf of the cell at constant pressure.

In physical chemistry, Eq. (9-68) is most useful when looked on as a means of measuring heats of reaction. The precise measurement of quantities of heat by direct calorimetric methods is one of the most difficult experimental techniques. Emf's, however, can readily be measured with high precision. If the reacting substances can be combined to form an electrolytic cell the heat of reaction can be computed very accurately from measurements of the emf and its rate of change with temperature.

Since the term $T(\partial\mathcal{E}/\partial T)_p$ is usually very small compared with $\mathcal{E}$, practically all of the energy available in a chemical reaction can be utilized directly as electrical energy provided the reacting substances will form a voltaic cell. (The electrical energy is even greater than the heat of reaction if $(\partial\mathcal{E}/\partial T)_p$ is positive.) It is interesting to speculate on the effect on our economy if a voltaic cell could be constructed of carbon and oxygen.

9-11 Thermodynamics of magnetism.

As another example of a process in which work other than "pdV" work is done, we consider a substance in a magnetic field, the specimen being in the form of a long rod so that demagnetizing effects are negligible. Let l represent the length of the rod, A its cross-sectional area, and suppose it to be wound uniformly with a magnetizing winding of N turns carrying a current i. Let B represent the flux density and $\Phi = BA$ the total flux. (We shall use rationalized mks units.) When the current in the windings is increased by di in time dt, the induced emf in the windings is

$$\mathcal{E} = N\frac{d\Phi}{dt} = NA\frac{dB}{dt}$$

and the work $d'A$ done in time dt is

$$d'A = \mathcal{E}idt = NAidB.$$

The magnetic intensity H is

$$H = Ni/l,$$

and eliminating i, we get

$$d'A = VHdB,$$

or,

$$d'a = vHdB,$$

where $V = Al = mv$ is the volume of the specimen. The expression above gives the work per unit mass done by the surroundings, and the work done by the system is the negative of this. Hence the combined first and second laws take the form

$$TdS = du + pdv - vHdB.$$

By definition,

$$B = \mu_0(H + M),$$

where M is the magnetization or magnetic moment per unit volume. Since molecular theories of magnetization lead to an expression for M, let us use the equation above to eliminate B. We have

$$vHdB = \mu_0 vHdH + \mu_0 vHdM.$$

The first term on the right is the work that would be required to increase the field in a vacuum, since in such a case M and dM would be zero. We shall therefore omit this term, since we are interested only in the work done *by the substance*, given by the second term. Also, since the magnetization proceeds at essentially constant volume, the term pdv can be omitted also. Therefore

$$Tds = du - \mu_0 vHdM.$$

The magnetization M is a function of the magnetic intensity H and of the temperature T. That is, there exists for every substance a "magnetic equation of state," $f(M,H,T) = 0$. Hence only two of the variables M, H, and T are independent, and we can consider s and u as functions of any pair of these variables. The situation is exactly analogous to that for a substance whose equation of state is $f(p,v,T) = 0$ and for which the combined first and second laws take the form

$$Tds = du + pdv. \tag{9-69}$$

The pressure p corresponds to the magnetic intensity H, v corresponds to $-\mu_0 vM$, and dv to $-\mu_0 vdM$. Constant pressure corresponds to constant H, and constant v to constant M. Since the methods of derivation are identical, we can write any number of thermodynamic equations for the magnetic case by analogy with those already derived. A few are given below, the number of the previously derived equation being given in the left-hand margin. The symbol c_H is the specific heat capacity at constant H. (In some of the earlier equations, which are given in "standard form" only, it is necessary to replace β and κ by their equivalents in terms of partial derivatives before using the analogies above.)

(5-14)
$$c_H = \left(\frac{\partial u}{\partial T}\right)_H - \mu_0 v H \left(\frac{\partial M}{\partial T}\right)_H,$$
(9-70)

(9-16)
$$\left(\frac{\partial u}{\partial H}\right)_T = \mu_0 v \left[H \left(\frac{\partial M}{\partial H}\right)_T + T \left(\frac{\partial M}{\partial T}\right)_H \right],$$
(9-71)

(9-20)
$$T ds = c_H dT + \mu_0 v T \left(\frac{\partial M}{\partial T}\right)_H dH.$$
(9-72)

A common technique in the production of extremely low temperatures, of the order of $1°$ K or less, is to cool a paramagnetic salt in liquid helium, magnetize it isothermally, removing heat in the process, and then demagnetize it adiabatically. The temperature drops in the adiabatic demagnetization, much as it does in the adiabatic expansion of a gas. The quantity of heat flowing into a substance when the magnetic intensity increases isothermally by an amount dH_T is found from Eq. (9-72) by setting $dT = 0$.

$$d'q_T = T ds_T = \mu_0 v T \left(\frac{\partial M}{\partial T}\right)_H dH_T.$$
(9-73)

The temperature change when the magnetic intensity changes adiabatically by an amount dH_s is obtained by setting $ds = 0$.

$$dT_s = -\frac{\mu_0 v T}{c_H} \left(\frac{\partial M}{\partial T}\right)_H dH_s.$$
(9-74)

All of the equations above are perfectly general and apply to any substance. To obtain numerical values of c_H and of the partial derivatives of M we must resort to experiment or to a molecular theory of the magnetization process. The elementary theory of a paramagnetic substance is discussed in Section 15-6. Experimentally, it is found that many paramagnetic substances, at temperatures that are not too low and in fields that are not too great, obey Curie's law, which states that the magnetization is directly proportional to the magnetic intensity and inversely proportional to the Kelvin temperature.

$$M = C \frac{H}{T},$$

where C is a constant called the *Curie constant*. This equation is the "magnetic equation of state" of the substance, and it approximates the behavior of actual paramagnetic materials much as $pv = RT$ approximates that of actual gases.

If Curie's law is obeyed, then

$$\left(\frac{\partial M}{\partial H}\right)_T = \frac{C}{T}, \quad \left(\frac{\partial M}{\partial T}\right)_H = -\frac{CH}{T^2}, \tag{9-75}$$

and from Eq. (9-71),

$$\left(\frac{\partial u}{\partial H}\right)_T = 0. \tag{9-76}$$

It is not difficult to show that the same result holds if M is any function of the ratio H/T. The fact that the internal energy does not depend on the magnetic intensity at constant temperature is analogous to the fact that the internal energy of an ideal gas, at constant temperature, does not depend on its pressure. When work is done on an ideal gas to compress it at constant temperature, an equal quantity of heat flows out of the gas to the reservoir which maintains the temperature constant. When work is done to magnetize a material obeying Curie's law, in an isothermal process, an equal quantity of heat flows out of the material.

Problems

1. Complete the derivation of Eqs. (9-16), (9-17), (9-18), and (9-19). Derive Eqs. (9-28) and (9-29) from Eq. (9-27) and the equation of state of an ideal gas.

2. Compute $(\partial u/\partial p)_T$ for (a) an ideal gas, (b) for a real gas obeying the equation of state

$$pv = RT + Bp,$$

where B is a function of temperature only.

3. (a) Is c_p for an ideal gas independent of p? (b) Is c_p for a van der Waals gas independent of p?

4. Assume that c_p for an ideal gas is given by

$$c_p = a + bT,$$

where a and b are constants. (a) What is the expression for c_v for this gas? (b) Use these expressions for c_p and c_v in Eqs. (9-24) and (9-26) to derive expressions for the specific entropy of this gas in terms of the entropy s_0 at some arbitrary reference state, and show that the three expressions obtained are equivalent.

5. 10 moles of a monatomic ideal gas ($c_v = \frac{3}{2}R$) are compressed isothermally and reversibly, at a temperature of 300° K, from an initial pressure of 1 atm to a final pressure of 10 atm. Compute the change in entropy of the gas.

6. An ideal gas for which $c_v = \frac{5}{2}R$ is carried reversibly around the cyclic path abc in Fig. 9-11. Fill in the blanks in the tables.

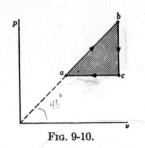

FIG. 9-10.

	$p(n/m^2)$	$V(m^3)$	$T(°K)$
Point a	2×10^5	3	100
Point b	4×10^5	6	400
Point c	2×10^5	6	200

	$W(j)$	$Q(j)$	$\Delta U(j)$	$\Delta S(j/\deg)$
Path ab	9×10^5	54×10^5	45×10^5	$36 \times 10^3 \times \ln 2$
Path bc	0	-30×10^5	-30×10^5	$-15 \times 10^3 \times \ln 2$
Path ca	-6×10^5	-21×10^5	-15×10^5	$-21 \times 10^3 \times \ln 2$
	$\Sigma W = 3$	$\Sigma Q = 3$	$\Sigma \Delta U = 0$	$\Sigma \Delta S = 0$

7. A system consisting of n moles of an ideal gas undergoes a free expansion from a volume V_1 to a volume $2V_1$. (a) What is the change in entropy of the gas? (b) of the universe? (c) If the expansion were performed reversibly and isothermally, what would be the change in entropy of the gas? (d) of the universe?

8. Oxygen gas, originally at a temperature of 300° K and a pressure of 1 atm, is compressed adiabatically and reversibly to 1/10th of its original volume. Find the final temperature, assuming (a) that oxygen is an ideal gas, (b) that it is a van der Waals gas. (Use Tables 2-1 and 12-3, and make any other assumptions that seem reasonable.)

9. Carbon dioxide at an initial pressure of 50 atm and a temperature of 300° K undergoes an adiabatic free expansion in which the final volume is 20 times the original volume. Find the change in temperature and the increase in entropy, assuming (a) that CO_2 is an ideal gas, (b) that it is a van der Waals gas.

10. Refer to Problem 12 in Chapter 3. Find (a) the heat flowing out of each system, and (b) the increase in internal energy of each. The density of the liquid is 10^3 kgm/m^3. At constant pressure, the specific heat capacity of the liquid is 4.18×10^3 joules/kgm-deg, and that of the gas is $5R/2$. The coefficient of volume expansion of the liquid is 4.3×10^{-4} deg^{-1}.

11. Refer to Fig. 2-7. Show the five processes in a T-s diagram.

12. The pressure on a block of copper at a temperature of 0° C is increased isothermally and reversibly from 1 atm to 1000 atm. Assume that β, κ, and ρ

are constant and equal respectively to 5×10^{-5} deg^{-1}, 8×10^{-12} (n/m²)$^{-1}$, and 8.9×10^3 kgm/m³. Calculate (a) the work done on the copper per kilogram, (b) the heat evolved. (c) How do you account for the fact that the heat evolved is greater than the work done? (d) What would be the rise in temperature of the copper, if the compression were adiabatic rather than isothermal?

13. The table below gives the volume of 1 gm of water at a number of temperatures and at a pressure of 1 atm.

$t(°C)$	$V(cm^3)$	$t(°C)$	$V(cm^3)$
0	1.00013	20	1.00177
2	1.00003	50	1.01207
4	1.00000	75	1.02576
6	1.00003	100	1.04343
10	1.00027		

Estimate as closely as you can the temperature change when the pressure on water in a hydraulic press is increased reversibly and adiabatically from a pressure of 1 atm to a pressure of 1000 atm, when the initial temperature is (a) 2° C, (b) 4° C, (c) 50° C. (d) What partial derivative needs to be evaluated to answer the question? Make any reasonable assumptions or approximations, but state what they are.

14. Water in a hydraulic press is compressed reversibly and adiabatically from a pressure of 1 atm to a pressure of 1000 atm. Find the final temperature, when the initial temperature is (a) 0° C, (b) 5° C, (c) 50° C. The values of β at these temperatures are

$t(°C)$	$\beta(deg^{-1})$
0	-67×10^{-6}
5	15×10^{-6}
50	465×10^{-6}

15. From Fig. 3-8, read as closely as you can the values of β and κ for copper, at temperatures of 200° K and 1200° K. Assume the density of copper constant and equal to 8.9×10^3 kgm/m³. The atomic weight of copper is 63. Compute the difference $c_p - c_v$ for copper at 200° K and 1200° K, and compare with the difference as read from the graphs in Fig. 4-3.

16. Find the difference $c_p - c_v$ for mercury at a temperature of 0° C and a pressure of 1 atm, taking the values of β and κ from Fig. 3-9. The density of mercury is 13.6×10^3 kgm/m³ and the atomic weight is 200.6. Express the answer in terms of R, and compare with $c_p - c_v$ for an ideal gas.

17. Ice originally at a temperature of $-2°$ C and atmospheric pressure is compressed adiabatically. Find the temperature and pressure at which the ice starts to melt. Take $c_p = 2090$ joules/kgm and $\rho = 920$ kgm/m³. See problem 11, Chapter 7, and construct diagrams like those called for in part (d) of that problem.

18. (a) Show that for an ideal gas

$$f = \int_{T_0}^{T} c_v dT - T \int_{T_0}^{T} c_v \frac{dT}{T} - RT \ln \frac{v}{v_0} - s_0 T + u_0,$$

$$g = \int_{T_0}^{T} c_p dT - T \int_{T_0}^{T} c_p \frac{dT}{T} + RT \ln \frac{p}{p_0} - s_0 T + u_0 + RT_0,$$

where s_0 and u_0 are respectively the specific entropy and internal energy in the reference state p_0, v_0, T_0.

(b) Verify equations (9-48) for an ideal gas by computing $(\partial f/\partial T)_v$ and $(\partial f/\partial v)_T$ from the first equation above.

19. The specific enthalpy of superheated steam at a pressure of 500 lb/in² and a temperature of 800° F is 1412 Btu/lb, and the specific entropy is 1.657 Btu/lb-deg F abs. Find the specific Gibbs function of superheated steam at this temperature and pressure, in engineering units.

20. Compute the values of Δu, Δs, Δh, and Δg, when one pound of water is evaporated at 300° F and 67 lb/in². Use the data in Problem 9 in Chapter 6.

21. One gram of water when converted to steam at atmospheric pressure, occupies a volume of 1671 cm³. The latent heat of vaporization at this temperature is 539 cal/gm.

(a) Compare the volume of steam with the volume that would be occupied at this temperature and pressure if water vapor were an ideal gas.

(b) Compute the increases in internal energy (ΔU), entropy (ΔS), enthalpy (ΔH), and in the Gibbs function (ΔG) when one gram of water is evaporated at this temperature and pressure. Express all answers in the same system of units.

22. (a) Show that the increase in vapor pressure $\Delta\pi$, when the total pressure on a liquid is increased isothermally from π_0 to p, is approximately

$$\Delta\pi = \frac{\pi_0 v''}{RT} (p - \pi_0).$$

(b) The vapor pressure of water at 20° C, when the total pressure equals the vapor pressure, is 17.5 mm of mercury. Find the change in vapor pressure when the water is open to the atmosphere. Neglect any effect of the dissolved air.

(c) Find the pressure required to increase the vapor pressure by 1 mm of mercury.

23. (a) Prove that the slope of a curve representing a reversible isothermal process in a Mollier diagram (h vs. s) is $T - (1/\beta)$.

(b) Prove that the slope of a curve representing a reversible isometric process is $T + [(\gamma - 1)/\beta]$.

24. The Joule-Kelvin coefficient μ for a substance undergoing a throttling process is defined as

$$\mu = (\partial T / \partial p)_h.$$

Compute μ (a) for an ideal gas, (b) for a van der Waals gas.

25. The vapor pressure of water over a limited range of temperature can be represented with sufficient accuracy by the empirical equation

$$p = K \exp\left(\frac{A + BT}{C + DT}\right),$$

where K, A, B, C, and D are constants. If the specific volume of the liquid is negligible and the vapor can be considered an ideal gas, find the form of the latent heat as a function of temperature that is implied by the equation above.

26. When zinc sulfate (valence $z = 2$) reacts chemically with copper, at a temperature of 273° K and atmospheric pressure, the heat evolved in the reaction is 2.31×10^8 joules/kilomole. The emf of a Daniell cell at 273° K is 1.0934 volts, and the emf decreases with temperature at the rate of 4.533×10^{-5} volt/deg. Calculate the heat of reaction from the data on the emf and compare with the directly measured value given above.

27. Prove that if Curie's law is obeyed, the heat per unit mass flowing into a paramagnetic substance when the magnetizing force is increased from zero to H at constant temperature T_1 is

$$q_{T_1} = -\frac{\mu_0 C v H^2}{2T_1}.$$

(b) Show that if the magnetizing force is now decreased adiabatically and reversibly from H to zero, and if C_H is constant, the final temperature T_2 is given by

$$T_2^2 = T_1^2 - \frac{2T_1 q_{T_1}}{c_H}.$$

(c) A sample of paramagnetic salt obeying Curie's law, and for which the total heat capacity $C_H = 10^{-3} T^3$ joule/deg, is cooled to 3° K in liquid helium, magnetized isothermally, and demagnetized adiabatically. If 5×10^{-3} joule of heat is removed in the isothermal magnetization, what is the temperature at the end of the process?

CHAPTER 10

SOME ENGINEERING APPLICATIONS OF THERMODYNAMICS

10-1 Thermodynamic properties of steam. In this chapter we describe briefly how the principles of thermodynamics are applied in engineering to the operation of reciprocating steam engines, turbines, and refrigerators. Numerical calculations are greatly aided by the use of tables and diagrams giving the entropy, internal energy, enthalpy, and other properties of the working substance over a range of pressures and temperatures. Such tables are available for water, ammonia, sulfur dioxide, and other materials commonly used in engines and refrigerators. We shall describe only the tables for water, commonly called "steam tables." In the tables used in the United States, pressures are in lb/in² abs, temperatures in degrees Fahrenheit or Fahrenheit absolute, (specific) volumes in ft³/lb, (specific) energy and enthalpy in Btu/lb, and (specific) entropy in Btu/lb-deg F abs.

Fig. 10-1 is a reproduction of portions of two of the tables found in "Thermodynamic Properties of Steam," by Keenan and Keyes. Table 1 covers the temperature range from 32° F to 705.4° F, the critical tempera-

Table 1. Saturation: Temperatures

Temp. Fahr.	Abs. Pressure Lb. Sq In.	In. Hg.	Specific Volume Sat. Liquid	Evap.	Sat. Vapor	Enthalpy Sat. Liquid	Evap	Sat. Vapor	Entropy Sat. Liquid	Evap	Sat. Vapor	Temp. Fahr.
t	p		v_f	v_{fg}	v_g	h_f	h_{fg}	h_g	s_f	s_{fg}	s_g	t
32	0 08854	0 1803	0 01602	3306	3306	0.00	1075.8	1075.8	0.0000	2 1877	2 1877	32°
33	0 09223	0 1878	0 01602	3180	3180	1.01	1075.2	1076.2	0.0020	2 1821	2 1841	33
34	0 09603	0 1955	0 01602	3061	3061	2.02	1074.7	1076.7	0.0041	2 1764	2 1805	34

Table 3. Superheated Vapor

Abs. Press. Lb./Sq. In. (Sat Temp)		Sat. Liquid	Sat. Vapor	Temperature—Degrees Fahrenheit												
				420°	440°	460°	480°	500°	520°	540°	560°	580°	600°	620°	640°	660°	680°
250 (400.95)	v	0.0187	1.8438	1 9077	1.9717	2.033	2.093	2.151	2.208	2.264	2.319	2.374	2.427	2.480	2.533	2.585	2.637
	h	376.0	1201.1	1214 2	1227.3	1239.7	1251.7	1263.4	1274.8	1285.9	1296.9	1307.7	1318.5	132v.1	1339.6	1350.1	1360.6
	s	0.5675	1.5263	1.5414	1.5560	1.5697	1.5826	1.5949	1.6067	1.6179	1.6288	1.6393	1.6495	1.6595	1.6691	1.6786	1.6878
255 (402 70)	v	0.0187	1.8086	1.8659	1.9292	1.9900	2.049	2.106	2.162	2.217	2.272	2.325	2.378	2.430	2.482	2.533	2.584
	h	377.9	1201.3	1213.3	1226.5	1239.0	1251.1	1262.8	1274.3	1285.5	1296.5	1307.3	1318.1	1328.7	1339.3	1349.8	1360.3
	s	0.5697	1.5246	1.5384	1.5531	1.5670	1.5800	1.5923	1.6041	1.6154	1.6263	1.6368	1.6471	1.6570	1.6667	1.6762	1.6855

700°	720°	740°	760°	780°	800°	850°	900°	950°	Temperature—Degrees Fahrenheit 1000°	1050°	1100°	1200°	1400°	1600°		Abs. Press. Lb./Sq. In. (Sat. Temp.)
2.688	2.740	2.791	2.841	2.892	2.942	3.068	3.192	3.316	3.439	3.562	3.684	3.928	4.413	4.896	v	250 (400.95)
1371.0	1381.4	1391.7	1402.1	1412.4	1422.7	1448.6	1474.5	1500.5	1526.6	1552.9	1579.3	1632.7	1741.8	1854.4	h	
1.6969	1.7058	1.7145	1.7230	1.7315	1.7397	1.7598	1.7793	1.7980	1.8162	1.8339	1.8512	1.8843	1.9464	2.0039	s	
2.634	2.684	2.734	2.784	2.834	2.884	3.006	3.128	3.250	3.371	3.491	3.611	3.850	4.326	4.799	v	255 (402.70)
1370.7	1381.1	1391.5	1401.8	1412.2	1422.5	1448.4	1474.3	1500.3	1526.5	1552.8	1579.2	1632.6	1741.8	1854.3	h	
1.6945	1.7034	1.7122	1.7207	1.7291	1.7374	1.7575	1.7770	1.7958	1.8140	1.8317	1.8489	1.8821	1.9442	2.0017	s	

FIG. 10-1. Reproduced by permission from *Thermodynamic Properties of Steam*, Keenan & Keyes. John Wiley & Sons, Inc.: New York, 1936.

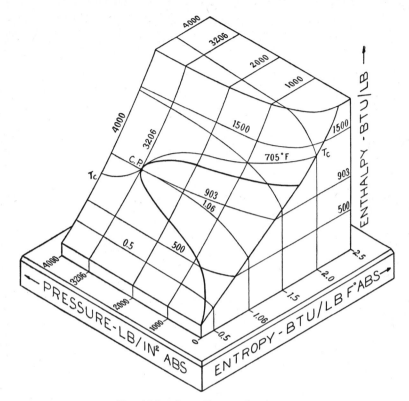

Fig. 10-2.   *h-s-p* diagram for water.

ture. It lists the saturation pressure and the specific volume, enthalpy, and entropy of saturated liquid and vapor, as well as the changes in the latter three in the evaporation process. Table 2, not reproduced, lists the same quantities as functions of pressure. Table 3 covers a range of pressure from 1 lb/in² to 5500 lb/in² and a range of temperature from 120° F to 1600° F. It lists the specific volume, enthalpy, and entropy of superheated steam as functions of pressure and temperature. Table 4, not reproduced, lists the specific volume, enthalpy, and entropy of the compressed liquid.

Fig. 10-2 is a drawing of the thermodynamic surface obtained by plotting the specific enthalpy of water vertically, and the pressure and specific entropy horizontally. The heavy line on the surface is the boundary of the liquid-vapor region, and the light lines are lines of constant *h*, *s*, and *p*. The figure is drawn to scale.

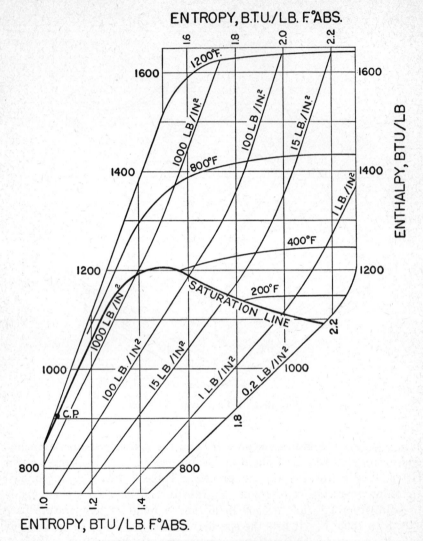

FIG. 10-3.   The Mollier diagram for water.

Fig. 10-3 is a projection of a portion of the *h-s-p* surface on the *h-s* plane, and is called a *Mollier diagram*. It covers the range of variables encountered in most engineering calculations. A large scale Mollier diagram is included with a set of steam tables. The quantities required for numerical calculations of work and efficiency can, in many instances, be read from the diagram with sufficient precision.

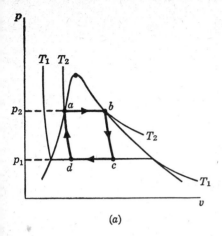

(a)

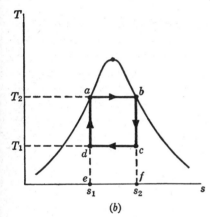

(b)

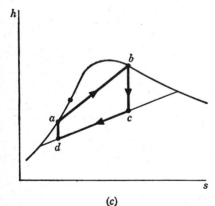

(c)

10-2 The Carnot steam cycle.

A Carnot cycle is any reversible cycle bounded by two isothermals and two adiabatics. The nature of the working substance is immaterial. Fig. 10-4(a) is a diagram in the p-v plane of a Carnot cycle operated in the liquid-vapor region. Starting at point a with saturated liquid in the cylinder of a Carnot engine, we carry out a reversible isothermal expansion at the temperature T_2 until the liquid is completely vaporized (point b). During this part of the cycle heat q_2 is withdrawn from a reservoir at temperature T_2. An adiabatic expansion then lowers the temperature to T_1 (point c). If the working substance is steam, this adiabatic expansion carries us back into the liquid-vapor region. In other words, some of the saturated vapor condenses. (Not all substances behave in this way. For some, the slope of the adiabatic is less than that of the saturation line and the point corresponding to c lies in the vapor region.) An isothermal compression is now carried out at the temperature T_1 to the state represented by point d, and heat q_1 is rejected to a reservoir. The cycle is completed by an adiabatic compression, during which the remainder of the vapor condenses and the state of the system returns to that represented by point a.

The same cycle is shown in a

Fig. 10-4. Carnot cycle in (a) a p-v diagram, (b) a T-s diagram, (c) an h-s diagram.

T-s diagram in Fig. 10-4(b) and in an h-s or Mollier diagram in Fig. 10-4(c). Since areas in a T-s diagram represent heat absorbed or liberated, the area $abef$ in Fig. 10-4(b) represents the heat q_2 absorbed in the reversible expansion at temperature T_2, the area $dcef$ the heat q_1 rejected at temperature T_1, and, from the first law, the area $abcd$ represents the net work w done in the cycle. (We are considering q_2, q_1, and w as all positive quantities.) The efficiency of the cycle is therefore

$$\eta = \frac{w}{q_2} = \frac{\text{area } abcd}{\text{area } abef}$$

$$= \frac{(T_2 - T_1)(s_2 - s_1)}{T_2(s_2 - s_1)}$$

$$= \frac{T_2 - T_1}{T_2}.$$

Consider next the same cycle, represented in the Mollier diagram in Fig. 10-4(c). Reversible adiabatics (isentropics) are represented by vertical lines, and isotherms and isobars (which are the same in the liquid-vapor region) by straight lines sloping upward to the right. Since the heat flowing into a system in any reversible isobaric process is equal to the increase in enthalpy of the system, the heat q_2 supplied in the isothermal-isobaric expansion from a to b is equal to $h_b - h_a$. The heat q_1 given up in the isothermal compression from c to d is $h_c - h_d$. The net work w done in the cycle is equal to the difference between the magnitudes of q_2 and q_1.

The efficiency is therefore

$$\eta = \frac{w}{q_2}$$

$$= \frac{h_b - h_a - h_c + h_d}{h_b - h_a}.$$

The advantage of the Mollier diagram is that heat, work, and efficiency can all be determined from the ordinates of points in the cycle, obviously a simpler procedure than measurements of area which must be made on a T-s diagram. Of course, the values of h at points a, b, c, and d may be taken from steam tables instead of being read from a graph.

10-3 The reciprocating steam engine and the turbine. In both the reciprocating steam engine and the turbine, the working substance, water, goes through essentially the same sequence of states. The boiler, in the schematic diagram of Fig. 10-5, receives heat from a heat source, and in it

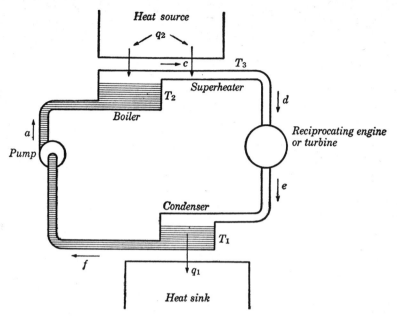

FIG. 10-5. Schematic diagram of processes in a reciprocating steam engine or turbine.

saturated liquid is converted to saturated vapor at a temperature determined by the pressure in this part of the system. This temperature is very much less than that of the heat source. For example, if the pressure in the boiler is 1000 lb/in², then the temperature is 544° F, while the flame temperature in the source where fuel is burned may be of the order of 3500° F. The saturated steam is led from the boiler to the superheater, where it receives more heat from the source and its temperature increases. The superheater is directly connected to the boiler, thus the pressure of the superheated steam does not rise above boiler pressure. In principle, the temperature of the superheated steam could be increased to that of the source, but a limit of about 1000° F, called the *metallurgical limit,* is set by the fact that above this temperature the materials available for piping are not strong enough to support the high pressures.

The superheated steam then flows to the reciprocating engine or turbine, where it delivers mechanical work and at the same time undergoes a drop in temperature and pressure. A portion is usually condensed in this part of the cycle also. The mixture of saturated liquid and vapor then flows to the condenser, where the remaining vapor is liquefied and the heat of condensation is given up to a heat sink, which may be the atmosphere or cooling water from a river or the ocean. The pressure in this part of the system is determined by the temperature of the heat sink. That is, the pressure is at least as great as the vapor pressure of water at the temperature of the sink. The condensed liquid is then forced into the boiler by the pump. This completes the cycle.

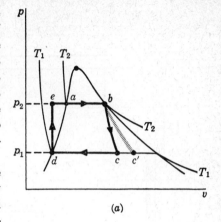

The reciprocating engine and the turbine differ only in the means by which internal energy is abstracted from the flowing steam and converted to mechanical work. In the former, a mass of steam in a cylinder expands against a piston. In the latter, the steam flows through nozzles as in Fig. 5-5, acquiring kinetic energy in the process. The rapidly moving steam then impinges on the buckets in the turbine rotor and gives up its kinetic energy. The process is approximately adiabatic in both devices but is not completely reversible and hence is not isentropic.

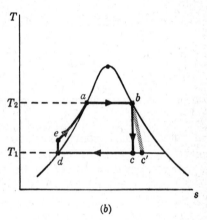

10-4 The Rankine cycle. The Rankine cycle is a reversible cycle which corresponds more nearly than does the Carnot cycle to the sequence of states assumed by the working substance in a reciprocating steam engine or turbine. We consider first a cycle in which the steam is not superheated, as shown in the three diagrams of Fig. 10-6. Start-

FIG. 10-6. The Rankine cycle in (a) a p-v diagram, (b) a T-s diagram, (c) an h-s diagram.

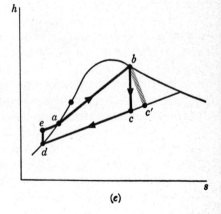

ing at point a, which corresponds to the boiler in Fig. 10-5, saturated liquid is converted reversibly to saturated vapor at temperature T_2 and pressure p_2 (point b). The vapor then expands reversibly and adiabatically to the pressure p_1 and temperature T_1 (point c). This stage corresponds to the passage of steam through the engine or turbine. The mixture of vapor and liquid is then completely liquefied at the temperature T_1, corresponding to the process in the condenser of Fig. 10-5 (point d). The liquid is then compressed reversibly and adiabatically to the boiler pressure p_2 (point e). This operation is performed by the pump in Fig. 10-5. As we have shown, the temperature of a liquid increases but very slightly in an adiabatic compression, so that heat must be supplied to the compressed liquid along the line ea in Fig. 10-6 to raise its temperature to T_2. In Fig. 10-5, this heating takes place after the liquid has been pumped into the boiler. If the cycle is to be reversible, however, the heat must be supplied by a series of heat reservoirs as in Fig. 1-1, ranging in temperature from that at point e (slightly greater than T_1) to T_2. The average temperature at which heat is supplied is therefore less than T_2, so the Rankine cycle has a lower efficiency than a Carnot cycle, which takes in heat only at the temperature T_2 and rejects it only at the temperature T_1.

The efficiency of the Rankine cycle can be determined directly from the Mollier diagram, Fig. 10-6(c), by the same method used in the Carnot cycle. Heat q_2 is supplied along the path eab and heat q_1 is rejected along the path cd. Although eab is not an isothermal process, it is isobaric (see Fig. 10-6(a)) and the heat q_2 supplied is equal to the enthalpy difference $h_b - h_e$. The heat q_1 rejected is $h_c - h_d$ and the net work w equals the difference between q_2 and q_1. The efficiency is therefore

$$\eta = \frac{w}{q_2} = \frac{h_b - h_e - h_c + h_d}{h_b - h_e}. \tag{10-1}$$

Note that while the expression for the efficiency in terms of enthalpy differences is the same as for the Carnot cycle (except for differences in labelling the diagrams), Eq. (10-1) does *not* reduce to

$$\eta = \frac{T_2 - T_1}{T_2},$$

as is obvious from a comparison of Fig. 10-4(b) and Fig. 10-6(b). As stated above, the efficiency of the Rankine cycle is less than that of a Carnot cycle operating between temperatures T_2 and T_1.

It was pointed out in Sec. 8-4, in connection with the general subject of entropy and irreversibility, that irreversible processes in a heat engine result in a decrease in efficiency. We can now see how irreversibility

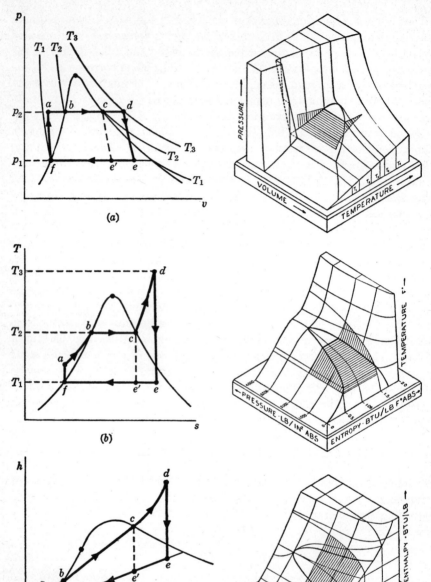

FIG. 10-7.   The Rankine cycle with
superheat.

FIG. 10-8.

affects the efficiency of a Rankine cycle. The full lines in the diagrams in Fig. 10-6 are drawn on the assumption that the expansion of the steam in a reciprocating engine or turbine is reversible as well as adiabatic, since only for a reversible adiabatic process is the entropy constant. Thus the line bc in Fig. 10-6(b) and (c) is vertical. The expansion in an actual engine is irreversible, so that the entropy is not constant but increases. This is shown in Fig. 10-6 by the dotted lines bc'. For a given condenser temperature, the expansion terminates at the same pressure and temperature in either case but the decrease in enthalpy is less in the irreversible than in the reversible expansion. Now apply the energy equation of steady flow to a turbine. The elevations at intake and exhaust can be assumed the same, the velocities at intake and exhaust are small and can be considered equal, and the process is very nearly adiabatic. The shaft work is therefore equal to the enthalpy difference between intake and exhaust. The efficiency of the irreversible cycle is therefore lower than that of the reversible, since $(h_b - h_c')$ is smaller than $(h_b - h_c)$ and the engine delivers less mechanical work for the same heat input.

10-5 The Rankine cycle with superheat. In practically all steam cycles the vapor is superheated to a temperature higher than that of the saturated vapor before it is expanded adiabatically. The superheating stage is represented by the segment cd in Fig. 10-7, where T_3 is the temperature of the superheated steam. There are two reasons for superheating. One is that the average temperature at which heat is absorbed is thereby increased above the temperature of vaporization, with a resulting increase in efficiency. The other, which is actually of greater importance, can be seen from an examination of Fig. 10-7. If the adiabatic expansion starts from the state of saturated vapor, point c, the state of the steam at the end of the expansion is represented by e'. The moisture content at e' is greater than that at e, the end point of the adiabatic expansion of superheated steam. If the moisture content of the steam is too great, mechanical wear on the turbine buckets becomes excessive. Hence superheating must be carried to a sufficiently high temperature to keep the moisture content down to a safe value.

In Fig. 10-7, heat q_2 is absorbed along the path $abcd$ and since this is isobaric, we again have $q_2 = h_d - h_a$. Since $q_1 = h_e - h_f$, the efficiency is

$$\eta = \frac{w}{q_2} = \frac{h_d - h_a - h_e + h_f}{h_d - h_a}.$$

Fig. 10-8 shows the Rankine cycle with superheat as it appears on the p-v-T surface, the s-p-T surface, and the h-s-p surface.

10-6 Methods of increasing efficiency. Several methods are employed for increasing the efficiency of a steam turbine over that obtainable with a simple Rankine cycle. In the *reheat* cycle, illustrated in the *T-s* diagram of Fig. 10-9, the steam is superheated to point *d*, allowed to expand adiabatically to point *e*, then returned to the heat source, superheated again to the same high temperature, and again expanded adiabatically to point *g*. The result is to increase the average temperature at which heat is absorbed.

In the *regenerative* cycle, a portion of the steam flowing through the turbine is withdrawn at an intermediate stage of the adiabatic expansion and, by means of a heat exchanger, is used to raise the temperature of the condensed liquid that has passed through all stages of the turbine. This eliminates to some extent the irreversible flow of heat that takes place if the condensed liquid is pumped directly into the boiler. In the latter case, the entire flow of heat into the condensate is from a system at a much higher temperature, while if some of this heat is supplied by steam withdrawn from an intermediate turbine stage, where its temperature is intermediate between that of the condenser and the boiler, there is an approximation to the reversible heating process illustrated in Fig. 1-1.

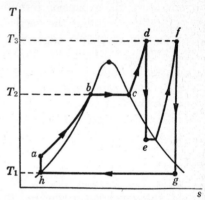

FIG. 10-9. The reheat cycle.

The critical temperature of water is 705° F, well below the metallurgical limit of 1000° F. It would be advantageous to carry out a Rankine cycle in which the working substance was evaporated at the metallurgical limit, since heat would then be absorbed at the maximum temperature possible. Evidently this cannot be done in a steam cycle. The critical temperature of mercury, however, is above 2800° F and its vapor pressure at 1000° F is 180 lb/in². It is therefore entirely feasible to design a cycle in which mercury is vaporized at the metallurgical limit. However, at a typical condenser temperature of 70° F the vapor pressure of mercury is so small and the specific volume so large that the size of the machinery required to handle the exhaust vapor renders the cost excessive. This difficulty is circumvented and the advantage of vaporizing at a high temperature is retained in the *mercury-steam binary-vapor engine*, where mercury is vaporized at a temperature near the metallurgical limit and expanded until its temperature drops to about 450° F. The heat flowing from the

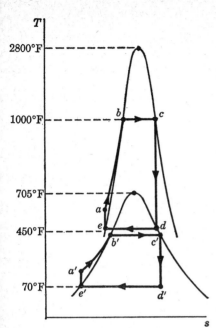

Fig. 10-10.　The mercury-steam binary-vapor cycle.

condensing mercury is used to generate steam at a pressure of about 450 lb/in², and the steam is then expanded to a condenser temperature of about 70° F. Fig. 10-10 is a T-s diagram of a mercury cycle superposed on a steam cycle. The General Electric Company has pioneered in the development of the binary-vapor engine and several plants of this type are now in operation.

10-7 The refrigeration cycle. If a Carnot cycle such as that in Fig. 10-4 is traversed in a counterclockwise direction, the Carnot engine becomes a Carnot refrigerator. Imagine the arrows in Fig. 10-4 to be reversed and consider a cycle starting at point a. The first stage of the process, ad, is a reversible adiabatic expansion. The second, dc, is an isothermal vaporization in which heat is absorbed from a reservoir at the low temperature T_1. The stage cb is a reversible adiabatic compression and the stage ba is an isothermal condensation during which heat is given up to a reservoir at the temperature T_2. Thus heat q_1 flows

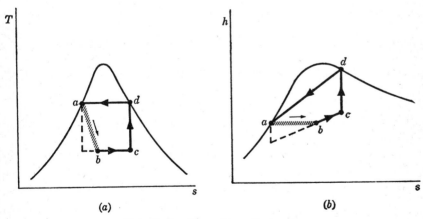

(a)　　　　　　　　(b)

Fig. 10-11.　The refrigeration cycle.

from a reservoir at a lower temperature to the working substance, and heat q_2 flows to a reservoir at a higher temperature.

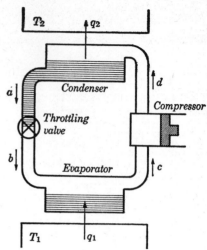

FIG. 10-12.   Principle of a refrigerating machine.

To carry out the adiabatic expansion ad reversibly, the working substance would have to expand against a piston.   It would be possible to design a refrigerator in which this was done and the mechanical work thus obtained could be utilized to do a part of the work of compression in the stage cb. However, the saving that would result from salvaging the work of expansion is more than offset by the added mechanical complexity and the increase in fixed charges incident to the change.   The reversible expansion is therefore replaced by an irreversible expansion through a throttling valve.   In this process, as explained in Sec. 5-9, the enthalpy in the initial and final states is the same.   The refrigeration cycle is shown in the $T\text{-}s$ and $h\text{-}s$ diagrams of Fig. 10-11, where ab is the irreversible throttling process.   (The process cannot be represented by a line, as it is not a succession of equilibrium states.)   A refrigerating machine is represented schematically in Fig. 10-12.   The letters a, b, c, and d correspond to the same letters in the cycle of Fig. 10-11.

10-8   The gas refrigerator.   A simplified diagram of the so-called *gas refrigerator* is given in Fig. 10-13.   In the generator, a solution of ammonia in water is heated by a small gas flame.   Ammonia is driven out of solution and ammonia vapor rises in the liquid lift tube, carrying with it some of the water in the same way that water is raised in the central tube of a coffee percolator.   This water collects in the separator, from which point it flows back through the absorber, while the ammonia vapor rises to the condenser.   Here the ammonia vapor is liquefied, its heat of condensation being removed by air circulating around the cooling vanes.   The liquid ammonia then flows into the evaporator, located in the cooling unit of the refrigerator, where it evaporates and in so doing absorbs heat from its surroundings.   The ammonia vapor continues on to the absorber, where

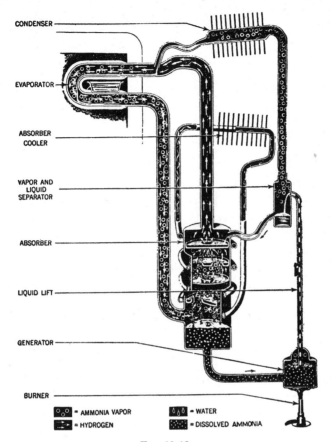

CONDENSER

EVAPORATOR

ABSORBER
COOLER

VAPOR AND
LIQUID
SEPARATOR

ABSORBER

LIQUID LIFT

GENERATOR

BURNER

○₀○ = AMMONIA VAPOR   ◊◊◊ = WATER
→ = HYDROGEN   = DISSOLVED AMMONIA

FIG. 10-13.

it dissolves in the water returning from the separator. The ammonia-water solution then flows to the generator, completing the cycle.

The absorber and evaporator also contain hydrogen gas, which is maintained in circulation by a convection process, brought about by the fact that the mixture of ammonia and hydrogen in the tube at the extreme left is denser than the pure hydrogen in the tube leading from the top of the absorber. This current of hydrogen, entering at the top of the evaporator, sweeps the ammonia vapor out of the evaporator and aids in rapid evaporation. Since ammonia is much more readily soluble in water than is hydrogen, most of the ammonia is dissolved in the water trickling down through the absorber, while the hydrogen passes upward through the absorber.

It is necessary that heat be removed from the absorber as well as from the condenser because heat is liberated when ammonia vapor dissolves in water. This is accomplished by the auxiliary circuit made up of the cooling coils around the absorber, and the absorber cooler.

The working substance in a gas refrigerator is completely enclosed in a rigid container and no work is done on it by its surroundings; the only interchange of energy is by a flow of heat. Heat is absorbed by the working substance at two different parts of the cycle, in the generator and in the evaporator. Heat is liberated in the condenser and in the absorber. Let T_3 represent the temperature of the generator, T_2 the temperature of the condenser and absorber (assumed equal for simplicity), and T_1 the temperature of the evaporator. Then $T_3 > T_2 > T_1$. If all processes were reversible, the temperatures of the gas flame and of the surroundings of the evaporator would be only infinitesimally greater than T_3 and T_1, and that of the air around the condenser and absorber would be only slightly less than T_2.

Let us consider an idealized reversible cycle in which a system absorbs heat Q_3 from a reservoir at temperature T_3, absorbs heat Q_1 from a reservoir at a temperature T_1, and rejects heat Q_2 to a reservoir at temperature T_2. The device is indicated schematically in Fig. 10-14. From the first law, considering all Q's as positive,

$$Q_1 + Q_3 = Q_2. \qquad (10\text{-}2)$$

From the second law, since the cycle is reversible, the change in entropy of the universe is zero. The entropy of the reservoir at temperature T_2 increases by Q_2/T_2, and the entropy of the other two reservoirs decreases by $Q_1/T_1 + Q_3/T_3$. Hence

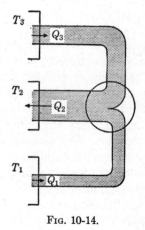

$$\frac{Q_1}{T_1} + \frac{Q_3}{T_3} = \frac{Q_2}{T_2}. \qquad (10\text{-}3)$$

The coefficient of performance of this refrigerator is defined as

$$E = \frac{Q_1}{Q_3},$$

since Q_1, the heat absorbed from the low temperature reservoir (i.e., the surroundings of the evaporator), is "what you get," while the heat Q_3

Fig. 10-14.

absorbed from the high temperature reservoir (i.e., the gas flame) is "what you pay for." Using Eqs. (10-2) and (10-3), we find

$$E = \frac{T_1(T_3 - T_2)}{T_3(T_2 - T_1)} . \tag{10-4}$$

For example, if $T_1 = -10°$ C $= 263°$ K, $T_3 = 100°$ C $= 373°$ K, $T_2 = 20°$ C $= 293°$ K, then

$$E \approx 2,$$

and about 2 joules are absorbed in the evaporator for every joule absorbed in the generator. The coefficient of performance of actual refrigerators is of course smaller than this because of unavoidable irreversible processes.

The "heat pump" portion of any refrigeration cycle consists of the flow of heat Q_1 from the low temperature T_1 to the higher temperature T_2. Such a flow in itself results in a decrease in entropy. In a mechanical refrigerator, this entropy decrease is compensated by the entropy increase when mechanical energy is converted to heat. In the gas refrigerator, it is compensated by the entropy increase resulting from the flow of heat Q_3 from the high temperature T_3 to the lower temperature T_2. The only condition imposed by the second law on either type of refrigerator is that the increase of entropy shall be at least as great as the decrease. It is a matter of indifference whether the increase results from a conversion of "work" to "heat," or from a flow of heat from a higher to a lower temperature.

Problems

1. Fig. 10-15, which is the same as Fig. 10-4(b), shows a Carnot cycle in the liquid-vapor region. The working substance is 1 kgm of water, and $T_2 = 453°$ K, $T_1 = 313°$ K. Steam tables list values of T, p, u, s, and h at points on the saturation lines and these are tabulated below, in mks units, for points a, b, e, and f. We wish to make a complete analysis of the cycle.

Point	t (°C)	T (°K)	p(n/m²)	u(j/kgm)	s(j/kgm-deg)	h(j/kgm)
a	180	453	10×10^5	7.60×10^5	2140	7.82×10^5
b	180	453	10×10^5	25.8×10^5	6590	27.7×10^5
e	40	313	$.074 \times 10^5$	1.67×10^5	572	1.67×10^5
f	40	313	$.074 \times 10^5$	24.3×10^5	8220	25.6×10^5

(a) Show that in the process ab,

$$q_{ab} = h_b - h_a, \quad w_{ab} = h_b - h_a - u_b + u_a.$$

(b) Show that in the process bc,

$$q_{bc} = 0, \quad w_{bc} = u_b - u_c.$$

(c) Show that in the process cd,

$$q_{cd} = h_d - h_c, \quad w_{cd} = h_d - h_c - u_d + u_c.$$

(d) Show that in the process da.

$$q_{da} = 0, \quad w_{da} = u_d - u_a.$$

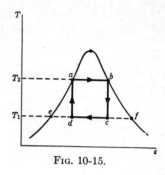

Fig. 10-15.

(e) Let x_2 and x_1 represent the fraction of the mass of the system in the vapor phase at points c and d respectively. Show that

$$x_2 = \frac{s_b - s_e}{s_f - s_e}, \quad x_1 = \frac{s_a - s_e}{s_f - s_e}.$$

(f) Show that

$$u_c = u_e + x_2(u_f - u_e), \quad h_c = h_e + x_2(h_f - h_e),$$

$$u_d = u_e + x_1(u_f - u_e), \quad h_d = h_e + x_1(h_f - h_e).$$

(g) Compute in joules the "expansion work" in the cycle, along the path abc.

(h) Compute in joules the "compression work," along the path cda, and find the ratio of expansion work to compression work.

(i) Compute from (g) and (h) the net work done in the cycle.

(j) Compute from (i) and (a) the efficiency of the cycle, and show that it is equal to $(T_2 - T_1)/T_2$.

(k) In any real engine there are unavoidable friction losses. To estimate the effect of these, assume that in the expansion stroke 5% of the work done by the system is lost, and that in the compression stroke 5% more work must be done than computed in part (h). Compute the net work delivered per cycle, and the efficiency.

Now consider a Carnot cycle using an ideal gas, also operating between reservoirs at 453° K and 313° K. Let the maximum pressure be $10 \times 10^5 \text{n/m}^2$, let $c_p = \frac{7}{2}R$, $c_v = \frac{5}{2}R$, $\gamma = 1.40$, and let the system absorb the same amount of heat from the high temperature source as the steam engine above.

(l) Compute the expansion work and the compression work in the ideal gas cycle, and find the ratio of expansion work to compression work.

(m) Compute the net work done in the cycle.

(n) Compute the efficiency of the cycle.

(o) Compute the efficiency, allowing 5% for losses in expansion and compression strokes, as in part (k).

(p) What conclusions can be drawn as to the relative practical merits of the two cycles?

2. A steam turbine operates in a reversible Rankine cycle. Superheated steam enters the turbine at a pressure of 100 lb/in² and a temperature of 800° F. The

pressure of the exhaust steam is 1 lb/in². (a) Find from Fig. 10-3 the work done per pound of steam. (b) If as a result of irreversible processes the specific entropy of the exhaust steam is 2 Btu/lb-deg F abs at the exhaust pressure of 1 lb/in², how much work is done per pound of steam?

3. Find the ratio of the efficiencies of two Carnot engines, one operating between temperatures of 450° F and 70° F, the other between temperatures of 1000° F and 70° F. (See Fig. 10-10.)

4. Refer to Fig. 10-11(a). (a) What would be the coefficient of performance of a reversible refrigeration cycle, represented by the rectangle, if $T_a = T_d = 330°$ K, and $T_b = T_c = 260°$ K? (b) What would be the coefficient of performance of the irreversible cycle $abcd$, if the specific entropy increase in the throttling process ab is one-third of the entropy difference $s_d - s_a$?

5. In Fig. 10-14, let $T_1 = 400°$ K, $T_2 = 300°$ K, $T_3 = 200°$ K. Assume all processes reversible. If 1200 joules are given up by the reservoir at 400° K, find the quantities of heat exchanged with the other reservoirs and state whether each reservoir gives up or absorbs heat.

6. Figure 10-16 represents a refrigeration cycle in which the adiabatic compression stage, cd, takes place in the vapor region. The expansion stage from d to a is at constant pressure and the irreversible expansion from a to b takes place through a throttling valve. (a) Sketch the cycle in an h-s diagram. (b) Show that the coefficient of performance of the cycle is given by

$$E = \frac{h_d - h_a}{h_d - h_c} .$$

(c) In a typical cycle using Freon-12 as a working substance, the specific enthalpies at points d, c, and a are respectively 90.6, 85.0, and 36.2 Btu/lb. The measured coefficient of performance of the cycle was 2.4. Compare with the value computed from the equation above, which assumes that all processes except ab are reversible.

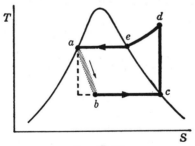

Fig. 10-16.

CHAPTER 11

KINETIC THEORY OF AN IDEAL GAS

11-1 Introduction. The subject of thermodynamics deals with the conclusions that can be drawn from certain experimental laws, and with the application of these conclusions to relations between properties of materials such as specific heats, coefficients of expansion, compressibilities, and so on. It makes no hypotheses about the nature of matter and is purely an experimental science.

While thermodynamic principles can predict many relations between the properties of matter, such as the difference between the specific heat capacities c_p and c_v or the variation of these quantities with pressure, it is not possible to derive from thermodynamic considerations alone the absolute magnitude of the heat capacities, or the equation of state of a substance.

We can go beyond the limitations of pure thermodynamics only by making hypotheses regarding the nature of matter, and by far the most fruitful of such hypotheses, as well as one of the oldest, is that matter is not continuous in structure but is composed of particles called molecules. In particular, the molecular theory of gases has been very completely developed, because the problems to be solved are much simpler than those encountered in dealing with liquids and solids. Theories of the solid and liquid states, however, are the subject of widespread investigation at the present time, and the problem appears to be well on the way toward a solution.

The properties of matter in bulk are predicted, starting with a molecular theory, from two different although related lines of attack. The first, called the *kinetic* or *dynamic* theory, applies the laws of mechanics (in imagination) to the individual molecules of a system, and from these laws derives, for example, expressions for the pressure of a gas, its internal energy, and its specific heat capacity. The approach of *statistical mechanics*, which is somewhat more general, is to ignore detailed considerations of molecules as individuals, and to apply considerations of *probability* to the very large numbers of molecules that make up any piece of matter. We shall see that the concept of entropy and the law of the increase of entropy have an elegant and simple interpretation from the viewpoint of statistical mechanics.

Both kinetic theory and statistical mechanics were first developed on the assumption (a natural one, since no alternative suggested itself) that the laws of mechanics, deduced from the behavior of matter in bulk, could be applied without change to particles like molecules, atoms, and electrons. As the sciences progressed it became evident that in some respects this assumption was not correct, that is, conclusions drawn from it by logical reasoning were not in accord with experimental facts. The failure of small-scale systems to obey the same laws as large-scale systems led to the development of the quantum theory and quantum mechanics, and statistical mechanics is closely connected with quantum ideas.

This section of the book will be devoted to the kinetic aspects of molecular theory and the third section to statistical mechanics. As we go along, we shall make many references to concepts and formulas that have already been discussed in the first section on thermodynamics, and we shall see how a much deeper insight into many questions can be attained with the help of a molecular theory as a background.

11-2 Basic assumptions. The simplest equation of state is that of an ideal gas, so we begin with an attempt (which will prove to be successful) to derive the equation of state of such a gas from a theory as to its molecular nature. We shall make the following assumptions.

Any finite volume of a gas consists of a very large number of molecules. This assumption is justified by all experimental evidence. Avogadro's number N_0 (the number of molecules in a kilogram-mole) is 6.03×10^{26}. Experimental methods for arriving at this figure are discussed in Chapter 17. At standard conditions, 1 kgm-mole occupies 22.4 m³. Hence at standard conditions there are approximately 3×10^{25} molecules in a cubic meter, 3×10^{19} in a cubic centimeter, and 3×10^{16} in a cubic millimeter.

The molecules are separated by distances large compared with their own dimensions and are in a state of continuous motion. The diameter of a molecule, considered to be spherical, is about 2 or 3×10^{-10} m. If we imagine one molar volume at standard conditions to be divided into cubical cells with one molecule per cell, the volume of each cell is $1/(3 \times 10^{25})$ m³ or approximately 30×10^{-27} m³. The length of one side of a cell is about 3×10^{-9} m, which means that the distance between molecules is of this order of magnitude, about 10 times the molecular diameter.

Molecules exert no forces on one another except when they collide. Therefore, between collisions with other molecules or with the walls of the container, and in the absence of external forces, they move in straight lines.

Collisions of molecules with one another and with the walls are perfectly elastic. The walls of a container can be considered perfectly smooth, thus there is no change of tangential velocity in a collision with the walls.

In the absence of external forces, the molecules are distributed uniformly throughout the container. If N represents the total number of molecules in a container of volume V, the average number of molecules per unit volume, n, is

$$n = \frac{N}{V}.$$

The assumption of uniform distribution then implies that in any volume element dV, wherever located, the number of molecules dN is

$$dN = ndV.$$

Obviously, the equation above is not true if dV is too small, since the number of molecules N, while large, is finite, and one can certainly imagine a finite volume element so small that it contains no molecules, in contradiction to the equation above. However, it is possible to divide a container into volume elements large enough so that the number of molecules per unit volume within them does not differ appreciably from the average, and at the same time small enough in comparison with the dimensions of physical apparatus so that they can be treated as infinitesimal in the mathematical sense and the methods of differential and integral calculus can be applied to them. For example, a cube $1/1000$ mm on a side is certainly small in comparison with the volume of most laboratory apparatus, yet at standard conditions it contains approximately 3×10^7 molecules.

All *directions* of molecular velocities are assumed equally probable. To put this assumption in analytic form, imagine that there is attached to each molecule a vector representing the magnitude and direction of its velocity. Let us transfer all these vectors to a common origin and construct a sphere of arbitrary radius r with center at the origin. The velocity vectors, prolonged if necessary, intersect the surface of the sphere in as many points as there are molecules and the assumption of uniform distribution in direction means that these points are uniformly distributed over the surface of the sphere. The average number of these points per unit area is

$$\frac{N}{4\pi r^2},$$

and the number in any element of area dA is

$$dN = \frac{N}{4\pi r^2} dA,$$

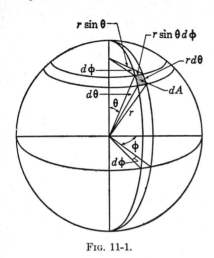

FIG. 11-1.

wherever the element is located. As in the preceding paragraph, the area must be large enough (i.e., it must include a large enough range of directions) so that the surface density of points within it does not differ appreciably from the average. Because of the large number of molecules, the range of directions can be made very small and still include a large number of points.

Let us carry this description of velocity directions one step further. Any arbitrary direction in space can be specified with reference to a polar coordinate system by the angles θ and ϕ, as in Fig. 11-1.   An element of area dA on the surface of a sphere of radius r is

$$dA = r^2 \sin \theta d\theta d\phi.$$

The number of points in this area, or the number of molecules having velocities in a direction between θ and $\theta + d\theta$, ϕ and $\phi + d\phi$, which we shall call $d^2N_{\theta\phi}$, is

$$d^2N_{\theta\phi} = \frac{N}{4\pi r^2} \times r^2 \sin \theta d\theta d\phi = \frac{N}{4\pi} \sin \theta d\theta d\phi. \qquad (11\text{-}1)$$

When both sides of this equation are divided by the volume V, we get

$$d^2n_{\theta\phi} = \frac{d^2N_{\theta\phi}}{V} = \frac{n}{4\pi} \sin \theta d\theta d\phi, \qquad (11\text{-}2)$$

where $d^2n_{\theta\phi}$ is the number of molecules per unit volume with velocities having directions between θ and $\theta + d\theta$, ϕ and $\phi + d\phi$.

Consider finally the *magnitudes* of the molecular velocities.   For brevity, we shall refer to the magnitude of the velocity as the *speed*.   It is clear that not all molecules have the same speed, although this assumption is sometimes made in elementary treatments.   Even if we could start them off in this way, intermolecular collisions would very quickly bring about differences in speed.   We shall show in Sec. 12-2 how to calculate the number that have speeds in any specified range, but for the presen-

we shall assume only that the speed can have any magnitude* from 0 to ∞. Let dN_v be the number of molecules with speeds between v and $v + dv$. Geometrically, this number is represented in Fig. 12-1 by the number of velocity vectors terminating in a thin shell of radius v and thickness dv.

As a result of collisions, the speed of any one molecule is continually changing, but we assume that in the equilibrium state the *number* of molecules with speeds in any specified range remains constant.

11-3 Collisions with the walls. In many problems it is desirable to know the number of molecules of a gas that strike (or cross) a surface, per unit area and per unit time. For example, when a liquid and vapor are in equilibrium, the number of molecules evaporating from the liquid surface, per unit area and per unit time, equals the number of vapor molecules striking the surface per unit area and per unit time, provided that every one striking the surface sticks to it. Hence the rate at which a liquid will evaporate when the vapor above its surface is pumped away can be found if we can compute the number of vapor molecules striking the surface at a given pressure and temperature. As another example, the free electrons in a metal behave in many ways like an "electron gas" and the rate of emission of electrons from a thermionic emitter depends on the rate at which electrons within the metal arrive at its surface.

A surface in contact with a gas is being continuously bombarded by molecules coming in from all directions and with all speeds. Consider the small element of area dA of such a surface in Fig. 11-2. Construct the normal to the element and some reference plane through the normal. We first ask how many molecules strike the surface in time dt, traveling in the particular direction θ, ϕ, and with specified speed v. Let us call this type of collision a $\theta\phi v$-collision. (To avoid continued repetition, let it be understood that this means in directions between θ and $\theta + d\theta$, ϕ and $\phi + d\phi$, and with speeds between v and $v + dv$.)

Construct the slanted cylinder shown in the figure, with edges in the direction θ, ϕ and of length $v dt$. This length is just the distance a molecule with speed v covers in the time dt. The number of $\theta\phi v$-collisions with dA in time dt is then equal to the number of $\theta\phi v$-molecules in this cylinder, where a $\theta\phi v$-molecule means one with speed v, traveling in the $\theta\phi$-direction.

To show that the statement above is true, we can see, first, that all $\theta\phi v$-molecules in the cylinder will be able to reach the surface within the

---

* It would be better to say, from zero to the speed of light. However, as we shall show, the number of molecules with speeds of even a small fraction of the speed of light is so small that for mathematical simplicity we may as well make the assumption above.

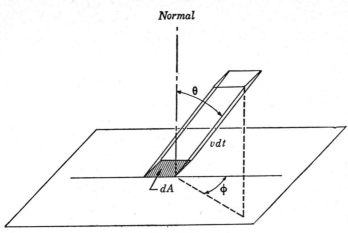

Fig. 11-2.

time dt and, on reaching it, will make a $\theta\phi v$-collision.   There are, of course, many other types of molecules in the cylinder and many other types of collisions with the surface.   Some of the other molecules in the cylinder will collide with the element dA in time dt and others will not.   Those that do *not* are either not traveling toward dA (i.e., are not $\theta\phi$-molecules) or are not traveling fast enough to reach it in time dt (i.e., they are not traveling with speed v).   Those within the cylinder that *do* collide with the surface are necessarily $\theta\phi$-molecules but unless they have speeds v they do not make a $\theta\phi v$-collision.   Hence, out of all the molecules in the cylinder, *only* the $\theta\phi v$-molecules will make $\theta\phi v$-collisions in time dt and *all* such molecules in the cylinder will make this type of collision.

Many other molecules, not in the cylinder, will strike the element dA in time dt.   Some of these will have a speed v, but they obviously are not $\theta\phi$-molecules, since they come in from other directions.   Therefore *all* $\theta\phi v$-molecules in the cylinder and *only* these molecules, will make $\theta\phi v$-collisions with dA in time dt.

How many of these molecules are there in the cylinder?   Here we make another assumption, justified because of the large number of molecules.   We assume that not only are the total number of molecules N uniformly distributed throughout the volume of the container, but that any subgroup such as the dN_v molecules or even the $dN_{\theta\phi v}$ molecules are also uniformly distributed.   To put it another way, if a certain fraction of the number of molecules in the entire volume V are v- or $\theta\phi v$-molecules, the same fraction of the molecules in the small cylinder are also of the v- or $\theta\phi v$-type.

Let dn_v represent the number of molecules per unit volume with speeds between v and $v + dv$. Then from Eq. (11-2) the number of $\theta\phi v$-molecules per unit volume is

$$d^3 n_{\theta\phi v} = \frac{1}{4\pi} dn_v \sin\theta d\theta d\phi.$$

The volume of the cylinder in Fig. 11-2 is

$$dV = dA \times vdt \cos\theta.$$

The number of $\theta\phi v$-molecules in the cylinder, which we have shown is equal to the number of collisions with dA in time dt, is therefore

$$d^3 n_{\theta\phi v} dV = dA dt \times \frac{vdn_v}{4\pi} \sin\theta \cos\theta d\theta d\phi,$$

and the number colliding per unit area and per unit time is

$$\frac{1}{4\pi} vdn_v \sin\theta \cos\theta d\theta d\phi. \tag{11-3}$$

The total number of collisions per unit area and per unit time made by molecules with speed v is now found by integrating over θ between 0 and $\pi/2$, and over ϕ between 0 and 2π. This gives

$$\tfrac{1}{4} vdn_v; \tag{11-4}$$

and the number of collisions made by molecules with speed v is jointly proportional to the number of molecules having this speed and to the speed. The *total* number of collisions per unit area and per unit time, by molecules having *all* speeds, is the integral of the expression above over the entire range of speeds and is given by

$$\frac{1}{4} \int vdn_v. \tag{11-5}$$

Let us express this result in terms of the average or arithmetic mean speed, $\bar{v}$. This quantity is found by adding together the speeds of all the molecules, and dividing by the total number of molecules. That is,

$$\bar{v} = \frac{\Sigma v}{N}.$$

But if there are N_1 molecules all with the same speed v_1, N_2 molecules all with the same speed v_2, etc., the sum of the speeds can also be found by multiplying the speed v_1 by the number of molecules N_1 having that speed, multiplying v_2 by the number of molecules N_2 having speed v_2, and so on, and adding these products.   The average speed is then the sum of all such products, divided by the total number of molecules N.   That is,

$$\bar{v} = \frac{N_1 v_1 + N_2 v_2 + \cdots}{N_1 + N_2 + \cdots} = \frac{\Sigma N_i v_i}{\Sigma N_i} = \frac{\Sigma N_i v_i}{N},$$

or, dividing numerator and denominator by the volume V,

$$\bar{v} = \frac{\Sigma n_i v_i}{n}. \tag{11-6}$$

It is important that this method of finding the average speed be clearly understood.   As a simple numerical example, suppose we have 2 molecules with speeds of 1 m/sec, 4 with speeds of 2 m/sec, and 3 with speeds of 3 m/sec.   Then $N_1 = 2$, $v_1 = 1$ m/sec; $N_2 = 4$, $v_2 = 2$ m/sec; $N_3 = 3$, $v_3 = 3$ m/sec.   Adding all the speeds directly gives

$$\Sigma v = (1 + 1) + (2 + 2 + 2 + 2) + (3 + 3 + 3) = 19 \text{ m/sec.}$$

The total number of molecules is

$$N = N_1 + N_2 + N_3 = \Sigma N_i = 2 + 4 + 3 = 9,$$

and the average speed is

$$\bar{v} = \frac{\Sigma v}{N} = \frac{19}{9} = 2.11 \text{ m/sec.}$$

Using the second method, we have

$$\bar{v} = \frac{N_1 v_1 + N_2 v_2 + N_3 v_3}{N_1 + N_2 + N_3}$$

$$= \frac{(2 \times 1) + (4 \times 2) + (3 \times 3)}{2 + 4 + 3}$$

$$= \frac{2 + 8 + 9}{2 + 4 + 3}$$

$$= \frac{19}{9} = 2.11 \text{ m/sec.}$$

If the molecules have a continuous distribution of speeds, and dn_v is the number with speed v, the sum in Eq. (11-6) becomes an integral, and

$$\bar{v} = \frac{\displaystyle\int v \, dn_v}{n}.$$

It follows that

$$\int v \, dn_v = n\bar{v}, \tag{11-7}$$

and hence from Eq. (11-5), the total number of collisions with the walls, per unit area and per unit time, including molecules coming in from all directions and with all speeds, is

$$\tfrac{1}{4}n\bar{v}. \tag{11-8}$$

At standard conditions, the number of molecules per cubic meter, n, is approximately 3×10^{25}. We shall show in Sec. 11-4 that the average speed of an oxygen molecule at $273°$ K is approximately 450 m/sec. The number of collisions with the walls of the container per square meter per second, made by oxygen molecules at standard conditions, is therefore

$$\frac{1}{4} \times 3 \times 10^{25} \times 450$$

$$\approx 3.3 \times 10^{27} \text{ collisions/m}^2\text{-sec.}$$

It is sometimes useful to put Eq. (11-3) in the following form. Consider the area dA in Fig. 11-2 to be located at the origin in Fig. 11-1 and to lie in the X-Y plane. The molecules colliding with the area in the direction defined by the angles θ and ϕ are those coming in to the area within the small cone in Fig. 11-1 which subtends the shaded area dA on the spherical surface in that diagram. This area is $r^2 \sin \theta d\theta d\phi$ and the solid angle of the cone, $d\omega$, is

$$d\omega = \frac{dA}{r^2} = \sin \theta d\theta d\phi.$$

Hence from Eq. (11-3) the number of molecules colliding per unit area and per unit time can be written

$$\frac{1}{4\pi} v \, dn_v \cos \theta d\omega,$$

and the number colliding per unit area, per unit time, and per unit solid angle, is

$$\frac{1}{4\pi} v \, dn_v \cos \theta. \tag{11-9}$$

The total number colliding per unit area, per unit time, and per unit solid angle, including all velocities, is evidently

$$\frac{1}{4\pi} \, n\bar{v} \cos \theta. \tag{11-10}$$

If we consider a number of small cones of equal solid angle with apices at dA in Fig. 11-2, the greatest number of molecules comes in to this area within the cone centered about the normal, since $\cos \theta$ has its maximum value for this cone, and the number decreases to zero for cones tangent to dA where $\theta = 90°$.

If the area dA is a hole in the walls of the vessel containing the gas, small enough so that leakage through the hole does not appreciably affect the equilibrium of the gas, then every molecule coming up to the hole escapes through it and Eqs. (11-3) and (11-10) also describe the distribution in direction of the molecules emerging from the hole. The number emerging per unit solid angle is a maximum in the direction normal to the plane of the hole and decreases to zero in the tangential direction.

11-4 Equation of state of an ideal gas. We next compute the average force exerted on an element of surface by the molecules of a gas colliding with it and from this get the average pressure and the equation of state. Fig. 11-3 shows a $\theta\phi v$-molecule before and after colliding with a surface. From our assumption of perfect elasticity, and considering the wall to be of infinite mass, the *magnitude* of the velocity v is the same before and after the collision, and from the assumption that the wall is perfectly smooth, the tangential component of velocity is also unaltered by the collision. It follows that the angle of reflection, θ, is equal to the angle of incidence and the normal component of velocity is reversed in the collision, from $v \cos \theta$ to $-v \cos \theta$.

The force exerted by any one molecule in a collision is an impulsive force, of short duration. The details of its variation with time are unknown, but it is not necessary to know them to compute the *average* force acting on a surface. We make use of the impulse-momentum theorem, which states that the impulse of a force is equal to the change in momentum produced by it. If m is the mass of a colliding molecule, the change in the normal component of momentum in a $\theta\phi v$-collision is

$$mv \cos \theta - (-mv \cos \theta) = 2 \, mv \cos \theta.$$

The number of $\theta\phi v$-collisions with an area dA in time dt is, from Eq. (11-3),

$$\frac{1}{4\pi} \, vdn_v \sin \theta \cos \theta d\theta d\phi dA dt.$$

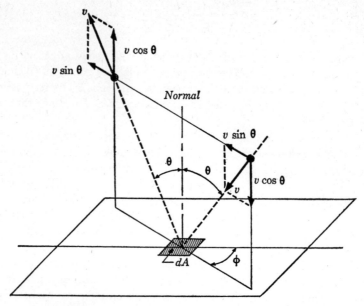

FIG. 11-3.   Changes in velocity in an elastic collision.

The change in momentum due to all $\theta\phi v$-collisions in time dt is

$$(2mv \cos \theta) \times \left(\frac{1}{4\pi} vdn_v \sin \theta \cos \theta d\theta d\phi dA dt \right)$$

$$= \frac{1}{2\pi} mv^2 dn_v \sin \theta \cos^2 \theta d\theta d\phi dA dt.$$

The change in momentum in all v-collisions is found by integrating over θ between 0 and $\pi/2$, and over ϕ between 0 and 2π. The first integral is $\frac{1}{3}$ and the second is 2π, and we get for the change in momentum,

$$\tfrac{1}{3}mv^2 dn_v dA dt.$$

To find the change in momentum resulting from collisions of molecules with all speeds, this expression must be summed over all values of v, giving

$$\frac{1}{3} m \left[\int v^2 dn_v \right] dA dt.$$

By definition, the product of the average value of a force, $\bar{F}$, and the time interval during which it acts, is the impulse of the force and is equal to the change in momentum produced by it. Hence

$$dF dt = \frac{1}{3} m \left[\int^c v^2 dn_v \right] dA dt. \tag{11-11}$$

The average pressure $\bar{p}$ exerted on the surface is the average force per unit area, dF/dA. Dividing Eq. (11-11) through by $dA dt$, we get

$$\bar{p} = \frac{dF}{dA} = \frac{1}{3} m \int^c v^2 dn_v. \tag{11-12}$$

Now the average value of the *square* of the speed of all the molecules is found by squaring all the speeds, adding these quantities, and dividing by the total number of molecules.

$$\overline{v^2} = \frac{\Sigma v^2}{N}.$$

Just as in calculating the average value of the speed, we can obtain Σv^2 more conveniently by multiplying v_1^2 by N_1, v_2^2 by N_2, etc., and adding these products. That is,

$$\overline{v^2} = \frac{\Sigma N_i v_i^2}{\Sigma N_i} = \frac{\Sigma N_i v_i^2}{N}, \qquad \text{or} \qquad \overline{v^2} = \frac{\Sigma n_i v_i^2}{n}.$$

If the molecules have a continuous distribution of speeds, and dn_v is the number with speed v, the sum becomes an integral and

$$\overline{v^2} = \frac{\int^c v^2 dn_v}{n}$$

or

$$\int^c v^2 dn_v = n\overline{v^2}. \tag{11-13}$$

Finally, since the pressure p that is measured experimentally is the same as the average pressure $\bar{p}$ exerted by the molecules, we have from Eqs. (11-12) and (11-13),

$$\boxed{p = \tfrac{1}{3} n m \overline{v^2}.} \tag{11-14}$$

Notice carefully that the mean value of the square of the speed, $\overline{v^2}$, is not the same thing as the square of the mean speed, $(\bar{v})^2$. Taking the simple distribution referred to in Sec. 11-3 as an example, we have

$$\overline{v^2} = \frac{\Sigma v^2}{N} = \frac{(1^2 + 1^2) + (2^2 + 2^2 + 2^2 + 2^2) + (3^2 + 3^2 + 3^2)}{2 + 4 + 3}$$

$$= \frac{45}{9} = 5(\text{m/sec})^2,$$

or

$$\overline{v^2} = \frac{\Sigma N_i v_i^2}{N} = \frac{2 \times 1^2 + 4 \times 2^2 + 3 \times 3^2}{2 + 4 + 3}$$

$$= \frac{45}{9} = 5(\text{m/sec})^2.$$

On the other hand, we have shown that the mean speed $\bar{v}$ is 2.11 m/sec, so the square of the mean speed is

$$(\bar{v})^2 = (2.11)^2 = 4.45 \ (\text{m/sec})^2.$$

Let us return now to Eq. (11-14). Remembering that n represents the number of molecules per unit volume, N/V, we can write this equation as

$$p = \frac{1}{3} \frac{N}{V} m\overline{v^2}, \tag{11-15}$$

or,

$$pV = \frac{1}{3} Nm\overline{v^2}. \tag{11-16}$$

This begins to look like the equation of state of an ideal gas,

$$pV = nRT,$$

where n represents the number of moles and does not have the same meaning as in Eq. (11-14). The number of moles is equal to the total number of molecules, N, divided by the number of molecules per mole, Avogadro's number N_0.

$$n = \frac{N}{N_0}.$$

We can therefore write the equation of state of an ideal gas as

$$pV = N \frac{R}{N_0} T.$$

The quotient R/N_0 occurs frequently in kinetic theory. It is called *the universal gas constant per molecule*, or *Boltzmann's constant*, and is represented by k. Since R and N_0 are universal constants, k is a universal constant also. That is, its magnitude depends only on the system of units employed. In the mks system,

$$k = \frac{R}{N_0} = \frac{8.3144 \times 10^3}{6.0251 \times 10^{26}}$$

$$= 1.3803 \times 10^{-23} \frac{\text{joule}}{\text{molecule-deg}}.$$

In terms of the Boltzmann constant, the equation of state of an ideal gas becomes

$$pV = NkT. \tag{11-17}$$

If this is to agree with the equation derived from molecular theory,

$$pV = \frac{1}{3} N m \overline{v^2},$$

we must set

$$NkT = \frac{1}{3} N m \overline{v^2},$$

or

$$\overline{v^2} = \frac{3kT}{m}. \tag{11-18}$$

The theory has thus led us to a goal we did not deliberately set out to seek, namely, it has given us a molecular interpretation of the concept of absolute temperature T, as a quantity proportional to the mean square speed of the molecules of a gas. It is even more significant to write Eq. (11-18) as

$$\tfrac{1}{2} m \overline{v^2} = \tfrac{3}{2} kT. \tag{11-19}$$

The product of one-half the mass of a molecule and the mean square speed is the same as the mean translational kinetic energy, and we see from the preceding equation that the mean translational kinetic energy of a gas molecule is proportional to the absolute temperature or, conversely, that temperature is proportional to the mean kinetic energy of translation. Furthermore, since the factor $3k/2$ is a universal constant, the mean kinetic energy depends only on the temperature and not on the pressure or volume or species of molecule. That is, the mean kinetic energies of the molecules of H_2, He, O_2, Hg, etc., are all the same at the same temperature despite the disparities in their masses.

We can compute from Eq. (11-19) what this energy is at any temperature. Let $T = 300°$ K. Then

$$\tfrac{3}{2}kT = \tfrac{3}{2} \times 1.38 \times 10^{-23} \times 300$$

$$= 6.21 \times 10^{-21} \text{ joule.}$$

If the molecules are oxygen, the mass m is

$$m = \frac{32}{6.03 \times 10^{26}} = 5.31 \times 10^{-26} \text{ kgm,}$$

and the mean square speed is

$$\overline{v^2} = \frac{2 \times 6.21 \times 10^{-21}}{5.31 \times 10^{-26}}$$

$$= 23.4 \times 10^4 \text{ (m/sec)}^2.$$

The square root of this quantity, or the root-mean-square speed v_{rms}, is

$$v_{rms} = 482 \text{ m/sec} = 1607 \text{ ft/sec} = 1100 \text{ mi/hr.}$$

By way of comparison, the speed of sound in air at standard conditions
is about 350 m/sec or 1100 ft/sec, and the speed of a .30 cal rifle bullet
is about 2700 ft/sec.

We shall show in the next chapter that the arithmetic mean speed of a
gas molecule is 0.925 times the *rms* speed.

$$\bar{v} = 0.925 \, v_{rms}.$$

The speed of a compressional wave in a fluid is given by

$$v = \sqrt{\frac{K_{ad}}{\rho}},$$

which, for an ideal gas, is equivalent to

$$v = \sqrt{\frac{\gamma kT}{m}},$$

where $\gamma = c_p/c_v$.

Since the root-mean square speed of a molecule is

$$v_{rms} = \sqrt{\frac{3kT}{m}},$$

we see that the two are nearly equal but that the speed of a sound wave is somewhat smaller than the *rms* molecular speed, as would be expected.

When electrons and ions are accelerated by an electric field, it is convenient to express their energies in electron-volts (abbreviated ev) where by definition

$$1 \text{ electron-volt} = 1.602 \times 10^{-19} \text{ joule.}$$

An electron-volt is the energy acquired by a particle of charge e ($= 1.602 \times 10^{-19}$ coul) accelerated through a potential difference of 1 volt.

At a temperature of 300° K,

$$\tfrac{3}{2}kT = 6.21 \times 10^{-21} \text{ joule,}$$

which in electron-volts is

$$\frac{6.21 \times 10^{-21}}{1.602 \times 10^{-19}} \approx 4 \times 10^{-2} \text{ ev.}$$

Hence at a temperature of 300° K the mean kinetic energy of a gas molecule is only a few hundredths of an electron-volt

11-5 Collisions with a moving wall. We now examine the nature of the mechanism by which an expanding gas does work against a moving piston, and show that if the process is adiabatic the work is done at the expense of the kinetic energy of the molecules (i.e., the internal energy of the gas) and that the temperature of the gas decreases. Fig. 11-4 represents a gas in a cylinder provided with a piston. Let the piston move up with a velocity u, small in comparison with molecular velocities and small enough so that the gas remains practically in an equilibrium state. From the thermodynamic viewpoint, then, the process is reversible.

When a molecule collides elastically with a stationary wall the magnitude of the normal component of velocity is unchanged. If the wall is moving, the magnitude of the *relative* velocity is unchanged. To take a simple numerical example, if a molecule approaches a stationary wall normally with a velocity of 15 cm/sec, referred to a coordinate system fixed in the laboratory, it rebounds with a velocity of 15 cm/sec. If the wall is moving away from the molecule with a velocity of 5 cm/sec, and if the molecule has

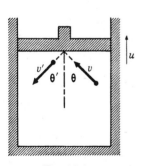

Fig. 11-4.

a velocity of 20 cm/sec, both relative to the laboratory coordinate system, the molecule is again approaching the wall with a relative velocity of 15 cm/sec. After the collision the magnitude of the velocity of the molecule relative to the wall will again be 15 cm/sec, but since the molecule is now moving in a direction opposite to that of the wall its velocity in the laboratory coordinate system is only 10 cm/sec.

In general, if the normal component of the velocity before collision is $v \cos \theta$, where θ is the angle between v and the normal to the wall, the velocity component after collision, $v' \cos \theta'$, is equal to $v \cos \theta - 2u$. The loss of kinetic energy in the collision is

$$\tfrac{1}{2}m(v \cos \theta)^2 - \tfrac{1}{2}m(v' \cos \theta')^2$$

$$= \tfrac{1}{2}m(v \cos \theta)^2 - \tfrac{1}{2}m(v \cos \theta - 2u)^2$$

$$= 2m \, vu \cos \theta$$

very nearly, since by hypothesis $u << v$. The kinetic energy of the molecule can decrease even if the collision is perfectly elastic, because in the collision process the molecule exerts a force against a *moving* wall and hence does work on the wall.

The loss of kinetic energy depends on the angle θ but not on ϕ. From Eq. (11-3), the number of molecules colliding with a wall with speed v, per unit area and per unit time, making angles with the normal between θ and $\theta + d\theta$, but including all angles ϕ between 0 and 2π, is

$$\tfrac{1}{2}vdn_v \sin \theta \cos \theta d\theta.$$

Multiplying this by the loss in kinetic energy in such a collision, we obtain for the loss in kinetic energy per unit area and per unit time, by molecules making θv-collisions,

$$muv^2dn_v \sin \theta \cos^2 \theta d\theta.$$

Next, integrate over θ between 0 and $\pi/2$ to get the loss in kinetic energy for all molecules with velocity v. This gives

$$\tfrac{1}{3}muv^2dn_v.$$

Finally, integrating over all values of v from 0 to ∞, and recalling the definition of $\overline{v^2}$, we get

$$\tfrac{1}{3}nm\overline{v^2}u$$

for the total loss of molecular kinetic energy, per unit area and per unit time. But $\tfrac{1}{3}nm\overline{v^2}$ equals the pressure p, and if the area of the moving piston in Fig. 11-4 is A, the decrease of molecular kinetic energy per unit time is

$$pAu = Fu.$$

The product Fu (force times velocity) gives the rate at which mechanical work is done on the piston or the power developed by the expanding gas, and we see that this is just equal to the rate of decrease of molecular kinetic energy. If the molecules do not receive energy from any other source, their kinetic energy and hence the temperature of the gas decreases. Note that it is not correct to say that the temperature *of a molecule* decreases. From the molecular point of view, temperature is an attribute of the assembly of molecules as a whole, namely, a quantity proportional to the mean kinetic energy. An individual molecule can have more or less kinetic energy but it does not have a higher or lower temperature.

The derivation above was based on the assumption that the piston velocity, u, was very much smaller than the molecular velocities, and does not hold if the piston is pulled up rapidly. In particular, if the piston velocity is very much greater than the molecular velocities, no molecules (or at least very few) will be able to overtake the piston and collide with it. Then there is no loss of kinetic energy and no decrease in temperature, intermolecular forces being neglected. Such a process is equivalent to an expansion into a vacuum, as in the Joule experiment, where we showed on thermodynamic grounds that the work and the change in internal energy were both zero.

11-6 The Clausius equation of state. We have made extensive use of the van der Waals equation of state in earlier chapters, not so much because of any great accuracy of this equation in describing the properties of real gases but because it shows in a general way, through the factor a, how these properties depend on intermolecular forces, and through the factor b how they depend on molecular sizes. The latter correction to the equation of state of an ideal gas was actually first introduced by Clausius.

Clausius reasoned that in the derivation in Sec. 11-4 one should use for the volume not the actual volume V of the container but the volume available to a single molecule, which will be somewhat less than V because of the volume occupied by the molecules themselves. Let us imagine that at a certain instant all the molecules of a gas except one are "frozen" in position, while the remaining molecule continues to move among the others and collide with them. We assume the molecules to be rigid spheres of radius ρ. At the instant of a collision the center-to-center distance of the colliding molecules is 2ρ, as in Fig. 11-5(a). The

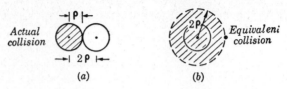

Actual collision   (a)   (b)   *Equivalent collision*

FIG. 11-5.

center-to-center distance would be the same if the moving molecule were to shrink to a geometrical point while the radius of the other were increased to 2ρ as in 11-5(b). The center of the moving molecule is thus excluded from a spherical volume of radius 2ρ, and this volume is called the "sphere of exclusion." However, only the hemisphere facing the moving molecule is effective in excluding the latter so we take as the effective volume b' unavailable to any one molecule, one-half of the total volume of the spheres of exclusion of all the other molecules.

$$b' = \tfrac{1}{2}N\tfrac{4}{3}\pi(2\rho)^3 = \tfrac{16}{3}N\pi\rho^3. \qquad (11\text{-}20)$$

Since the volume of a spherical molecule of radius ρ is $\tfrac{4}{3}\pi\rho^3$, the unavailable volume, b', is 4 times the total molecular volume, and the available volume is $V - b'$. Hence instead of Eq. (11-14) we have

$$p(V - b') = \tfrac{1}{3}Nm\overline{v^2}.$$

or, replacing $\tfrac{1}{3}Nm\overline{v^2}$ by nRT,

$$p(V - b') = nRT. \qquad (11\text{-}21)$$

This is the Clausius equation of state.

11-7 The van der Waals equation of state. Van der Waals, in 1873, included a second correction term in the equation of state to take into account the forces between molecules. Let us assume that the molecules of a gas exert forces of attraction on one another, but that these forces decrease so rapidly with distance (for example, as $1/r^6$) that they are appreciable only between a molecule and its nearest neighbors. Molecules within the body of a gas are on the average attracted equally in all directions, but those in the outermost layer experience a net inward force. The inward force that the walls must exert, to reverse the momentum of the molecules colliding with it, is therefore less than that calculated in Sec. 11-4, and hence the pressure is less.

Let us call p' the pressure computed from a consideration of molecular impacts. The reduction of the observed pressure below p' will be proportional both to the number of molecules per unit volume in the surface layer, on which the inward forces act, and to the number per unit volume in the next layer beneath them, which are doing the attracting. Hence the pressure is reduced by an amount proportional to $\left(\dfrac{N}{V}\right)^2$, or equal to $a'\left(\dfrac{N}{V}\right)^2$, where a' is a factor dependent on the strength of the attractive forces. The observed pressure p can therefore be written

$$p = p' - a'\left(\frac{N}{V}\right)^2,$$

or,

$$p' = p + a'\left(\frac{N}{V}\right)^2.$$

Combining this with the Clausius equation, we get

$$\left[p + a'\left(\frac{N}{V}\right)^2\right](V - b') = nRT, \tag{11-22}$$

which is one form of van der Waals equation. If we introduce two new quantities a and b, defined as

$$a = a'N_0^2, \quad b = b'N_0/N,$$

where N_0 is Avogadro's number, Eq. (11-22) reduces to the form we have used,

$$\left(p + \frac{a}{v^2}\right)(v - b) = RT.$$

It follows from the definitions of b and b', and from the fact that the molal specific critical volume of a van der Waals gas equals $3b$, that b equals 4 times the total volume of the (spherical) molecules in one mole of a van der Waals gas, and that the critical volume equals 12 times the total molecular volume.

A more accurate analysis of intermolecular forces and collisions, for which the reader is referred to more advanced texts, shows that both a and b are functions of temperature, and not simply constants of proportionality.

Problems

1. (a) Find the length of one side of a cubical volume of a gas at standard conditions which contains a number of molecules equal to the population of the United States. (b) The wave length of light in the yellow-green portion of the spectrum is 5000 A or 5×10^{-7} m. At standard conditions, how many molecules are there in a cubical volume of a gas 5×10^{-7} m on a side?

2. (a) Compute the number of molecules per unit volume in a gas at 300° K when the pressure is 10^{-3} mm of mercury. (b) How many molecules are there in a cube 1 mm on a side under these conditions?

3. (a) In Fig. 11-1, let $\theta = 45°$, $d\theta = 0.01$ radian, $\phi = 60°$, $d\phi = 0.01$ radian. What fraction of the molecules of a gas have velocity vectors within the narrow cone which intercepts the shaded area dA? (b) Consider a second cone intercepting the same area on the spherical surface, but for which $\theta = 90°$, $\phi = 0$. Sketch this cone in Fig. 11-1, and compare the number of velocity vectors included within it, with those in the cone in part (a).

4. (a) Approximately what fraction of the molecules of a gas have velocities for which the angle θ in Fig. 11-1 lies between 29.5° and 30.5°, while ϕ lies between 44.5° and 45.5°? (b) What fraction have velocities for which θ lies between 29.5° and 30.5°, regardless of the value of ϕ? Note: Angles must be expressed in radians.

5. Compute the average or arithmetic mean speed, and the square root of the mean square speed, of the following group of particles:

N_i	2	4	6	8	2
v_i(cm/sec)	1	2	3	4	5

6. Consider the following distributions of the speeds of six particles:
(a) all 6 have speeds of 10 m/sec;
(b) 3 have speeds of 5 m/sec and 3 have speeds of 10 m/sec;
(c) 2 have speeds of 5 m/sec and 4 have speeds of 10 m/sec;
(d) 3 are at rest and 3 have speeds of 10 m/sec.
For each distribution, compute $\bar{v}$ and v_{rms}.

7. (a) Compute the mean translational kinetic energy of a gas molecule at 300° K. (b) Compute the rms speed if the gas is hydrogen ($H_2 = 2$), oxygen ($O_2 = 32$), mercury vapor ($Hg = 201$).

8. Compute the rms speed of (a) helium atoms at 2° K, (b) nitrogen molecules at 27° C, (c) mercury atoms at 100° C.

9. At what temperature is the mean translational kinetic energy of a molecule equal to that of a singly charged ion of the same mass that has been accelerated from rest through a potential difference of (a) 1 volt, (b) 1000 volts, (c) 1,000,000 volts? Neglect relativistic effects.

10. What form would Eq. (11-14) take if several kinds of molecules were present in a gas? Does the answer agree with Dalton's law?

11. Derive an expression equivalent to Eq. (11-14) for a two-dimensional gas, i.e., one whose molecules can move only in a plane. (The concept corresponding to pressure, or force-per-unit-area, becomes force-per-unit-length.)

12. (a) How many molecular impacts are made per second on each square centimeter of a surface exposed to air at a pressure of 1 atm and at 300° K? The mean molecular weight of air is 29. (b) What would be the length of a cylinder 1 cm² in cross section containing this number of air molecules at 1 atm and 300° K?

13. A cubical box 1 m on a side, containing O_2 at standard conditions, contains approximately 3×10^{25} molecules. Compare this with the total number of collisions made with the walls of the box in 1 sec.

14. A closed vessel contains liquid water in equilibrium with its vapor at 100° C and 1 atm. One gram of water vapor at this temperature and pressure occupies a volume of 1670 cm³. The heat of vaporization at this temperature is 2250 joules/gm.
   (a) How many molecules are there per cm³ of vapor?
   (b) How many vapor molecules strike each cm² of liquid surface per second?
   (c) If each molecule which strikes the surface condenses, how many evaporate from each cm² per second?
   (d) Compare the mean kinetic energy of a vapor molecule with the energy required to transfer one molecule from the liquid to the vapor phase.

15. When a liquid and its vapor are in equilibrium, the rates of evaporation of the liquid and condensation of the vapor are equal. Assume that every molecule of the vapor striking the liquid surface condenses, and assume that the rate of evaporation is the same when the vapor is rapidly pumped away from the surface, as when liquid and vapor are in equilibrium. The vapor pressure of mercury at 0° C is 185×10^{-6} mm of mercury and the latent heat of vaporization is 80.5 cal/gm. Compute the rate of evaporation of mercury into a vacuum, in gm/cm²-sec, (a) at a temperature of 0° C, (b) at −20° C.

16. A thin-walled vessel of volume V, kept at constant temperature, contains a gas which slowly leaks out through a small hole of area A. The outside pressure is low enough so that leakage back into the vessel is negligible. Find the time required for the pressure in the vessel to decrease to $1/e$th of its original value. Express your answer in terms of A, V, and the mean molecular velocity $\bar{v}$.

17. The pressure in a vacuum system is 10^{-3} mm of mercury. The external pressure is 1 atm and $T = 300°$ K. There is a pinhole in the walls of the system, of area 10^{-10} cm². Assume that every molecule "striking" the hole passes through. (a) How many molecules leak into the system in 1 hour? (b) If the volume of the system is 2 liters, what rise in pressure would result in the system? (c) Show that the number of molecules that leak out is negligible.

18. A vessel of volume $2V$ is divided into compartments of equal volume by a thin partition. The left side contains initially an ideal gas at a pressure p_0, and the right side is initially evacuated. A small hole of area A is punched in the partition. Derive an expression for the pressure p_1 on the left side as a function of time. Assume the temperature to remain constant and to be the same on both sides of the partition. *not on quiz*

19. What is the form of a graph of pv/T vs p, as in Fig. 2-1, for a gas obeying the Clausius equation of state?

20. (a) Let ω represent the volume of a spherical molecule of diameter σ. Prove that for a van der Waals gas,

$$b = 4N_0\omega,$$

$$v_c = 12N_0\omega,$$

where N_0 is Avogadro's number.

(b) From the data in Table 2-1, compute the "diameter" of an oxygen molecule, and of a helium atom.

21. The critical temperature of CO_2 is 31.1° C and the critical pressure is 73 atm. Assume that CO_2 obeys the van der Waals equation. (a) Compute the critical density of CO_2 in gm/cm^3. (b) Estimate the diameter of a molecule of CO_2.

CHAPTER 12

THE DISTRIBUTION OF MOLECULAR VELOCITIES

12-1 The distribution of molecular velocities. In the preceding chapter we assumed that the molecules of a gas had different velocities but left unanswered the question as to how many molecules had a velocity of any specified magnitude and direction. For the problems considered in that chapter a knowledge of the form of the so-called *distribution function* was unnecessary, since the number of collisions with a surface and the pressure exerted by a gas on a surface depend only on the arithmetic mean and the rms speeds respectively and are independent of any specific velocity distribution.

The problem of determining the distribution function was first worked out in 1859 by Clerk Maxwell (known also for his contributions to electromagnetic theory). The theory was later put on a sounder basis by Ludwig Boltzmann, using the methods of statistical mechanics. We shall give in this section what was essentially Maxwell's original derivation.

Let us imagine that at a certain instant the velocity vectors of all the molecules of a gas are transferred to a common origin. Construct a rectangular coordinate system as in Fig. 12-1, where the three axes represent the X-, Y-, and Z-components of velocity. We shall call these components v_x, v_y and v_z respectively, and let v represent the magnitude of the velocity or the speed. Then for any velocity vector,

$$v^2 = v_x^2 + v_y^2 + v_z^2.$$

Each velocity vector in Fig. 12-1 is completely defined by the coordinates of its end point (the arrowhead of the vector). We can therefore speak of these *points*, instead of the vectors themselves, and describe our problem as that of determining the way in which these representative points are distributed in the *velocity space* of Fig. 12-1. Thus the number of points in any small volume element $dv_x dv_y dv_z$, whose coordinates are v_x, v_y, and v_z, gives the number of molecules having velocities with components v_x, v_y, and v_z or, more precisely, with components between v_x and $v_x + dv_x$, v_y and $v_y + dv_y$, and v_z and $v_z + dv_z$.

The same limitations are imposed on the permissible smallness of a volume element in velocity space as on a volume element of a gas in ordinary space. The element must be large enough to contain a large number of representative points, but small in comparison with the total range of velocities. The problem may be stated in another way. We are going

223

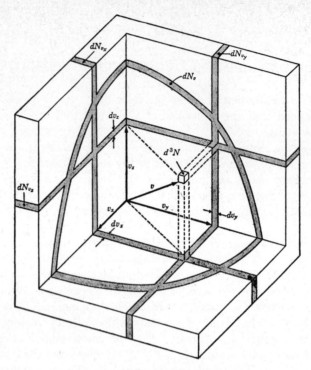

FIG. 12-1.   Diagram of velocity space.

to attempt to describe the velocity distribution by a *continuous function* of velocities, whereas the actual distribution, since there are only a finite number of molecules, is necessarily discontinuous.   That is, out of the triple infinity of geometrical points in velocity space, only a finite number are occupied and most of the space is empty.   The distribution function that we will obtain, then, cannot be expected to give correct results if applied to a volume element that contains only a small number of representative points.   This aspect of the theory will become clearer after we have discussed it again later in the section.

We first ask, out of the total number of N molecules, or N representative points, what fraction have X-components of velocity between some arbitrary value v_x and a slightly larger value $v_x + dv_x$?   Geometrically, this is the same as asking how many representative points in Fig. 12-1 lie in the thin slice of thickness dv_x, parallel to the v_y-v_z plane and at a perpendicular distance v_x from this plane.   It should be evident that any velocity vector terminating in this slice has an X-component of velocity between v_x and $v_x + dv_x$, regardless of the magnitudes of the Y- and Z-components of its velocity. Let dN_{v_x} represent the number of points in the slice. The fraction of the total number N lying in the slice is then

$$\frac{dN_{v_x}}{N}.$$

This fraction will certainly depend on the location of the slice considered, that is, it will be some function of v_x. Also, if the thickness of the slice is small, the fraction will be proportional to this thickness. The function of v_x is unknown at this point (the derivation of the form of the function is precisely our problem), so all we can do for the present is to write it as $f(v_x)$. That is, we let

$$\frac{dN_{v_x}}{N} = f(v_x)dv_x. \tag{12-1}$$

The number of molecules with X-velocity components between v_x and $v_x + dv_x$ is therefore

$$dN_{v_x} = Nf(v_x)dv_x. \tag{12-2}$$

Now in the absence of any mass motion of the gas, all *directions* in velocity space are equivalent. Hence the fractional number of molecules in slices perpendicular to the v_y- and v_z-axes must be given by functions of v_y and v_z having precisely the same form as the unknown function of v_x, and

$$\frac{dN_{v_y}}{N} = f(v_y)dv_y, \tag{12-3}$$

$$\frac{dN_{v_z}}{N} = f(v_z)dv_z. \tag{12-4}$$

We next ask, what fraction of the molecules with X-velocity components between v_x and $v_x + dv_x$ have at the same time Y-velocity components between v_y and $v_y + dv_y$? Although the subgroup of dN_{v_x} molecules is only a small fraction of the total, it still comprises a very large number of molecules. (That is, we must take dv_x large enough so that the subgroup *does* contain a large number of molecules. Fortunately, the total number N is so large that we can do this and still keep the velocity range dv_x relatively small.) Eq. (12-3) gives the fraction of the *total* number of molecules with velocity components between v_y and $v_y + dv_y$. Maxwell assumed that if one considered any subgroup of this total number, the same fraction of the subgroup would have velocity components between v_y and $v_y + dv_y$, provided the subgroup was large enough.

To take an example from another field, a certain fraction of the population of the United States is between 15 and 20 years old. Consider as a subgroup the population of New York State. The argument above is equivalent to assuming that the same fraction of the population of this subgroup is between 15 and 20 years old. Obviously the subgroup taken cannot be too small. Out of a subgroup as small as 10 persons, for example, there is no assurance that the fraction in the 15 to 20 year age group is the same as it is for the entire population of the U. S. Also, the subgroup must be selected in such a way that it avoids obvious weightings in favor of any particular age group. The population ratios in California, for example, where many elderly people find it so pleasant to live, may be quite different from those in Vermont. This aspect of the question, as it applies to molecular velocities, means that we assume that the possession of a Y-velocity of magnitude v_y is not affected by the fact that a molecule already has an X-velocity of magnitude v_x. This assumption was one of the weaker points of Maxwell's theory and it can best be justified by the fact that the theory works; that is, it predicts a velocity distribution in agreement with experiment.

Making the assumptions above, then, we set the fractional number of v_x-component molecules having Y-components between v_y and $v_y + dv_y$, equal to the fraction of the total number having Y-components in this same range. Let $d^2N_{v_x v_y}$ represent the number of molecules having simultaneously X-components of velocity between v_x and $v_x + dv_x$, and Y-components between v_y and $v_y + dv_y$. We write $d^2N_{v_x v_y}$, since this is a small fraction of an already small fraction, or a differential of second order. The fractional number of v_x-component molecules with Y-components between v_y and $v_y + dv_y$ is then

$$\frac{d^2N_{v_x v_y}}{dN_{v_x}}.$$

The fraction of the *total* number with Y-components between v_y and $v_y + dv_y$ is, from Eq. (12-3),

$$\frac{dN_{v_y}}{N} = f(v_y)dv_y.$$

Equating these fractions, we get

$$d^2N_{v_x v_y} = dN_{v_x}f(v_y)dv_y.$$

But from Eq. (12-2),

$$dN_{v_x} = Nf(v_x)dv_x.$$

Hence

$$d^2N_{v_x v_y} = Nf(v_x)f(v_y)dv_x dv_y.$$

Geometrically, $d^2N_{v_x v_y}$ is the number of representative points in that portion of velocity space that is common to two slices perpendicular to the v_x- and v_y-axes respectively. A portion of such a common volume is indicated by dotted lines in Fig. 12-1. It is in the form of a prism of rectangular cross section (square cross section if dv_x and dv_y are equal) and extends from $-\infty$ to $+\infty$.

By exactly the same reasoning as above, the number of molecules simultaneously having X-components of velocity between v_x and $v_x + dv_x$, Y-components between v_y and $v_y + dv_y$, and Z-components between v_z and $v_z + dv_z$, is

$$d^3N_{v_x v_y v_z} = Nf(v_x)f(v_y)f(v_z)dv_x dv_y dv_z. \tag{12-5}$$

This is the number of representative points in the volume element $dv_x dv_y dv_z$ in Fig. 12-1, or in the element common to the vertical prism and the slice between v_z and $v_z + dv_z$.

The number of representative points per unit volume, or the "density" of points in velocity space, which we shall represent by ρ, is

$$\rho = \frac{d^3N_{v_x v_y v_z}}{dv_x dv_y dv_z} = Nf(v_x)f(v_y)f(v_z). \tag{12-6}$$

Since the velocity distribution is isotropic, the density is the same in any other volume element at the same radial distance v from the origin, where

$$v^2 = v_x^2 + v_y^2 + v_z^2.$$

In other words, the density is the same at all points within any thin spherical shell with center at the origin.

Consider now a second volume element near the first, and in which, in general, the density is different from that in the first. The change in density when v_x, v_y, and v_z are changed by dv_x, dv_y, and dv_z respectively, is

$$d\rho = \frac{\partial \rho}{\partial v_x} dv_x + \frac{\partial \rho}{\partial v_y} dv_y + \frac{\partial \rho}{\partial v_z} dv_z. \tag{12-7}$$

Since $f(v_x)$ is by hypothesis a function of v_x only, and $f(v_y)$ and $f(v_z)$ are independent of v_x, then from Eq. (12-6),

$$\frac{\partial \rho}{\partial v_x} = N \left[\frac{d}{dv_x} f(v_x) \right] f(v_y)f(v_z)$$

$$= Nf'(v_x)f(v_y)f(v_z),$$

where

$$f'(v_x) \equiv \frac{d}{dv_x} f(v_x).$$

By the same method, we find

$$\frac{\partial \rho}{\partial v_y} = N f(v_x) f'(v_y) f(v_z),$$

$$\frac{\partial \rho}{\partial v_z} = N f(v_x) f(v_y) f'(v_z).$$

Now consider the special case where the changes dv_x, dv_y, and dv_z are such that the second volume element lies in the same spherical shell as the first. Then $d\rho = 0$, and from Eq. (12-7) and the preceding expressions for the partial derivatives, we obtain

$$\frac{f'(v_x)}{f(v_x)} dv_x + \frac{f'(v_y)}{f(v_y)} dv_y + \frac{f'(v_z)}{f(v_z)} dv_z = 0. \tag{12-8}$$

But if the second element does lie in the same spherical shell as the first,

$$v_x^2 + v_y^2 + v_z^2 = v^2 = \text{const},$$

and

$$v_x dv_x + v_y dv_y + v_z dv_z = 0. \tag{12-9}$$

That is, if we are to stay in the same spherical shell, so that $d\rho = 0$, the differentials dv_x, dv_y, and dv_z in Eq. (12-8) are not independent. They cannot be given any arbitrary values but must satisfy Eq. (12-9), a so-called *condition equation*.

If dv_x, dv_y, and dv_z in Eq. (12-8) *were* independent, the only way the equation could always be satisfied would be if the coefficient of each were equal to zero. Suppose dv_x, dv_y, and dv_z were independent, i.e., any value could be assigned to any one, independently of the values assigned to the others. Then we might say, let $dv_x = dv_y = 0$, $dv_z \neq 0$. Obviously the coefficient of dv_z would have to be zero to satisfy Eq. (12-8) and, by the same argument, the other coefficients would have to be zero also. But in our problem dv_x, dv_y, and dv_z are not independent, since they have to satisfy Eq. (12-9). We see from this equation that if we let $dv_x = dv_y = 0$, then dv_z must also equal zero (since in general $v_z \neq 0$) and we are not free to assume $dv_z \neq 0$, which would be necessary to prove that the coefficient of dv_z was zero.

Using a method invented by Lagrange, known as the *method of undetermined multipliers*, we can combine Eq. (12-8) and the condition equation and *in effect* obtain an equation in which dv_x, dv_y, and dv_z *are* independent.

Let us multiply the condition equation, (12-9), by a constant λ whose value we shall determine later (λ is then our undetermined multiplier) and add the resulting equation to (12-8).   This gives

$$\left(\frac{f'(v_x)}{f(v_x)} + \lambda v_x\right) dv_x + \left(\frac{f'(v_y)}{f(v_y)} + \lambda v_y\right) dv_y + \left(\frac{f'(v_z)}{f(v_z)} + \lambda v_z\right) dv_z = 0. \quad (12\text{-}10)$$

Now let us assign a value to λ which makes

$$\frac{f'(v_x)}{f(v_x)} + \lambda v_x = 0. \quad (12\text{-}11)$$

Eq. (12-10) then reduces to

$$\left(\frac{f'(v_y)}{f(v_y)} + \lambda v_y\right) dv_y + \left(\frac{f'(v_z)}{f(v_z)} + \lambda v_z\right) dv_z = 0. \quad (12\text{-}12)$$

But any *two* of the variables dv_x, dv_y, and dv_z can be considered independent, so let us assume that dv_y and dv_z are independent.   Then the coefficients of each must vanish, as we have shown.   Hence

$$\frac{f'(v_y)}{f(v_y)} + \lambda v_y = 0, \quad (12\text{-}13)$$

$$\frac{f'(v_z)}{f(v_z)} + \lambda v_z = 0. \quad (12\text{-}14)$$

In effect, then, dv_x, dv_y, and dv_z in Eq. (12-10) are independent, since the coefficient of each is equal to zero.

We can now determine the form of the function f from any one of the equations (12-11), (12-13), or (12-14).   From Eq. (12-11),

$$\frac{1}{f(v_x)} \frac{d}{dv_x} f(v_x) + \lambda v_x = 0,$$

$$\frac{d(f(v_x))}{f(v_x)} = -\lambda v_x dv_x,$$

and integrating

$$\ln f(v_x) = -\frac{\lambda v_x^2}{2} + \ln \alpha,$$

where $\ln \alpha$ is an integration constant.   Going over to the exponential form,

$$f(v_x) = \alpha e^{-\frac{\lambda v_x^2}{2}}.$$

or, for brevity,

$$f(v_x) = \alpha \exp\left(-\beta^2 v_x^2\right), \quad (12\text{-}15)$$

where β is a new constant defined by the equation

$$\beta^2 \equiv \frac{\lambda}{2}.$$

Since $f(v_y)$ and $f(v_z)$ obey the same differential equation as $f(v_x)$, we have

$$f(v_y) = \alpha \exp(-\beta^2 v_y^2), \tag{12-16}$$

$$f(v_z) = \alpha \exp(-\beta^2 v_z^2). \tag{12-17}$$

The *form* of the function $f(v_x)$ is therefore determined, although we still have to find the meaning of the constants α and β.

Inserting the expressions for $f(v_x)$, $f(v_y)$, and $f(v_z)$ in Eq. (12-5), we get for the number of representative points in a volume element $dv_x dv_y dv_z$ in velocity space,

$$d^3N = N\alpha^3 \exp\left[-\beta^2(v_x^2 + v_y^2 + v_z^2)\right]dv_x dv_y dv_z,$$

or

$$d^3N = N\alpha^3 \exp(-\beta^2 v^2)dv_x dv_y dv_z. \tag{12-18}$$

The number of points per unit volume is

$$\rho = \frac{d^3N}{dv_x dv_y dv_z} = N\alpha^3 \exp(-\beta^2 v^2). \tag{12-19}$$

The density is seen to be a function of v only, in accord with our original assumption of an isotropic distribution, and it is plotted in Fig. 12-2 as a function of v (v is always positive). The density is a maximum at the origin where $v = 0$ and it falls off exponentially with v^2. If velocity space is divided into small elements of equal volume, the element at the origin contains the largest number of representative points. Because of the inverse exponential dependence of ρ on v^2, the density decreases rapidly as v increases.

The quantity

$$N\alpha^3 \exp(-\beta^2 v^2)$$

is the *Maxwell velocity distribution function*. It is often more convenient, however, to express the distribution in other forms. Very often, one wishes to know only the number of molecules having *speeds* within a certain range but including all directions in space. The range

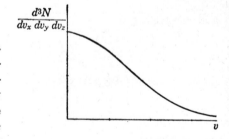

FIG. 12-2.   Graph of Maxwell-Boltzmann velocity distribution function.

may be infinitesimal, as between v and $v + dv$, or it may include all molecules with speeds greater or less than some particular value. Geometrically, referring to Fig. 12-1, the molecules with speeds between v and $v + dv$ are those with representative points in a thin shell between v and $v + dv$, those with speeds less than v_0 include all points within a sphere of radius v_0, and so on.

The simplest way of calculating the number of molecules with speeds between v and $v + dv$ is to recall that the density of points is uniform in any thin spherical shell of radius v. The volume of such a shell is

$$4\pi v^2 dv, \tag{12-20}$$

and since the density at a radial distance v from the origin is

$$\rho = N\alpha^3 \exp{(-\beta^2 v^2)},$$

the number of points in the shell, dN_v, is

$$dN_v = N\alpha^3 \exp{(-\beta^2 v^2)} \times 4\pi v^2 dv,$$

or

$$dN_v = 4\pi N\alpha^3 v^2 \exp{(-\beta^2 v^2)}dv. \tag{12-21}$$

The ratio dN_v/dv or, what is the same thing, the coefficient of dv in Eq. (12-21), is the Maxwell distribution function of molecular *speeds*. Unlike the velocity distribution function, it does not represent the number of points per unit volume, but the number per unit range of speed dv. The speed distribution function is plotted in Fig. 12-3. Because of the factor v^2, which does not occur in the velocity distribution function, the graph in Fig. 12-3 is zero when $v = 0$, rises to a maximum, and then decreases with increasing v. The number of molecules with speeds between v and $v + dv$ is represented in this graph by the *area* (not the ordinate)

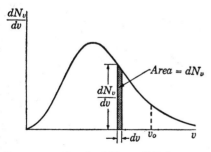

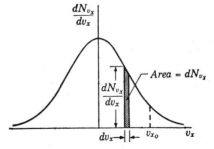

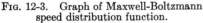

FIG. 12-3.   Graph of Maxwell-Boltzmann speed distribution function.

FIG. 12-4.   Maxwell-Boltzmann distribution function for a single component of velocity.

of a narrow vertical strip such as the one shaded. The height of such a strip is dN_v/dv, its width is dv, and its area is therefore dN_v. The number of molecules with speeds less than v_0 equals the area under the curve to the left of v_0, and so on.

Notice that although the density ρ, or the number of representative points per unit volume, is a maximum at the origin, the spherical shell enclosing the maximum number of points is the one with radius v_m, lying at the maximum of the speed distribution curve. The reason for this apparent discrepancy is that as we proceed outward from the origin the volumes of successive spherical shells continually increase (see Eq. (12-20)), while the number of representative points per unit volume continually decreases (see Eq. (12-19)). The volume of the innermost shell (which is actually a small sphere of radius dv) is essentially zero, so that although the density is a maximum for this shell the number of points within it is practically zero because its volume is so small. In other words, practically none of the molecules is at rest.

The number of molecules with X-*components* of velocity in any specified narrow range is obtained by inserting the expression for $f(v_x)$ in Eq. (12-2). This gives

$$dN_{v_x} = N\alpha \exp\left(-\beta^2 v_x^2\right)dv_x, \qquad (12\text{-}22)$$

or

$$\frac{dN_{v_x}}{dv_x} = N\alpha \exp\left(-\beta^2 v_x^2\right), \qquad (12\text{-}23)$$

with similar expressions for Y and Z. The ratio dN_{v_x}/dv_x is the number of molecules per unit range of X-velocity, and is plotted in Fig. 12-4. As in Fig. 12-3, the area of a narrow vertical strip under this graph, at any value of v_x, is equal to dN_{v_x}, or the number of molecules in the corresponding thin slice of velocity space. It will be seen that the slice containing the largest number of molecules is the one at $v_x = 0$, and that the curve is symmetrical and extends from $v_x = -\infty$ to $v_x = +\infty$. The number of molecules with positive X-components of velocity greater than some arbitrary value such as v_{x_0} equals the area under the graph to the right of v_{x_0}, and so on.

12-2 Evaluation of α and β.

We next consider the evaluation of the constants α and β. Let us first make use of the fact that the integral of dN_v over all values of v from zero to infinity equals the total number of molecules, N.

$$N = \int dN_v = 4\pi N\alpha^3 \int_0^\infty v^2 \exp(-\beta^2 v^2)dv.$$

The definite integral, from Table 12-1, is

$$\sqrt{\pi}/4\beta^3,$$

and hence

$$\alpha^3 = \pi^{-3/2}\beta^3. \tag{12-24}$$

The speed distribution function can therefore be expressed wholly in terms of β.

$$dN_v = \frac{4N}{\sqrt{\pi}} \beta^3 v^2 \exp(-\beta^2 v^2)dv.$$

The physical significance of the constant β can now be determined by computing the average speed, the mean square speed, or the most probable speed. The average speed is

$$\bar{v} = \frac{\displaystyle\int v\,dN_v}{N}$$

$$= \frac{4\beta^3}{\sqrt{\pi}} \int_0^\infty v^3 \exp(-\beta^2 v^2)dv.$$

The definite integral, from Table 12-1, is

$$1/2\beta^4,$$

so

$$\bar{v} = \frac{2}{\beta\sqrt{\pi}}, \quad \beta = \frac{2}{\sqrt{\pi}}\frac{1}{\bar{v}}. \tag{12-25}$$

The root-mean-square speed is

$$v_{rms} = \sqrt{\bar{v^2}} = \left[\frac{\displaystyle\int v^2\,dN_v}{N}\right]^{1/2}$$

$$= \left[\frac{4\beta^3}{\sqrt{\pi}} \int_0^\infty v^4 \exp(-\beta^2 v^2)dv\right]^{1/2}.$$

The definite integral is

$$3\sqrt{\pi}/8\beta^5,$$

so

$$v_{rms} = \sqrt{\frac{3}{2}}\frac{1}{\beta}, \qquad \beta = \sqrt{\frac{3}{2}}\frac{1}{v_{rms}} . \qquad (12\text{-}26)$$

The most probable speed v_m is that corresponding to the radius of the spherical shell in velocity space containing the largest number of representative points. In other words, more molecules have the speed v_m than have any other speed. To determine v_m, we find the value of v for which the speed distribution function is a maximum, by setting its first derivative with respect to v equal to zero.

$$\frac{d}{dv}\left[\frac{4N}{\sqrt{\pi}}\beta^3 v^2 \exp(-\beta^2 v^2)\right] = 0.$$

TABLE 12-1.

$$f(n) = \int_0^\infty x^n e^{-ax^2}\, dx.$$

$$\int_{-\infty}^{\infty} e^{-x^2}dx = \sqrt{\pi}$$

n	$f(n)$	n	$f(n)$
0	$\dfrac{1}{2}\sqrt{\dfrac{\pi}{a}}$	1	$\dfrac{1}{2a}$
2	$\dfrac{1}{4}\sqrt{\dfrac{\pi}{a^3}}$	3	$\dfrac{1}{2a^2}$
4	$\dfrac{3}{8}\sqrt{\dfrac{\pi}{a^5}}$	5	$\dfrac{1}{a^3}$
6	$\dfrac{15}{16}\sqrt{\dfrac{\pi}{a^7}}$	7	$\dfrac{3}{a^4}$

If n is even, $\qquad\displaystyle\int_{-\infty}^{+\infty} x^n e^{-ax^2}dx = 2f(n).$

If n is odd, $\qquad\displaystyle\int_{-\infty}^{+\infty} x^n e^{-ax^2}dx = 0.$

This gives

$$v_m = 1/\beta, \quad \beta = 1/v_m. \tag{12-27}$$

The constant β can therefore be expressed in terms of any one of these speeds. However, let us make use of the result derived in Sec. 11-4, that the root-mean-square speed is related to the temperature by the equation

$$v_{rms} = \sqrt{\frac{3kT}{m}}.$$

Then

$$\beta = \sqrt{\frac{m}{2kT}},$$

and we see that while β is a constant for any given equilibrium state, its magnitude is inversely proportional to the square root of the Kelvin temperature. We can now eliminate β as well as α from the three distribution functions and write

$$dN_v = (4N/\sqrt{\pi})(m/2kT)^{3/2}v^2 \exp(-mv^2/2kT)dv, \tag{12-28}$$

$$d^3N_{v_xv_yv_z} = (N/\pi^{3/2})(m/2kT)^{3/2} \exp(-mv^2/2kT)dv_xdv_ydv_z, \tag{12-29}$$

$$dN_{v_x} = (N/\sqrt{\pi})(m/2kT)^{1/2} \exp(-mv_x^2/2kT)dv_x, \tag{12-30}$$

with corresponding expressions for dN_{v_y} and dN_{v_z}. Eq. (12-28) gives the number of molecules with velocity vectors terminating in a thin spherical shell in velocity space, of radius v and thickness dv. Eq. (12-29) gives the number with velocity vectors terminating in a volume element $dv_xdv_ydv_z$ of velocity space, the element being located at a radial distance v from the origin. Eq. (12-30) gives the number with velocity vectors terminating in a thin slice perpendicular to the v_x-axis and at a distance v_x from the origin.

Each of the distribution functions depends on the temperature, both through the coefficient of the exponential term and the exponent of that term. Fig. 12-5 shows three graphs of the function dN_v/dv, at

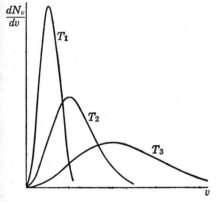

FIG. 12-5. Distribution function at three different temperatures, $T_3 > T_2 > T_1$.

three different temperatures. The areas under all three curves are the same, since the area represents the total number of molecules.

Let us now return to a consideration of the average, root-mean-square, and most probable speeds. From the relations between each of these quantities and β, and from the expression for β in terms of T, we find

$$v_m = \sqrt{2 \frac{kT}{m}}, \qquad (12\text{-}31)$$

$$\bar{v} = \sqrt{\frac{8}{\pi} \frac{kT}{m}} = \sqrt{2.55 \frac{kT}{m}}, \qquad (12\text{-}32)$$

$$v_{rms} = \sqrt{3 \frac{kT}{m}}. \qquad (12\text{-}33)$$

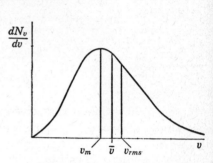

The relative magnitudes of the three, at a given temperature, are

$$v_m : \bar{v} : v_{rms} = 1 : 1.128 : 1.224,$$

and the three are shown in Fig. 12-6.

Fig. 12-6. Most probable, arithmetic mean, and root-mean-square velocities.

12-3 The error function. One often wishes to compute the number of particles with speeds or velocity components greater or less than a specified value, or lying between two specified values. These numbers are represented graphically by areas under the graphs of the appropriate distribution functions and bounded by vertical lines. In velocity space, they are the number of representative points lying outside or inside a sphere of specified radius, or between two spheres, or on one side or the other of a plane perpendicular to some axis of velocity. Analytically, they are computed by integration of the appropriate distribution function between the proper limits, but while the integrals of these functions between 0 and ∞ reduce to the relatively simple expressions given in Table 12-1, the same is not true of the integral between finite limits.

As a specific example, suppose we wish to compute the number $N_{0 \to v_{x_0}}$ of molecules, out of a total number N, having X-components of velocity between 0 and some arbitrary value v_{x_0}. In Fig. 12-4, this number is represented by the area under the graph of the distribution function and bounded by the vertical axis and the dotted line at v_{x_0}. Analytically, the number is

$$N_{0 \to v_{x_0}} = \int_0^{v_{x_0}} dN_{v_x}.$$

The expression for dN_{v_x} is given in Eq. (12-22) or (12-30). For simplicity, let us use Eq. (12-22) and express the velocity as a fraction of the most probable velocity v_m or $1/\beta$. That is, we define a quantity x by the equation

$$x = \frac{v_x}{v_m} = \beta v_x.$$

Then

$$dx = \beta dv_x,$$

and making use of Eq. (12-24), Eq. (12-22) becomes

$$dN_x = \frac{N}{\sqrt{\pi}} \exp(-x^2)dx,$$

and hence

$$N_{0 \to x} = \frac{N}{\sqrt{\pi}} \int_0^x e^{-x^2}dx. \qquad (12\text{-}34)$$

The value of the definite integral in this equation is a function of its upper limit. The integral can be evaluated by expanding e^{-x^2} in a series and integrating term by term. Tables of the integral, as a function of the upper limit, are available. It is customary to include the factor $2/\sqrt{\pi}$, and the integral is called the *error function*, written $erf(x)$.

$$erf(x) \equiv \frac{2}{\sqrt{\pi}} \int_0^x e^{-x^2}dx. \qquad (12\text{-}35)$$

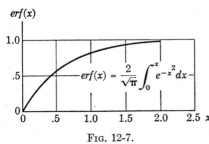

FIG. 12-7.

An abbreviated table of values of the error function is given in Table 12-2 and a graph in Fig. 12-7. We see from Table 12-1, setting $n = 0$ and $a = 1$, that

$$erf(\infty) = \frac{2}{\sqrt{\pi}} \int_0^\infty e^{-x^2}dx = 1,$$

so that the limiting value of $erf(x)$ as x increases is exactly unity. From Table 12-2, the function is practically equal to 1 for values of x greater than about 2.

Returning now to Eq. (12-34), the number $N_{0 \to x}$ can be written

$$N_{0 \to x} = (N/\sqrt{\pi})(\sqrt{\pi}/2) \, erf(x),$$

$$= \frac{N}{2} \, erf(x). \tag{12-36}$$

For example, let us compute the number of particles having X-components of velocity between 0 and v_m. Then $x = 1$ and

$$N_{0 \to 1} = \frac{N}{2} \, erf(1)$$

$$= \frac{N}{2} \times .843$$

$$= 0.422N.$$

TABLE 12-2.

Values of the error function $erf(x) = \dfrac{2}{\sqrt{\pi}} \displaystyle\int_0^x e^{-x^2} dx.$

x	$erf(x)$	x	$erf(x)$
0	0	1.6	.9763
0.2	.2227	1.8	.9891
0.4	.4284	2.0	.9953
0.6	.6039	2.2	.9981
0.8	.7421	2.4	.9993
1.0	.8427	2.6	.9998
1.2	.9103	2.8	.9999
1.4	.9523		

For values of x larger than those given in the table, $erf(x)$ can be computed from the semiconvergent series

$$erf(x) = 1 - \frac{e^{-x^2}}{\sqrt{\pi}x}\left(1 - \frac{1}{2x^2} + \frac{1 \cdot 3}{(2x^2)^2} - \frac{1 \cdot 3 \cdot 5}{(2x^2)^3} + \cdots\right).$$

The number of particles with (positive) X-components of velocity between 0 and ∞ is obviously $N/2$. Hence the number with X-components greater than an arbitrary value v_x is $N/2$, minus the number with velocity components between 0 and v_x. That is,

$$N_{x \to \infty} = \frac{N}{2} - \frac{N}{2}\, erf(x)$$

$$= \frac{N}{2}\,(1 - erf(x)). \tag{12-37}$$

It is left as a problem to show that the number with *speeds* between 0 and v is

$$N_{0 \to x} = N\left[erf(x) - \frac{2}{\sqrt{\pi}} x e^{-x^2} \right] \tag{12-38}$$

where $x = v/v_m$.

12-4 The energy distribution function.

The translational kinetic energy w of a molecule of mass m, traveling with a speed v, is

$$w = \tfrac{1}{2}mv^2,$$

and the energy w_x associated with a velocity component v_x is

$$w_x = \tfrac{1}{2}mv_x^2.$$

The exponential terms in the Maxwell distribution functions, Eqs. (12-28) to (12-30), are therefore

$$\frac{w}{kT}, \quad \frac{w}{kT}, \quad \text{and} \quad \frac{w_x}{kT}.$$

That is, each exponent is the (negative) ratio of an energy to the quantity kT. (The term kT represents an energy also, since, as we have shown, the mean translational kinetic energy of the molecules of a gas at a temperature T is $\tfrac{3}{2}kT$.)

We shall show later that the Maxwell distribution function is a special case of a more general distribution principle derived by Boltzmann, where the ratio (energy/kT) is not restricted to kinetic energy of translation. Because of the generalization introduced by Boltzmann, following Maxwell's earlier work, the distribution function is often called a Maxwell-Boltzmann distribution.

It is useful to have an expression for the number of molecules with translational kinetic energies within a certain prescribed range, say between w and $w + dw$. Since $w = mv^2/2$,

$$dw = mvdv,$$

$$dv = \frac{dw}{mv} = \frac{dw}{m\sqrt{\dfrac{2w}{m}}} = (2mw)^{-1/2}dw.$$

Then from Eq. (12-28),

$$dN_w = (4N/\sqrt{\pi})\left(\frac{m}{2kT}\right)^{3/2}\frac{2w}{m}\exp\,(-w/kT)(2mw)^{-1/2}dw$$

$$= (2N/\sqrt{\pi})(kT)^{-3/2}\,w^{1/2}\exp\,(-w/kT)dw. \qquad (12\text{-}39)$$

We have changed the notation from dN_v to dN_w, since the distribution function is now expressed in terms of w. A graph of dN_w/dw is given in Fig. 12-8, plotted as a function of w/kT. The most probable energy is $kT/2$.

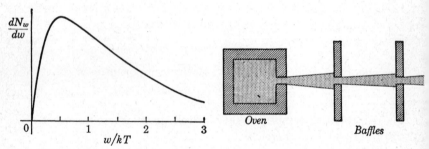

FIG. 12-8. Maxwell-Boltzmann energy distribution function.

FIG. 12-9. Production of a beam of neutral particles.

12-5 Molecular beams. An important technique in atomic physics is the production of a collimated beam of neutral particles in a so-called *molecular beam*. A beam of *charged* particles, electrons or ions, can be accelerated and decelerated by an electric field, and guided and focused by either an electric or a magnetic field. These methods cannot be used if the particles are uncharged. Molecular beams can be produced by allowing molecules of a gas to escape from a small opening in the walls of a container into a region in which the pressure is kept low by continuous pumping. A series of baffles, as in Fig. 12-9, limits the beam to a small cross section. Since one often wishes to work with molecules of a material such as silver, which is a solid at room temperature, the temperature in the container must be great enough to produce a sufficiently high vapor pressure. Hence the container is often a small electric furnace or oven.

We have shown in Sec. 11-3 that the number of molecules with speed v, striking the surface of a container per unit area and per unit time, is

$$\tfrac{1}{4}v\,dn_v, \tag{12-40}$$

where dn_v is the number of molecules per unit volume with speed v.

If the molecules have a Maxwellian velocity distribution, the number per unit volume with a speed v is

$$dn_v = \frac{4n}{\sqrt{\pi}}\left(\frac{2kT}{m}\right)^{-3/2} v^2 \exp\left(-mv^2/2kT\right)dv.$$

If there is a hole in a wall of the oven, small enough so that leakage through the hole does not appreciably affect the equilibrium state of the gas in the oven, Eq. (12-40) gives the number with speed v escaping through the hole, per unit area and per unit time. We wish to compute the rms speed of those that escape. Following the standard method, the mean square speed of the escaping molecules is found by multiplying by v^2 the number that escape with speed v, integrating over all values of v, and dividing by the total number. The rms speed is the square root of the result. It is left as a problem to show that

$$v_{rms} = \sqrt{\frac{4kT}{m}}. \tag{12-41}$$

The rms speed of the molecules *in* the oven is

$$v_{rms} = \sqrt{\frac{3kT}{m}},$$

so that those escaping have a somewhat higher speed than those in the oven.

The distribution in *direction* of the molecules escaping through the hole is given by Eq. (11-10). That is, the number per unit solid angle in the emerging beam is a maximum in the direction of the normal to the plane of the opening and decreases to zero in the tangential direction.

12-6 Experimental verification of Maxwell velocity distribution.

Direct measurements of the distribution of velocities in a molecular beam have been made by a number of methods. Fig. 12-10 is a diagram of the apparatus used by Zartman and Ko in 1930-1934, a modification of a technique developed by Stern in 1920. In Fig. 12-10, O is an oven and S_1 and S_2 are slits defining a molecular beam. C is a cylinder that can be rotated at approximately 6000 rpm about the axis A. If the cylinder is at rest, the molecular beam enters the cylinder through a slit S_3 and strikes a curved glass plate G. The molecules stick to the glass plate, and the number arriving at any portion can be determined by removing the plate and measuring with a recording microphotometer the darkening that has resulted.

Now suppose the cylinder is rotated. Molecules can enter it only during the short time intervals during which the slit S_3 crosses the molecular beam. If the rotation is clockwise, as indicated, the glass plate moves toward the right while the molecules cross the diameter of the cylinder. They therefore strike the plate at the left of the point of

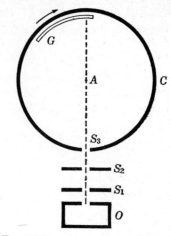

FIG. 12-10. Apparatus used by Zartman and Ko in studying distribution of velocities.

impact when the cylinder is at rest, and the more slowly they travel, the farther to the left is this point of impact. The blackening of the plate is therefore a measure of the "velocity spectrum" of the molecular beam.

A more recent and more precise experiment, making use of the free fall of the molecules in a beam, was performed by Estermann, Simpson, and Stern, in 1947. A simplified diagram of the apparatus is given in Fig. 12-11. A molecular beam of cesium emerges from the oven slit O, passes through the collimating slit S, and impinges on a hot tungsten wire D. The pressure of the residual gas in the apparatus is of the order of

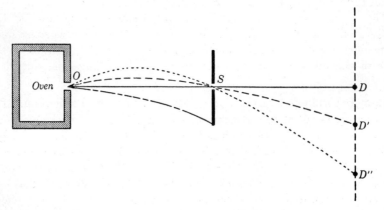

FIG. 12-11. Schematic diagram of apparatus of Estermann, Simpson, and Stern.

10^{-8} mm of mercury. Both the slits and the detecting wire are horizontal. The cesium atoms striking the tungsten wire become ionized, re-evaporate, and are collected by a negatively charged cylinder surrounding the wire but not shown in the diagram. The ion current to the collecting cylinder then gives directly the number of cesium atoms impinging on the wire per second.

In the absence of a gravitational field, only those atoms emerging in a horizontal direction would pass through the slit S, and they would all strike the collector in the position D regardless of their velocities. Actually, the path of each atom is a parabola, and an atom emerging from the slit O in a horizontal direction, as indicated by the dot and dash line, (with the vertical scale greatly exaggerated) would not pass through the slit S. The dashed line and the dotted line represent the trajectories of two atoms that can pass through the slit S, the velocity along the dashed trajectory being greater than that along the dotted. Hence as the detector is moved down from the position D, those atoms with velocities corresponding to the dashed trajectory will be collected at D', those with the slower velocity corresponding to the dotted trajectory will be collected at D'', etc. Measurement of the ion current as a function of the vertical height of the collector then gives the velocity distribution.

Fig. 12-12 is a graph of the results. The ordinate is proportional to the collector current and the abscissa to the vertical distance S of the collector below the position D in Fig. 12-11. The points are experimental values and the solid line is the theoretical curve computed from the Maxwell velocity distribution. The measured currents at large distances (small velocities) are somewhat smaller than the predicted values, an effect resulting from collisions of molecules in the beam with one another near the oven slit. The general agreement between theory and experiment is excellent.

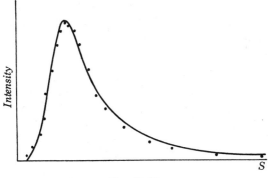

Fig. 12-12.

12-7 The principle of equipartition of energy. Suppose we have a mixture of gases that do not react chemically with one another, and that the temperature and density are such that their behavior approximates that of an ideal gas. It is found experimentally that the total pressure of the mixture is the sum of the pressures that each gas alone would exert if a mass of each, equal to the mass of that gas in the mixture, occupied the entire volume of the mixture. The pressure that would be exerted by each gas if present alone is called its *partial pressure* and the experimental law above is *Dalton's law of partial pressures.* If the gases are distinguished by subscripts, we can then write

$$p_1V = N_1kT, \quad p_2V = N_2kT, \text{ etc.,}$$

where p_1, p_2, etc., are the partial pressures of the component gases, N_1, N_2, etc., are the numbers of molecules of each, and V and T are the volume and temperature, common to all of the gases.

Let m_1, m_2, etc., represent the masses of the molecules of the components and $\overline{v_1^2}$, $\overline{v_2^2}$, etc., the respective mean square speeds. By the methods of Sec. 11-4, considering the collisions of each type of molecule with the walls and computing the pressure produced by each, we would find

$$p_1V = \tfrac{1}{3}N_1m_1\overline{v_1^2}, \quad p_2V = \tfrac{1}{3}N_2m_2\overline{v_2^2}, \text{ etc.}$$

Equating corresponding expressions for p_1V, p_2V, etc., gives

$$\tfrac{1}{2}m_1\overline{v_1^2} = \tfrac{3}{2}kT, \quad \tfrac{1}{2}m_2\overline{v_2^2} = \tfrac{3}{2}kT, \text{ etc.}$$

The terms on the left side of the preceding equations are the mean translational kinetic energies of the molecules of the various gases and we conclude that in a mixture of gases the mean kinetic energies of the molecules of each gas are the same. That is, in a mixture of hydrogen and mercury vapor, although the masses of the molecules are in the ratio of 2 to 200, the mean translational kinetic energy of the hydrogen molecules equals that of the mercury molecules.

The example above is one illustration of the *principle of equipartition of energy.* We know now that this principle is not a universal law of nature but rather a limiting case under certain special conditions. However, it has been a very fruitful principle in the development of molecular theories.

Let us give another example. The translational kinetic energy associated with the X-component of the velocity of a molecule of mass m is

$$w_x = \tfrac{1}{2}mv_x^2.$$

The mean value of the square of the X-components of velocity of molecules having a Maxwell distribution is

$$\overline{v_x^2} = \frac{\displaystyle\int v_x^2 dN_{v_x}}{N} = \frac{kT}{m}.$$

The mean kinetic energy of a molecule, associated with the X-component of its velocity, is therefore

$$\overline{w}_x = \tfrac{1}{2}m\overline{v_x^2} = \tfrac{1}{2}kT,$$

with corresponding expressions for the Y- and Z-components.

But we have shown that the mean *total* translational kinetic energy is

$$\overline{w} = \tfrac{3}{2}kT.$$

It follows that the translational kinetic energy associated with each component of velocity is just one-third of the total (not a surprising result since the X-, Y-, and Z-directions are all equivalent). Each independent quantity that must be specified to determine the energy of a molecule is called a *degree of freedom*. Since the translational kinetic energy of a molecule is determined by the three velocity components of its center of mass, it has three translational degrees of freedom and we see that the translational kinetic energy is divided equally among them. In other words, we have *equi*partition of the energy among the three translational degrees of freedom.

Molecules, however, are not geometrical points but are of finite size. They have moments of inertia, as well as mass, and can therefore have kinetic energy of rotation as well as of translation. Furthermore, we would expect them to rotate because of the random collisions with other molecules and with the walls. Since the angular velocity vector of a rotating molecule can have a component along all three coordinate axes, a molecule would be expected to have three rotational degrees of freedom or, if it is a rigid body, six degrees of freedom in all. However, molecules are not perfectly rigid structures and can also be expected to oscillate or vibrate as the result of collisions with other molecules, giving rise to still more degrees of freedom. (It may be mentioned at this point that rotations and vibrations of molecules are facts that are as well established as most of our other information about molecular properties. The best experimental method of studying rotations and vibrations consists of a spectroscopic analysis of the light emitted or absorbed by molecules in the infrared.) Without committing ourselves to any specific number, let us say that in general a molecule has f degrees of freedom, of which 3 only are translational, however complex the molecule.

We shall show in Chapter 14, on the basis of the Maxwell-Boltzmann statistics, that if the energy associated with any degree of freedom is a quadratic function of the variable specifying the degree of freedom, the mean value of the corresponding energy equals $\frac{1}{2}kT$. For example, the kinetic energy associated with the velocity component v_x is a quadratic function of v_x, and, as shown above, the mean value of w_x is $\frac{1}{2}kT$. Similarly for rotation, where the kinetic energy is $\frac{1}{2}I\omega^2$, the mean rotational kinetic energy is $\frac{1}{2}kT$, and for a harmonic oscillator, where the potential energy is $\frac{1}{2}kx^2$ (k being the force constant) the mean potential energy is $\frac{1}{2}kT$. Hence all of the degrees of freedom for which the energy is a quadratic function have associated with them, on the average, equal amounts of energy, and if all degrees of freedom are of this nature the total energy is shared equally among them. This is the general statement of the principle of equipartition of energy. The mean *total* energy of a molecule with f degrees of freedom, assuming the equipartition principle holds, is therefore

$$\bar{w} = \frac{f}{2}kT, \qquad (12\text{-}42)$$

and the total energy of N molecules is

$$N\bar{w} = \frac{f}{2}NkT = \frac{f}{2}nRT,$$

where n is the number of moles and R the universal gas constant.

12-8 Classical theory of specific heat capacity. In thermodynamics, the internal energy U of a system is defined by the equation

$$U_2 - U_1 = Q - W.$$

Only changes in internal energy can be measured, from measurements of heat and work.

Starting with a molecular model of a system, we can identify the internal energy with the sum of the energies of the individual molecules. In the preceding section we have derived a theoretical expression for the total energy associated with the f degrees of freedom of each of the N molecules of a gas. We therefore set this equal to the internal energy U.

$$U = \frac{f}{2}NkT = \frac{f}{2}nRT. \qquad (12\text{-}43)$$

The specific internal energy per mole is

$$u = \frac{U}{n} = \frac{f}{2} RT. \qquad (12\text{-}44)$$

How can we test the validity of the assumptions made in the foregoing derivation? The most direct way is from measurements of specific heat capacities. The molar specific heat capacity at constant volume is

$$c_v = \left(\frac{\partial u}{\partial T}\right)_v .$$

Hence, if the hypothesis above is correct, we should have

$$c_v = \frac{d}{dT}\left(\frac{f}{2} RT\right) = \frac{f}{2} R. \qquad (12\text{-}45)$$

We also know from thermodynamic reasoning that for an ideal gas,

$$c_p = c_v + R.$$

Hence

$$c_p = \frac{f}{2} R + R = \frac{f+2}{2} R, \qquad (12\text{-}46)$$

and

$$\gamma = \frac{c_p}{c_v} = \frac{\dfrac{f+2}{2}}{\dfrac{f}{2}} = \frac{f+2}{f} . \qquad (12\text{-}47)$$

Thus while the principles of thermodynamics could give us only an expression for the *difference* between the specific heat capacities at constant pressure and constant volume, molecular theory, together with the equipartition principle, predicts the actual **magnitudes of the specific heats** and their ratio γ, in terms of the number of degrees of freedom f and the experimentally determined universal constant R. Note that, according to the theory, c_v, c_p, and γ are all constants independent of the temperature.

Consider first a gas whose atoms are monatomic and for which the energy is wholly kinetic energy of translation. Since there are three translational degrees of freedom, $f = 3$, and we would expect

$$c_v = \frac{f}{2} R = \frac{3}{2} R,$$

$$\gamma = \frac{f+2}{f} = \frac{3+2}{3} = \frac{5}{3} .$$

This is in good agreement with the values of c_v and γ for the monatomic gases listed in Table 12-3. Furthermore, the specific heats of these gases are found to be practically independent of temperature, in agreement with the theory.

Consider next a diatomic molecule having the dumbbell structure shown in Fig. 12-13. Its moment of inertia about the X- and Z-axes is very much greater than that about the Y-axis, and if the latter can be neglected, the molecule has two rotational degrees of freedom, the two

TABLE 12-3.

Molar specific heat capacities of a number of gases, at temperatures near room temperature. The quantities measured experimentally are c_p and γ. The former is determined by use of a continuous flow calorimeter and the latter is obtained from measurements of the velocity of sound in the gas.

Gas	γ	c_p/R	c_v/R	$\dfrac{c_p - c_v}{R}$
He	1.659	2.52	1.519	1.001
Ne	1.64			
A	1.67	2.52	1.509	1.008
Kr	1.68			
Xe	1.66			
H_2	1.410	3.42	2.438	.9995
O_2	1.401	3.52	2.504	1.004
N_2	1.404	3.50	2.448	1.005
CO	1.404	3.50	2.488	1.005
NO	1.400	3.52	2.512	1.005
Cl_2	1.36	4.12	3.02	1.09
CO_2	1.304	4.40	3.38	1.027
NH_3	1.31	4.48	3.42	1.06
$C_4H_{10}O$	1.08	16.6	15.4	1.23

quantities specifying the rotational kinetic energy being the components of angular velocity about the X- and Z-axes. Also, since the atomic

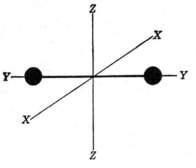

FIG. 12-13.   A dumbbell molecule.

bond is not perfectly rigid, the atoms can vibrate along the line joining them. This introduces two vibrational degrees of freedom, since the vibrational energy is part kinetic and part potential and is specified by the velocity and the separation of the atoms. We might therefore expect seven degrees of freedom for a diatomic molecule (3 for translation, 2 for rotation, and 2 for vibration). For $f = 7$, the theory predicts

$$c_v = \tfrac{7}{2}R = 3.5R, \quad \gamma = \tfrac{9}{7} = 1.29.$$

These values are not in good agreement with those observed for the diatomic gases listed in Table 12-3.   However, letting $f = 5$, we find

$$c_v = \tfrac{5}{2}R = 2.5R, \quad \gamma = \tfrac{7}{5} = 1.40.$$

These are almost exactly equal to the average values of c_v and γ for the diatomic molecules in the second part of the table (Cl^2 is an interesting exception).   Thus, near room temperature, these molecules behave as if either the rotational or vibrational degrees of freedom, but not both, shared equally with the translational degrees of freedom in the total molecular energy.

As the number of atoms in a molecule increases, the number of degrees of freedom can be expected to increase, and the theory predicts a decreasing ratio of specific heats, in general agreement with experiment.

The main features of the theory are fairly well borne out.   It predicts that γ is never greater than 1.67 or less than 1 and this is in fact true. However, if we insert in Eq. (12-47) the measured values of γ and solve for f, the result is in general not exactly an integer.   Now a molecule either has a degree of freedom or it has not—degrees of freedom are counted, not weighed.   It is meaningless to speak of a fraction of a degree of freedom, and the simple concept of equipartition is certainly not the whole story.

When we examine the temperature variation of specific heats, the divergences between experiment and the simple theory above become even more apparent.   Except for gases whose atoms are monatomic, the specific heats of all gases increase with increasing temperature and decrease as the temperature is lowered.   In fact, at a temperature of 20° K, the specific heat of hydrogen (the only diatomic gas that remains a gas at very low temperatures) decreases to $\frac{3}{2}R$, the value predicted by theory for a monatomic gas.   Thus at this low temperature neither the rotational nor the vibrational degrees of freedom of the hydrogen molecule appear to share at all in the internal energy.

All of the difficulties mentioned above are removed, however, when the principles of quantum mechanics and of statistics are taken into consideration.   These are discussed in Sec. 15-4.

12-9 Specific heat capacity of a solid.   The molecules of a solid, unlike those of a gas, are constrained to oscillate about fixed points by the relatively large forces exerted on them by other molecules.   Let us imagine that each executes simple harmonic motion.   Each has three degrees of freedom, considered as a mass point, but the *potential* energy associated with its motion, which could be neglected for the widely separated molecules of a gas, is on the average just equal to the kinetic energy, if the motion is simple harmonic.   Hence, if the equipartition principle is valid for solids, we must assign an energy kT to each degree of freedom ($\frac{1}{2}kT$ for kinetic energy, $\frac{1}{2}kT$ for potential energy) rather than just $\frac{1}{2}kT$ as for the molecules of a gas.   The total energy of N molecules is then

$$U = 3NkT,$$

and the molar specific heat capacity at constant volume, from the theory, is

$$c_v = 3R = 3 \times 8.31 \times 10^3 = 24.9 \times 10^3 \text{ joules/mole-deg.}$$

But the well-known Dulong-Petit law states that at temperatures which are not too low, the molar specific heat capacities at constant volume of all pure substances in the solid state are very nearly equal to $3R$ and again we have reasonably good agreement with experiment at high temperatures.   At low temperatures the agreement is definitely bad, since the specific heats of solids all approach zero as the temperature approaches absolute zero.   This is another problem to which the classical theory does not provide the right answer and where the methods of quantum mechanics must be used.

One other discrepancy between simple theory and experiment should be pointed out here.   There is good reason to believe that in metals, which are electrical conductors, each atom parts with one or more of its outer electrons and that these electrons form a sort of electron cloud or electron gas, occupying the volume of the metal and constrained by electrical forces at the metal surfaces in much the same way that ordinary gases occupy a containing vessel. This electron gas can be considered quite independently of the metal and it should have a molar specific heat equal to that of any other monatomic gas, namely, $\frac{3}{2}R$. That is, as the temperature of the metal is increased, energy must be supplied to make the electrons move faster as well as to increase the amplitude of vibrations of the metallic ions. The latter should have a specific heat capacity of $3R$, so the total heat capacity of a metal should be at least $3R + \frac{3}{2}R = \frac{9}{2}R$. Actually, metals obey the Dulong-Petit law as well as do nonconductors, so apparently the electrons do not share in the thermal energy. This was a very puzzling thing for many years, but again it has a very satisfactory explanation when quantum methods are used.

Problems

1. The Maxwell-Boltzmann distribution function of molecular speeds can be written

$$\frac{dN_x}{dx} = F(x^2),$$

where

$$v_m = \sqrt{2kT/m}, \quad x = v/v_m, \quad F(x^2) = \frac{4N}{\sqrt{\pi}} x^2 e^{-x^2}.$$

Construct a graph, plotting x horizontally and

$$y = \frac{\sqrt{\pi}}{4N} F(x^2)$$

vertically.   Compute y at the following values of x:

$$x = 0, .2, .4, .6, .8, 1.0, 1.2, 1.5, 2.0, 3.0.$$

2. Compute enough points to construct graphs of the speed distribution function dN_v/dv, for 1 kilomole of oxygen at temperatures of $100°$ K, $200°$ K, $400°$ K.

3. Compute enough points to construct graphs of the velocity distribution function $dN_{v_x v_y v_z}/dv_x dv_y dv_z$, for oxygen at temperatures of $100°$ K, $200°$ K, $400°$ K.

4. In Fig. 12-1, let $N =$ Avogadro's number, 6.03×10^{26} molecules.   Let $v_x = v_y = v_z = v_m$, and approximate the differentials dv_x, dv_y, and dv_z by $0.01\ v_m$. Compute the number of representative points in the following volume elements of velocity space:
   (a) the slice of thickness dv_y,
   (b) the rectangular cylinder common to two slices,
   (c) the volume element $dv_x dv_y dv_z$,
   (d) the spherical shell, if its radius is $\sqrt{3}\ v_m$ and its thickness $0.01\ v_m$.

5. (a) What would be the answer to part (c) of problem 4, if the differentials dv_x, dv_y, dv_z were taken as small as $10^{-9}\ v_m$, instead of $10^{-2}\ v_m$?   (b) What fraction of the molecules of a gas have speeds exactly equal to v_m (or exactly equal to any arbitrary value)?

6. (a) What is the "distance" v_x, in Fig. 12-1, of a slice at right angles to the v_x-axis, if the slice contains one-half as many representative points as a parallel slice of the same thickness passing through the origin?   Express the answer in terms of v_m.   (b) At what radial "distance" v from the origin of velocity space in Fig. 12-1 is the "density" of representative points one-half as great as at the origin?

7. (a) Compute to three significant figures the rms, arithmetic mean, and most probable speeds of an oxygen molecule at a temperature of $300°$ K.   (b) Compute the most probable speed of an oxygen molecule at the following temperatures: $100°$ K, $300°$ K, $1000°$ K, $10,000°$ K.

8. Find the fractional number of molecules of a gas having (a) velocities with X-components between v_m and $1.01\,v_m$, (b) speeds between v_m and $1.01\,v_m$, (c) velocities with X-, Y-, and Z-components each between v_m and $1.01\,v_m$.

(Approximate dv by $\Delta v = .01\,v_m$.)   Interpret the answers above graphically, in terms of volume elements in velocity space.

9. Complete the derivation of Eq. (12-38).

10. Find the fractional number of molecules of a gas with speeds between v_m and $1.2\,v_m$, (a) from Eq. (12-28), letting $v = v_m$ and $dv = 0.2\,v_m$, (b) from Eq. (12-28), letting $v = 1.1\,v_m$ and $dv = 0.2\,v_m$, (c) from Eq. (12-38).

11. What fraction of the molecules of a gas have positive X-components of velocity greater than $2\,v_m$?

12. (a) What fraction of the molecules of a gas have speeds greater than some arbitrary value v? Express your answer in terms of $x = v/v_m$. Compute this fraction if (b) $v = v_m$, (c) $v = 2\,v_m$.

13. What fraction of the molecules of a gas have (a) velocities with X-components between 0 and $+v_m$, $+v_m$ and $+\infty$, 0 and $+\infty$? Illustrate graphically in terms of the velocity distribution function.

(b) What fraction have speeds between 0 and v_m, v_m and ∞, 0 and ∞? Illustrate graphically in terms of the speed distribution function.

14. What fraction of the molecules of a gas have X-components of velocity between $-v_m$ and $+v_m$?

15. How many oxygen molecules, out of 1 mole, have speeds greater than 10^3 m/sec at a temperature of (a) $100°$ K, (b) $1000°$ K, (c) $10,000°$ K? Illustrate graphically in terms of the distribution function.

16. Find the number of molecules colliding with a surface, per unit area and per unit time, with components of velocity at right angles to the surface greater than some arbitrary value $v = xv_m$.

17. Calculate the average reciprocal speed, $(1/v)_{av}$, in terms of the temperature, in a Maxwell distribution.

18. Find the average speed of those molecules of a gas with speeds (a) between 0 and v_m, (b) greater than v_m.

19. What is the most probable energy w_m of molecules having a Maxwellian velocity distribution?   Is it equal to $\frac{1}{2}\,mv_m^2$?

20. The speed distribution function of a group of N particles is given by

$$dN_v = kdv, \qquad\qquad (V > v > 0)$$

$$dN_v = 0. \qquad\qquad (v > V)$$

(a) Draw a graph of the distribution function, (b) find the constant k in terms of N and V, (c) compute the average and rms speeds in terms of V.

21. The speed distribution function of a group of N particles is given by

$$dN_v = kv\,dv, \qquad\qquad (V > v > 0)$$

$$dN_v = 0. \qquad\qquad (v > V)$$

(a) Draw a graph of the distribution function, (b) find the constant k in terms of N and V, (c) compute the average speed, the rms speed, and the most probable speed in terms of V.

22. The oven in Fig. 12-10 contains bismuth at a temperature of 827° K, the drum is 10 cm in diameter and rotates at 6000 rpm. Find the displacement on the glass plate G, measured from a point directly opposite the slit, of the points of impact of the molecules Bi and Bi_2. Assume that all the molecules of each species escape with the rms speed appropriate to that species.

23. A spherical bulb 10 cm in radius is pumped continuously to a high vacuum. In the bulb is a small vessel, closed except for a circular hole 0.2 mm in diameter located at the center of the bulb. The vessel contains mercury at 100° C, at which temperature its vapor pressure is 0.28 mm of mercury. (a) Compute the average speed $\bar{v}$ of the molecules of mercury vapor in the small vessel. (b) Compute the rate of efflux of mercury through the hole, in milligrams/hr. (c) How long a time is required for 1 microgram of mercury to be deposited on a square centimeter of the inner surface of the bulb, in a direction making an angle of 45° with the normal to the hole? (See Fig. 12-14.)

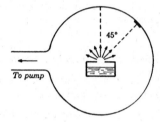

Fig. 12-14.

24. A spherical bulb 10 cm in radius is maintained at a temperature of 27° C, except for one square centimeter, which is kept at a very low temperature. The bulb contains water vapor originally at a pressure of 10 mm of mercury. Assuming that every water molecule striking the cold area condenses and sticks to the surface, how long a time is required for the pressure to decrease to 10^{-4} mm of mercury?

25. In a molecular beam experiment, the source is a tube containing hydrogen at a pressure $p_s = 0.15$ mm of mercury and at a temperature $T = 400°$ K. In the tube wall is a slit 30 mm $\times$ 0.025 mm, opening into a highly evacuated region. Opposite the source slit and 1 meter away from it is a second detector slit parallel to the first and of the same size. This slit is in the wall of a small enclosure in which the pressure p_d can be measured.

When the steady state has been reached: (a) What is the discharge rate of the source slit, in micrograms/sec? (b) What is the rate of arrival of hydrogen at the detector slit, in micro-micrograms/sec, and in molecules/sec? (c) How many molecules that will eventually reach the detector slit are in the space between source and detector at any instant? (d) What is the equilibrium pressure p_d in the detector chamber?

26. The distances OS and SD in the apparatus of Estermann, Simpson, and Stern in Fig. 12-11, are each 1 meter. Calculate the distance of the detector below the central position D, for cesium atoms having a speed equal to the rms speed

in a beam emerging from an oven at a temperature of 460° K. Calculate also the "angle of elevation" of the trajectory. The atomic weight of cesium is 133.

27. A molecule consists of four atoms at the corners of a tetrahedron. (a) What is the number of translational, rotational, and vibrational degrees of freedom for this molecule? (b) On the basis of the equipartition principle, what are the values of c_v and γ for a gas composed of these molecules?

28. Complete the derivation of Eq. (12-41).

29. The neutron flux across an area at the center of the Brookhaven pile is about 4×10^{16} neutrons/m²-sec. Assume that the neutrons have a Maxwellian velocity distribution corresponding to a temperature of 300° K ("thermal" neutrons). (a) Find the number of neutrons per cubic meter. (b) Find the "partial pressure" of the neutron gas.

CHAPTER 13

TRANSPORT PHENOMENA

13-1 Mean free path. In the derivation of the equation of state of an ideal gas, collisions between molecules were ignored, which is equivalent to treating the molecules as geometrical points. This neglect of collisions was justified because the pressure depends only on the average value of the squares of the speeds of all the molecules. Collisions will change the velocities of individual molecules, but will leave unaltered the *number* of molecules having any particular velocity. In other words, when some particular molecule "loses" some particular velocity as a result of a collision, another molecule somewhere else in the gas acquires, as a result of a collision, the same velocity that was "lost" by the first molecule.

We now consider a number of properties of a gas which depend on the fact that molecules have a finite size and do make collisions with one another. These properties would not exist, or would be of a very different nature, if molecules were strictly geometrical points.

In Fig. 13-1, a particular molecule represented by the solid circle has been singled out and its path among the other molecules indicated.

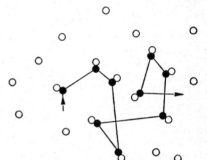

FIG. 13-1.   Molecular free paths.

Each segment of the path between successive collisions is called a *free path* and we wish to compute the average lengths of these free paths, or the *mean free path*, represented by λ.

We imagine that at a certain instant all of the molecules of a gas, except one, are "frozen" in position, while the remaining molecule continues to move among the others with a speed equal to the average speed $\bar{v}$. Let us assume the molecules to be perfectly elastic spheres of radius ρ. At the instant of a collision, the center-to-center distance of the colliding molecules is 2ρ, as in Fig. 11-5(a). The center-to-center distance would be the same if the radius of the moving molecule were increased to 2ρ while the stationary molecules were shrunk to geometrical points, as in Fig. 11-5(b). The effective cross-sectional area of the moving molecule, or its *collision cross section* σ, is therefore

$$\sigma = 4\pi\rho^2.$$

In a time interval t, the moving molecule covers a distance $\bar{v}t$ along an irregular zigzag path, and sweeps out a cylindrical volume of length $\bar{v}t$ and cross section σ. In this time it makes collisions with all the other molecules whose centers lie within this volume. If there are n molecules per unit volume, the number with centers in the cylinder swept out by the moving molecule is

$$\sigma n \bar{v}t.$$

This is therefore the number of collisions in time t, and the number of collisions per unit time, or the *collision frequency z*, is

$$\boxed{z = \sigma n \bar{v}.} \tag{13-1}$$

At standard conditions, the number of molecules per cubic meter is about 3×10^{25}. The mean speed of oxygen molecules at room temperature is about 450 m/sec, and the radius of an oxygen molecule is about 1.8×10^{-10} m. The collision cross section σ is $\sigma = 4\pi\rho^2 = 4\pi(1.8 \times 10^{-10})^2 \approx 4 \times 10^{-19}$ m². The collision frequency in oxygen at standard conditions is therefore about

$$z \approx 4 \times 10^{-19} \times 3 \times 10^{25} \times 450$$

$$\approx 5.5 \times 10^9 \text{ collisions/sec.}$$

The average distance between collisions, or the mean free path, equals the total distance covered in time t, divided by the number of collisions in this time. Hence

$$\lambda = \frac{\bar{v}t}{\sigma n \bar{v}t},$$

or

$$\lambda = \frac{1}{\sigma n}. \tag{13-2}$$

At a given temperature, the number of molecules per unit volume is directly proportional to the pressure, and the mean free path is inversely proportional to the pressure. For oxygen at standard conditions,

$$\lambda \approx \frac{1}{4 \times 10^{-19} \times 3 \times 10^{25}}$$

$$\approx 8 \times 10^{-8} \text{ m} = 8 \times 10^{-6} \text{ cm.}$$

The distance between molecules at standard conditions is of the order of 3×10^{-9} m, so the mean free path is of the order of 10 times the intermolecular distance, the latter being about 10 times the molecular diameter. Fig. 13-1 is therefore somewhat misleading. The free paths should on the average be much greater than the distances between molecules.

More complete theories of the mean free path take into account the motion of all the molecules of a gas, the fact that not all molecules have the same speed, and other factors. The only change in the end result is to alter the numerical coefficient of the right side of Eq. (13-2). The inverse dependence on the number of molecules per unit volume, and on the collision cross section, remains unaltered. In particular, if the molecules are all assumed to have the same speed and account is taken of their relative velocities, we obtain

$$\lambda = \frac{3}{4}\frac{1}{\sigma n} = \frac{0.75}{\sigma n},$$

a result derived by Clausius. On the assumption of a Maxwellian distribution of velocities the mean free path is

$$\lambda = \frac{1}{\sqrt{2}}\frac{1}{\sigma n} = \frac{0.707}{\sigma n}. \tag{13-3}$$

The preceding equations are for the mean free path of a molecule of radius ρ moving among other molecules of the same radius. In gas discharge tubes one often wishes to know the mean free path of an electron moving among molecules of a gas. The "radius" of an electron is so much smaller than that of a molecule that the electron can be treated as a point and the center-to-center distance in a collision (see Fig. 11-4) becomes ρ rather than 2ρ, where ρ is the *molecular* radius. Furthermore, the velocities of the electrons are so much greater than those of the molecules that the latter can be assumed at rest and the correction for relative velocities need not be made. There are two reasons for the large electronic velocity. First, because of the relatively small electronic mass, we would expect a much greater electronic velocity from the equipartition principle if the electrons were at the same temperature as the gas. Second, as a result of the electric field in a gas discharge, the electronic velocities are even greater than would be the case if thermal equilibrium existed. Hence the effective "electron temperature" may be many thousands of degrees, while the gas temperature is only a few hundred degrees.

From the considerations above, the *electronic mean free path* is

$$\lambda_e = 4\frac{1}{\sigma n}.$$

13-2 The distribution of free paths. In the preceding section we computed the mean length of the free path of a molecule. Our next problem is to derive the form of the distribution function of the free paths. That is, out of a large number of free paths, how many have a specified length, say between x and $x + dx$?

Consider a large number of molecules N_0 at a certain instant. We propose to follow this group, in imagination, as they make collisions with other molecules. Each collision removes a molecule from the group. Let N represent the number remaining in the group (i.e., the number that have not yet made a collision) after those remaining in the group have traveled a distance x, measured along the free path of each molecule. In the next short distance dx, a certain number of molecules will make collisions and be removed from the group. We assume that this number is proportional to the number of molecules N remaining in the group, and to the distance dx. Since every collision removes a molecule from the group and decreases N, the change in N in the distance dx is necessarily negative, and we write

$$dN = -P_c N dx, \qquad (13\text{-}4)$$

where P_c is a proportionality constant called the *collision probability* and which depends on the physical conditions in the gas but not on N or x. Then

$$\frac{dN}{N} = -P_c dx,$$

$$\ln N = -P_c x + \text{const.}$$

When $x = 0$, $N = N_0$, so the integration constant is $\ln N_0$ and

$$\boxed{N = N_0 \exp(-P_c x).} \qquad (13\text{-}5)$$

The number remaining in the group therefore falls off exponentially with x. Inserting this expression for N in Eq. (13-4) gives

$$\boxed{dN = -P_c N_0 \exp(-P_c x) dx.} \qquad (13\text{-}6)$$

In this equation, dN, taken with a positive sign, represents the number of molecules with free paths of length between x and $x + dx$. The *mean free path* λ is found by multiplying any particular free path of length x by the number of molecules dN having that free path, adding these products, and dividing by the total number of molecules N_0. That is,

$$\lambda = \frac{\int x dN}{N_0} = \frac{\int_0^\infty P_c N_0 x \exp (-P_c x) dx}{N_0} = \frac{1}{P_c} \cdot$$

The collision probability P_c is therefore equal to the reciprocal of the mean free path. Also, since $\lambda = 1/\sigma n$, it follows that

$$P_c = \sigma n$$

and the collision probability is jointly proportional to the collision cross section and the number of molecules per unit volume.

Equations (13-5) and (13-6) can now be written

$$N = N_0 \exp (-x/\lambda), \tag{13-7}$$

$$dN = -\frac{N_0}{\lambda} \exp (-x/\lambda) dx. \tag{13-8}$$

To repeat, the first of these equations, known as the survival equation, gives the number of molecules N, out of a number N_0, having free paths longer than x, while the second, with positive sign, gives the number with free paths between x and $x + dx$. Fig. 13-2 is a graph of N/N_0, plotted as a function of x/λ. The *ordinate* of the curve gives the fractional

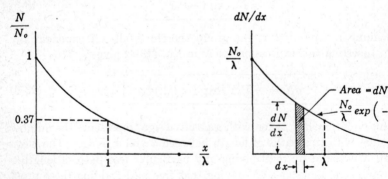

FIG. 13-2. Graph of the survival equation.   FIG. 13-3.

number of molecules with free paths longer than any fraction of the mean free path. Note that the fraction with free paths longer than the mean is e^{-1} or 37%, while the number with free paths shorter than the mean is 63%.

Fig. 13-3 is a graph of dN/dx, taken with positive sign, plotted as a function of x. The ordinate of this curve is the number of molecules *per unit length of path* with free paths between x and $x + dx$. The actual number dN of free paths between x and $x + dx$ is represented by the area of a narrow vertical strip.

One interesting aspect of the theory of the distribution of free paths is that the N_0 molecules considered originally are not necessarily just starting out on their free paths after having made a collision. We merely make a random selection of a large number of molecules at any instant and inquire into their *future* without asking questions about their *past*. Sometimes, however, it is the past rather than the future that is of interest. That is, we may fix our attention on a group of molecules at some instant and instead of asking, as we did above, how far each will travel on the average before it makes its *next* collision, ask how far each has traveled on the average since making its *last previous* collision. The same reasoning as that used above shows that this average distance is also the mean free path λ, and that the distribution of "past" free paths of the group is the same as the distribution of "future" free paths. Hence when we consider a large number of molecules in a gas at any instant, the average distance they have yet to travel before their next collision is equal to the average distance they have already traveled since their last previous collision, and both distances are equal to the mean free path λ. Eq. (13-7) gives the number of both "past" and "future" free paths longer than x, and Eq. (13-8) the number of "past" and "future" free paths of length between x and $x + dx$.

This raises the following interesting question. If the average distance traveled by the group *before* we consider it is λ, and the average distance *after* we consider it is also λ, why is not the mean free path equal to 2λ, rather than λ?

13-3 Coefficient of viscosity. In this section we give an elementary treatment of three properties of a gas from the molecular viewpoint. These are its viscosity, thermal conductivity, and coefficient of diffusion. These properties can be explained in terms of the transport across some imagined surface within the gas of momentum, energy, and mass respectively, by the molecules crossing the surface. Consider first the coefficient of viscosity.

In Fig. 13-4, the lower plate is at rest and the upper plate is moving toward the right at constant velocity. There is a gas in the space between the plates and it is well known that as a consequence of the viscosity or internal friction, a force is necessary to maintain the upper plate in motion. The coefficient of viscosity η of a fluid is defined by the equation

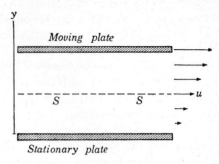

FIG. 13-4. Gas between a moving and a stationary plate.

$$F = \eta A \frac{du}{dy}, \qquad (13\text{-}9)$$

where F is the viscous force, parallel to the direction of motion, exerted on an area A when the velocity gradient at right angles to the area is du/dy.

The dotted line SS in Fig. 13-4 represents an imagined surface within the gas at an arbitrary height above the lower fixed plate. Let u represent the velocity of the gas toward the right, at this elevation, and du/dy the rate of change of velocity, at this height. The velocity u is superposed on the random thermal velocities of the molecules, so that the gas is not in thermodynamic equilibrium. However, in most practical problems the thermal velocities are so much greater than the velocity associated with any mass motion that we can use results previously derived for an equilibrium condition.

Molecules are continuously crossing the dotted surface both from above and from below. We shall assume that at its last collision before crossing the surface, each molecule acquires a flow velocity toward the right, corresponding to the particular height at which the collision was made. Since the flow velocity above the dotted surface is greater than that below the surface, molecules crossing from above transport a greater momentum (toward the right) across the surface than do the molecules crossing from below. There results a net rate of transport of momentum across the surface, and from Newton's second law we can equate the net rate of transport of momentum, per unit area, to the viscous force per unit area.

Thus the viscosity of a gas arises not from any "frictional" forces between its molecules, but from the fact that they carry momentum across a surface as a result of their random thermal motion. The process is analogous to that of two freight trains of open coal cars moving in the same direction on parallel tracks at slightly different speeds, with a gang of laborers in each car, each laborer shoveling coal from his car into the opposite car on the other train.   The cars in the slower train are continually being struck by pieces of coal traveling slightly faster than the cars, with the result that there is a net forward force on that train.   Conversely, there is a net backward force on the faster train, and the effect is the same as if the sides of the cars were rubbing together and exerting forces on one another through the mechanism of sliding friction.

Let us first compute the average height $\bar{y}$ above (or below) the surface SS at which a molecule makes its last collision before crossing.   In Fig. 13-5, dV is a small volume element at a distance r from an element of area dA in the plane SS, in a direction making an angle θ with the normal to dA.   If z is the collision frequency of any one molecule and n the number of molecules per unit volume, the total number of molecules in dV is ndV and the total number of collisions within dV in time dt is

$$\frac{1}{2}zndVdt,$$

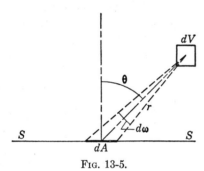

Fig. 13-5.

the factor $\frac{1}{2}$ occurring since otherwise each collision would be counted twice.   At each collision, two new free paths originate, so the total number of free paths originating in dV in time dt is

$$zndVdt.$$

These paths start off uniformly in all directions, so the number headed toward dA is

$$\frac{d\omega}{4\pi}\,zndVdt,$$

where $d\omega$ is the solid angle subtended at dV by the area dA, and is equal to $dA\cos\theta/r^2$.

From the survival equation, the number of molecules that reach dA without having made a collision is the number above multiplied by $\exp(-r/\lambda)$.   Replacing dV by the expression for a volume element in spherical coordinates, $dV = r^2\sin\theta d\theta d\phi dr$, we get for the number of molecules leaving dV in time dt and crossing dA without having made a collision,

$$\frac{1}{4\pi}\,zndAdt\,\sin\theta\,\cos\theta\,\exp(-r/\lambda)d\theta d\phi dr. \qquad (13\text{-}10)$$

To find the total number crossing dA in time dt from all directions and all distances, we integrate over θ from 0 to $\pi/2$, over ϕ from 0 to 2π, and over r from 0 to ∞. The result is

$$\frac{1}{4}zn\lambda dAdt, \tag{13-11}$$

which, since $z = \bar{v}/\lambda$, gives for the number crossing SS from either side, per unit area and per unit time,

$$\frac{1}{4}n\bar{v}.$$

This is the same as the result derived in Sec. 11-3, where the effect of collisions was ignored.

Now to return to the calculation of the average height of the last collision before crossing. The height of the volume element dV above SS is $r\cos\theta$. The number of molecules crossing dA directly from dV is given by Eq. (13-10). The average height for all molecules is found by multiplying the height $r\cos\theta$ by the number crossing from dV, integrating over θ, ϕ and r, and dividing by the total number crossing dA. The integral to be evaluated is

$$\frac{1}{4\pi}zndAdt \int_0^{\pi/2} \sin\theta\,\cos^2\theta d\theta \int_0^{2\pi} d\phi \int_0^\infty r\exp(-r/\lambda)dr$$

$$= \frac{1}{6}zn\lambda^2 dAdt.$$

Dividing by the total number crossing dA in time dt, given by Eq. (13-11), we get

$$\bar{y} = \frac{\frac{1}{6}zn\lambda^2 dAdt}{\frac{1}{4}zn\lambda dAdt}$$

$$= \frac{2}{3}\lambda.$$

Hence, on the average, each molecule crossing the plane made its last collision before crossing at a height equal to two-thirds of the mean free path above (or below) the surface.

At a height $\frac{2}{3}\lambda$ above the plane SS in Fig. 13-4, the flow velocity of the gas is

$$u + \frac{2}{3}\lambda\frac{du}{dy},$$

if the velocity gradient du/dy can be considered constant over distances of the order of a free path. The momentum of a molecule with this velocity (we consider only the momentum in the direction of flow, since there is no net transfer of random momentum across the surface) is

$$m\left(u + \frac{2}{3}\lambda\frac{du}{dy}\right).$$

Hence the net momentum in the direction of flow, carried across the surface per unit area and per unit time, by the molecules crossing the surface from above, is

$$\frac{1}{4}n\bar{v}m\left(u + \frac{2}{3}\lambda\frac{du}{dy}\right).$$

Similarly, the net momentum carried across the surface by the molecules crossing it in an upward direction from below is

$$\frac{1}{4}n\bar{v}m\left(u - \frac{2}{3}\lambda\frac{du}{dy}\right).$$

The net rate of transport of momentum, per unit area and per unit time, is the difference between these quantities, or

$$\frac{1}{3}nm\bar{v}\lambda\frac{du}{dy},$$

and, from Newton's second law, this is equal to the viscous force per unit area. Hence, by comparison with the definition of the coefficient of viscosity in Eq. (13-9), we have

$$\eta = \frac{1}{3}nm\bar{v}\lambda. \tag{13-12}$$

Introducing in Eq. (13-12) the expression for λ from Eq. (13-3) gives

$$\eta = \frac{1}{3}\frac{m\bar{v}}{\sqrt{2}\sigma}. \tag{13-13}$$

An unexpected conclusion from this equation is that *the viscosity of a gas is independent of the pressure*, or density, and is a function of temperature alone through the dependence of $\bar{v}$ on T,

$$\bar{v} = \sqrt{\frac{8kT}{\pi m}}.$$

Experiment, however, bears this out except at very low pressures where the mean free path becomes of the order of the dimensions of the apparatus. The theory above would not be expected to hold under these conditions, where a molecule could go bouncing from one wall to the other without making a large number of collisions on the way.   The predicted dependence on the square root of the Kelvin temperature is also in reasonably good agreement with experiment.   As for the dependence on the cross section σ, Eq. (13-13) is, as a matter of fact, one of the relations that is commonly used to "measure" collision cross sections (and hence molecular radii), since all of the terms in it except σ can be directly measured.   (The relation between $\bar{v}$ and T can be considered as well established experimentally.) Some values of the molecular radius ρ for a number of gases, computed from viscosity measurements, are given in Table 13-1.   They should not, of course, be considered as actual measurements of the radii of spherical molecules, but only to mean that as far as viscosity is concerned, these gases behave *as if* their molecules were elastic spheres having these radii. When the actual force fields around molecules are taken into account, the whole concept of "collisions" between molecules, and of free paths, loses its significance.   One molecule can influence another at an appreciable distance, and the trajectory of a molecule is deviated gradually as it approaches other molecules, rather than suddenly at a well-defined collision. Nevertheless, the concepts of free paths and cross sections are extremely useful and can be given a purely experimental significance in the following way.   There are many experimental methods of measuring the number of

TABLE 13-1.

Gas	$\eta(15°\text{ C})$ $\dfrac{\text{newt-sec}}{\text{m}^2}$	$\lambda(15°\text{ C, 1 atm})$ m	ρ m
He	19.4×10^{-6}	18.6×10^{-8}	1.09×10^{-10}
Ne	31.0	13.2	1.30
A	22.0	6.66	1.82
H_2	8.71	11.8	1.37
N_2	17.3	6.28	1.88
O_2	20.0	6.79	1.80
CO_2	14.5	4.19	2.30
NH_3	9.7	4.51	2.22
CH_4	10.8	5.16	2.07

particles N, out of a number N_0, that travel a distance greater than any arbitrary value in a gas. These methods are simplest (although not simple) when the particles are ions or electrons. Then, in the survival equation,

$$N = N_0 \exp(-x/\lambda),$$

the quantities N, N_0, and x are experimentally determined, and this equation can be used to *define* a mean free path (or an "effective" mean free path) λ. This experimental value of λ can then be inserted in Eq. (13-2) and this equation used to *define* an "effective" collision cross section σ. Thus the quantities λ and σ are a matter of experiment and definition and are independent of any theory.

13-4 Thermal conductivity. The thermal conductivity of a gas is handled in the same way as its viscosity. Let the upper and lower plates in Fig. 13-5 be at rest but at different temperatures, so that there is a temperature gradient, rather than a velocity gradient, in the gas. Let T be the temperature at the dotted plane and dT/dy the temperature gradient. The mean energy of a molecule at a temperature T, from Eq. (12-42), is

$$\frac{f}{2} kT,$$

and the energy carried across the plane, per unit area and per unit time, by the molecules crossing it from above, is

$$\frac{1}{4} n\bar{v} \times \frac{f}{2} k \left(T + \frac{2}{3} \lambda \frac{dT}{dy} \right).$$

The energy carried by those crossing from below is

$$\frac{1}{4} n\bar{v} \times \frac{f}{2} k \left(T - \frac{2}{3} \lambda \frac{dT}{dy} \right).$$

The net rate of flow of energy per unit area, which we identify with the rate of flow of heat per unit area across the plane, is

$$\frac{1}{6} n\bar{v}fk\lambda \frac{dT}{dy}. \tag{13-14}$$

The definition of the thermal conductivity K is

$$H = KA \frac{dT}{dy},$$

where H is the heat flowing per unit time across an area A where the

TABLE 13-2.

Gas	K joule/m- sec-deg	M kgm/mole	$\eta(0°\ C)$ newt-sec/m²	c_v joule/mole-deg	$\dfrac{KM}{\eta c_v}$
He	144×10^{-3}	4.002	18.8×10^{-6}	12.6×10^3	2.44
Ne	46.3	20.18	29.9	12.7	2.47
A	15.9	39.94	21.0	12.7	2.42
H_2	174	2.016	8.4	20.1	2.06
N_2	23.7	28.02	16.6	20.9	1.91
O_2	24.0	32.00	19.2	20.9	1.92
CO_2	142	44.00	13.8	27.8	1.64
NH_3	21.5	17.03	9.15	28.6	1.40
CH_4	30.1	16.03	10.3	26.8	1.75

temperature gradient is dT/dy. The coefficient of dT/dy in Eq. (13-14) is therefore the thermal conductivity K.

$$K = \frac{1}{6}n\bar{v}fk\lambda. \tag{13-15}$$

When we insert the expression for λ from Eq. (13-3), this reduces to

$$K = \frac{1}{6}\frac{\bar{v}fk}{\sqrt{2}\sigma}. \tag{13-16}$$

The thermal conductivity, like the viscosity, should therefore be independent of density. This is also in good agreement with experiment, down to pressures so low that the mean free path becomes of the same length as the dimensions of the container.

The ratio of thermal conductivity to viscosity, from Eqs. (13-16) and (13-13), is

$$\frac{K}{\eta} = \frac{\bar{v}fk}{6\sqrt{2}\sigma} \times \frac{3\sqrt{2}\sigma}{m\bar{v}} = \frac{fk}{2m}.$$

But $$c_v = \frac{f}{2}R, \quad k = \frac{R}{N_0}, \quad m = \frac{M}{N_0},$$

where M is the molecular weight, and N_0 is Avogadro's number. Hence

$$\frac{K}{\eta} = \frac{c_v}{M},$$

or

$$\frac{KM}{\eta c_v} = 1,$$

and the elementary theory predicts that, for all gases, this combination of experimental properties should equal unity. Some figures are given in Table 13-2 for comparison. The ratio $KM/\eta c_v$ does have the right order of magnitude, but we see again the influence of molecular complexity. By dropping the assumption that the molecules are rigid spheres and assuming a repulsive force between them that varies with the inverse 5th power of the center-to-center distance, the theoretical value of the ratio can be brought into good agreement with the experimental results.

13-5 Diffusion. The vessel in Fig. 13-6 is divided by a partition, on opposite sides of which are two different gases A and B at the same temperature and pressure, so that the number of molecules per unit volume is the same on both sides. If the partition is removed there is no mass motion of the gas in either direction, but after a sufficiently long time has elapsed one finds that both gases are uniformly distributed throughout the entire volume. This phenomenon, as a result of which each gas gradually permeates the other, is called *diffusion*. It

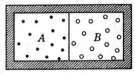

Fig. 13-6.

is not restricted to gases but occurs in liquids and solids as well. Diffusion is a consequence of random molecular motion and occurs whenever there is a concentration gradient of any molecular species, that is, when the number of particles per unit volume on one side of a surface differs from that on the other side. The phenomenon can be described as a transport of matter (i.e., of molecules) across a surface. Diffusion will also take place in a gas if there is a temperature gradient and hence a gradient in random thermal velocity.

In practice, the phenomenon of diffusion is often complicated by (a) the superposition of a hydrodynamic flow arising from pressure differences, (b) the effects of molecules rebounding from the walls of the vessel, and (c) by the fact that when more than one type of molecule is present the rates of diffusion of one into another are not the same. We can simplify the problem and still bring out the essential ideas by (a) considering the diffusion of molecules of a single species into others of the same species (so-called *self-diffusion*), (b) by assuming the containing vessel large enough in comparison with the mean free path so that collisions with the walls can be neglected in comparison with collisions with other molecules, and (c) by assuming a uniform pressure so that there is no hydrodynamic flow.

If all of the molecules of a system were *exactly* alike, any calculation of interdiffusion among them would be of academic interest only, since there would be no experimental method by which the diffusing molecules could be distinguished from the others. However, molecules that are isotopes of the same element, or molecules whose nuclei have been made radioactive, differ only in their nuclear structure and are essentially identical as far as collision cross sections are concerned. (Their mean kinetic energies will differ slightly because of differences in mass.) It is thus possible to "tag" certain molecules so that they can be distinguished from others and yet to treat the diffusion problem as if the molecules were all alike.

Let the vertical line in Fig. 13-7 represent an imaginary surface within a very large vessel. The vessel contains a mixture of tagged and untagged molecules, the total number of molecules per unit volume being the same at all points, so that the pressure is uniform. We assume the temperature uniform also. Let n represent the number of tagged molecules per unit volume at any point. We shall assume that n is a function of x only, where the X-axis is normal to the vertical plane. We assume also that the concentration gradient dn/dx is uniform and is positive, so that n increases from left to right. Then if n_0 is the concentration of tagged molecules at the vertical plane, the concentration at a distance x from the plane is

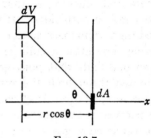

Fig. 13-7.

$$n = n_0 + x \frac{dn}{dx}. \qquad (13\text{-}17)$$

Since the concentration is greater at the right than at the left, the number of tagged molecules crossing the plane from right to left will exceed the number crossing in the opposite direction. The net number crossing the plane from left to right, in the positive X-direction, per unit area and per unit time, will be represented by Γ. The *coefficient of self-diffusion D* is then defined by the equation

$$\Gamma = -D \frac{dn}{dx}, \qquad (13\text{-}18)$$

where the negative sign is inserted since if dn/dx is positive, Γ is negative, as explained above. We now proceed to compute Γ.

We first wish to find the number of tagged molecules that start their free paths in the volume element dV in Fig. 13-7, in time dt. Let n' represent the *total* number of molecules per unit volume, the same at all points. As explained in Sec. 13-3, the *total* number of free paths originating in dV in time dt is

$$zn'\, dV\, dt.$$

If n represents the number of tagged molecules per unit volume in the element dV, the ratio of such molecules to the total number is n/n', and the same fraction of the free paths will be those of tagged molecules. Hence the number of free paths of tagged molecules is

$$\frac{n}{n'}\, zn'\, dV\, dt = zn\, dV\, dt.$$

The number crossing dA without making a collision is, from Eq. (13-10),

$$\frac{1}{4\pi}\, zn\, dA\, dt \sin\theta \cos\theta \exp\left(-r/\lambda\right) d\theta d\phi dr. \qquad (13\text{-}19)$$

From Eq. (13-17), and the geometry of the system,

$$n = n_0 - r\cos\theta\, \frac{dn}{dx}.$$

Inserting this in Eq. (13-19), we get

$$\frac{1}{4\pi}\, zn_0\, dA\, dt \sin\theta \cos\theta \exp\left(-r/\lambda\right) d\theta d\phi dr$$

$$-\frac{1}{4\pi}\, z\, \frac{dn}{dx}\, dA\, dt \sin\theta \cos^2\theta\, r \exp\left(-r/\lambda\right) d\theta d\phi dr.$$

We now integrate both of these expressions over θ from 0 to $\pi/2$, over ϕ from 0 to 2π, and over r from 0 to ∞. The first term is the same as Eq. (13-10), except that n is replaced by n_0, and leads to Eq. (13-11),

$$\frac{1}{4}\, zn_0\lambda\, dA\, dt.$$

The second term is like the unnumbered integral following Eq. (13-11), and leads to

$$-\frac{1}{6}\, z\lambda^2\, \frac{dn}{dx}\, dA\, dt. \qquad (13\text{-}20)$$

Hence the number crossing the plane from left to right, per unit area and per unit time, which we can represent by $\underset{\rightarrow}{\Gamma}$, is

$$\underset{\rightarrow}{\Gamma} = \frac{1}{4} z n_0 \lambda - \frac{1}{6} z \lambda^2 \frac{dn}{dx} . \tag{13-21}$$

By exactly the same argument, the number crossing from right to left is

$$\underset{\leftarrow}{\Gamma} = \frac{1}{4} z n_0 \lambda + \frac{1}{6} z \lambda^2 \frac{dn}{dx} . \tag{13-22}$$

The net number Γ crossing from left to right is now given by Eq. (13-21) minus Eq. (13-22),

$$\Gamma = - \frac{1}{3} z \lambda^2 \frac{dn}{dx} . \tag{13-23}$$

From Eq. (13-17), the diffusion coefficient D is therefore

$$D = \frac{1}{3} z \lambda^2, \tag{13-24}$$

or, since $z = \bar{v}/\lambda$,

$$D = \frac{1}{3} \bar{v} \lambda. \tag{13-25}$$

The mean free path λ is

$$\lambda = \frac{1}{\sqrt{2}\, \sigma n'},$$

where n' is the total number of molecules per unit volume.

Hence we can also write

$$D = \frac{\bar{v}}{3\sqrt{2}\, \sigma n'} . \tag{13-26}$$

Using Eq. (13-13) and the fact that the density ρ equals the product $n'm$, we have a relation between diffusion coefficient and viscosity,

$$D = \frac{\eta}{\rho} . \tag{13-27}$$

The phenomenon of diffusion through fine capillary pores in a ceramic material is one of the methods used to separate the isotopes U^{235} and U^{238}. Naturally occurring uranium is converted to the hexafluoride UF_6, a gas, and the mixture of isotopes flows by diffusion through a porous barrier. The phenomenon is more complicated than the simple case described above because the free path is no longer small compared with the dimensions of the capillaries and collisions with the walls become an important factor. However, we can see qualitatively that because of the slightly smaller mass of U^{235} compared with U^{238}, the mean speed $\bar{v}$ of the hexa-fluoride molecules containing U^{235} will be slightly greater than for the others. The diffusion coefficient is slightly greater also, so that this component is slightly enriched in the gas that has diffused through the pores.

The problem of gaseous self-diffusion in a capillary tube is carefully analyzed in a recent article by W. G. Pollard and R. D. Present in the Physical Review, Vol. 73, p. 762 (1948).

The operation of a pile is also dependent on the phenomenon of diffusion. The neutrons in a pile behave like a gas that is continuously being generated throughout the pile by fission processes, and which diffuses through the pile and eventually escapes from the surface. In order that the pile may operate successfully, conditions must be such that the rate of generation of neutrons is at least as great as the loss by diffusion, plus the losses due to collisions in which the neutrons are absorbed.

Problems

1. What is the collision frequency of a nitrogen molecule, (a) at 300° K and atmospheric pressure? (b) at 300° K and a pressure of 10^{-6} atm?

2. The mean free path of the molecules of a certain gas at a temperature of 25° C is 2.63×10^{-5} m. (a) If the radius of the molecule is 2.56×10^{-10} m, find the pressure of the gas. (b) Calculate the number of collisions per meter of path made by a molecule.

3. Oxygen gas (O_2) is contained in a one-liter flask at atmospheric pressure and a temperature of 300° K. (a) How many collisions per second are made by any one molecule, with other molecules? (b) How many molecules strike one square centimeter of the surface of the flask, per second? (c) How many molecules are there in the flask?

4. The mean free path in a certain gas is 10 cm. Consider 10,000 free paths. How many are longer than (a) 10 cm? (b) 20 cm? (c) 50 cm? (d) How many are longer than 5 cm but shorter than 10 cm? (e) How many are between 9.5 and 10.5 cm in length? (f) How many are between 9.9 and 10.1 cm in length? (g) How many are exactly 10 cm in length?

5. A group of oxygen molecules start their free paths at the same instant. The pressure is such that the mean free path is 2 cm. After how long a time will half of the group still remain, i.e., half the group will not as yet have made a collision? Assume all particles to have a speed equal to the average speed. The temperature is 300° K.

6. The total length of the apparatus of Estermann, Simpson, and Stern, in Fig. 12-11, is about 2 m and the pressure of the residual gas of the order of 10^{-8} mm

of mercury. Estimate the mean free path of the cesium atoms, and the fraction that travel a distance greater than 2 m before making a collision.

7. To what pressure, in mm of mercury, must a cathode-ray tube be evacuated in order that 90% of the electrons leaving the cathode shall reach the anode, 20 cm away, without making a collision?

8. A beam of electrons is projected from an electron gun into a gas at a pressure p, and the number remaining in the beam at a distance x from the gun is determined by allowing the beam to strike a collecting plate and measuring the current to the plate. The electron current emitted by the gun is 100 μa, and the current to the collector when $x = 10$ cm and $p = 100$ n/m² (about 1 mm of mercury) is 37 μa. (a) What is the electron mean free path? (b) What current would be collected if the pressure were reduced to 50 n/m²?

9. Compute the "radius" of an oxygen molecule, (a) from the experimental value of the viscosity of oxygen in Table 13-2, (b) from the experimental values of K and c_v in Table 13-2.

10. The viscosity of carbon dioxide over a range of temperatures is given in the table below. Compute the ratio $\eta/\sqrt{T}$ at each temperature.

$t°$ C	-21	0	100	182	302
$\eta \times 10^6$	12.9	14.0	18.6	22.2	26.8

11. A singly charged oxygen ion starts a free path in a direction at right angles to an electric field of intensity 10^4 volts/m. The pressure is one atmosphere and the temperature 300° K.
(a) Compute the distance moved in the direction of the field in a time equal to that required to traverse one mean free path.
(b) What is the ratio of the mean free path to this distance?
(c) What is the average velocity in the direction of the field?
(d) What is the ratio of the thermal velocity to this velocity?
(e) What is the ratio of the energy of thermal agitation to the energy gained from the field in one mean free path?

12. A large number of throws are made with a single die. (a) What is the average number of throws between the appearances of a six? At any stage of the process, what is the average number of throws (b) before the next appearance of a six, (c) since the last appearance of a six?

13. An electron with an energy of 100 electron volts is produced in an atmosphere of helium at a pressure of 1 mm of mercury and at a temperature of 300° K.
(a) Prove that in a head-on elastic collision between a body of mass m and a second body of mass M, initially at rest, the fractional decrease in energy of the first body is approximately $4m/M$, if $m \ll M$. (b) If on the average the electron loses this fraction of its kinetic energy in each collision with a helium atom, after how many collisions does its energy decrease to within 10% of the average thermal energy of the helium atoms? (That is, after how many collisions is its energy 110% of the average thermal energy of the helium atoms?) (c) What is the original collision

frequency of the electron, when its kinetic energy is 100 electron volts?   (d) Assuming that the collision frequency is constant, find the time required for the process in part (b).

14. A tube 2 m long and 10^{-4} m² in cross section contains CO_2 at atmospheric pressure and at a temperature of 273° K.   The carbon atoms in one-half of the CO_2 molecules are the radioactive isotope C^{14}.   At time $t = 0$, all of the molecules at the extreme left end of the tube contain radioactive carbon, and the number of such molecules per unit volume decreases uniformly to zero at the other end of the tube.   (a) What is the initial concentration gradient of radioactive molecules?   (b) Initially, how many radioactive molecules per second cross a cross section at the mid-point of the tube from left to right?   (c) How many cross from right to left?   (d) What is the initial net rate of diffusion of radioactive molecules across the cross section, in molecules per second and in micrograms per second?

CHAPTER 14

THE MAXWELL-BOLTZMANN STATISTICS

14-1 Introduction. The methods of statistical mechanics were first developed during the latter part of the last century, largely by Boltzmann, in Germany, and Gibbs, in the United States. The history of this branch of theoretical physics is typical of many others. Early work led to results that were in part in excellent agreement with experiment, while in other parts the agreement was not as good or was definitely bad. Then in the first decades of the present century an entirely new approach to the problem was introduced, as a consequence of which the older theory fell into its rightful place as a limiting form of the new, clearly applicable to the problems where it had been found to work but inapplicable to problems where it did not. Although it would be logical to present the new statistics first, and then the old as a limiting case, we shall follow the historical order and begin with the "classical" or Maxwell-Boltzmann statistics.

Statistical mechanics, like kinetic theory, presupposes a molecular model of matter but does not concern itself with detailed consideration of such things as collisions of molecules with one another or with a surface. Instead, it takes advantage of the fact that molecules are very numerous and that many properties of an assembly of molecules can be predicted with accuracy even in the absence of any information about specific individuals. Thus an actuary for a life insurance company can predict with high precision the average life expectancy of all persons in the U. S. born in a given year, without knowing the state of health of any one of them.

14-2 Phase space. The simplest system to consider, from the statistical viewpoint, is a monatomic gas. A complete specification of the state of the gas, from the molecular viewpoint, calls for a statement of the position and velocity of each of its molecules. That is, the six quantities

$$x, \ y, \ z, \ v_x, \ v_y, \ v_z,$$

must be specified for each molecule.

In Sec. 12-1, where we derived the Maxwell velocity distribution function, we found it helpful to introduce the concept of *velocity space* and to speak of the number of representative points per unit "volume" in velocity space. This imposed no great strain on the imagination, since we had but three velocity components to deal with. Now we wish to consider all six of the quantities listed above. Although the entire argument can be carried out on a purely mathematical basis, most people find it helpful to use the language of geometry and to speak of the three position co-ordinates and the three velocity coordinates of a molecule as determining the position of a point in a six-dimensional hyperspace or *phase space.**

Let us subdivide phase space into small six-dimensional elements of volume, which for brevity we call *cells*, with sides of length dx, dy, dz, dv_x, dv_y, dv_z. The differentials $dx \cdots dv_z$ are small compared with the dimensions of the system and the range of velocities of the molecules, but large enough so that each cell contains a large number of representative points. The volume of this cell, or the product of the six quantities above, will be represented by H. Every molecule of the gas has its representative point in phase space and for brevity we speak of these as phase points. Imagine the cells to be numbered $1, 2, \ldots i, \ldots$, and let $N_1, N_2, \ldots N_i, \ldots$ stand for the number of phase points in the corresponding cells. The number of phase points per unit volume, or the "density" in phase space, which we represent by ρ, is then

$$\rho = \frac{N_i}{H}, \quad N_i = \rho H, \tag{14-1}$$

where the subscript i is the number of some arbitrary cell. The density ρ will be some function of the six coordinates of the ith cell, and the fundamental problem of statistical mechanics is to determine the form of this function.

Notice the analogy between what we are doing here and the method of deriving the Maxwell distribution function, where we derived an expression for ρ, the density of representative points in velocity space.

14-3 Microstates and macrostates. A complete specification of the six coordinates of each molecule of a system, within the limits of the dimensions of the cell in which its representative point lies, is said to define a *microstate* of the system. Such a specification states where each molecule is, within the limits dx, dy, dz, and how fast and in what direction it is moving, within the limits of the differentials of velocity. This detailed

---

* A more general approach is to consider a large number of identical systems of N molecules each, and a phase space of $6N$ dimensions. The coordinates of a single point in this space then give the position and velocity of all N molecules of any one system, and the methods of statistics are applied to the large number of points representing the large number of systems.

description is quite unnecessary to determine the observable properties of the gas. For example, the density (in the ordinary sense of mass per unit volume) is the same if there are the same *number* of molecules in each volume element of ordinary space, regardless of *which* molecules lie in any volume element. Similarly, the pressure exerted by the gas depends only on *how many* molecules have specified velocities, not at all on *which* molecules have those velocities. In other words, the observable properties depend only on how many phase points lie in each cell of phase space. A specification of the *number* of phase points in each cell of phase space, i.e., of the numbers N_i, is said to define a *macrostate* of the system.

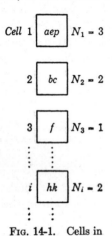

Fig. 14-1. Cells in phase space.

The distinction between microstates and macrostates is illustrated in Fig. 14-1. The cells in phase space are numbered 1, 2, 3, etc., and the phase points are lettered a, b, c, etc. A particular microstate is specified by stating that phase points a, e, p, are in cell 1, phase points b, c, are in cell 2, and so on. The corresponding macrostate is specified by merely giving the total number N_1 of phase points in cell 1, the number N_2 in cell 2, and, in general, the number N_i in the ith cell.

Whether we can specify it or not (and of course we cannot) a microstate *exists* for a given gas at every instant, at least according to the concepts of classical mechanics. But no microstate can persist without change, because the molecules are all in motion. In the intervals between collisions, every phase point moves through phase space because of the continuous change in its x, y, and z coordinates, although its components of velocity remain the same. When a collision between two molecules takes place, the components of velocity of both molecules change very suddenly and the phase points of the colliding molecules jump to two other volume elements having the same position coordinates but different velocity coordinates. The continuous shifting around of phase points in phase space is like the motion of the molecules of a gas in ordinary space, except that it is even more complicated. The important point is that the gas is continuously and spontaneously changing from one microstate to another.

One of the fundamental hypotheses of statistical mechanics is that *all microstates are equally probable*. That is, over a long period of time, any one microstate occurs as often as any other. At first this does not seem reasonable. One particular microstate, for example, is that in which every molecule in a box is located in a small volume element in one corner of the box, with all molecules traveling in the same direction. In another microstate the molecules are uniformly distributed throughout the box, with molecule a at some specified point, molecule b at some other specified point, and so on. Molecule a has some specified velocity in magnitude and direction, molecule b has another specified velocity, etc. Although the two microstates described above are very different, and while the second appears more probable than the first, it will be seen that in both microstates *the position and velocity of every molecule is completely specified.* The specifications are *different*, but they are *complete*, and it is the fact that they are complete that makes the microstates equally probable.

It may be objected that the two microstates will not occur equally often. It would be a rare thing indeed to find all the molecules in a box gathered in one corner and moving in the same direction, while it is very likely that they will be uniformly distributed and have velocities in random directions. True, but the latter description is not that of the second microstate described above. There we said not only that the molecules were uniformly distributed, but that some particular molecule was at a particular point and traveling in a particular direction, another particular molecule was at another point and traveling in another specified direction, and so on. Picture, if you can, the microstate of a sample of gas at the present moment, and imagine how long you would have to wait before, as a result of collisions, you would again find *every* molecule at the point it now occupies and traveling in exactly the same direction and with the same speed it now has. You would have to wait just as long to find all the molecules gathered in one corner and moving in the same direction. As K. K. Darrow has expressed it, the feature that distinguishes the two microstates is not their relative probability, but their symmetry. The two are equally probable.

Let us give one other example. A bridge hand consisting of 13 spades is a rare occurrence. You have probably never been dealt one. But any other hand in which all 13 cards are specified is just as likely to be dealt you as a hand consisting of 13 spades. Of course, a hand containing 4 spades, 3 hearts, 3 diamonds, and 3 clubs, is very likely to turn up. This is a *macrostate*, in which we specify not *which* spades, hearts, etc., the hand contains, but only *how many*. A completely specified distribution such as

S	A, K, J, 10
H	A, K, 3
D	9, 8, 2
C	K, Q, J

is not only a good hand but occurs just as often, and no more often, than a 13-spade hand. Both the hand above and the 13-spade hand are *microstates*.

It is easily seen that many different microstates, whether of the molecules of a gas or the 13 cards in a bridge hand, correspond to the same macrostate. Any shift of the phase points in phase space that does not change the *numbers* of points in each volume element, leaves unaltered the macrostate of the gas and its observable properties. As time goes on, and the microstates of a gas continuously change, the macrostate that occurs most frequently will be that for which there are the largest number of microstates. If, as turns out to be the case, there is one particular macrostate for which there are many more microstates than any other, that macrostate will be practically the only one ever observed. Others will be observed occasionally and these rare occurrences are responsible, among other things, for the scattering of blue light from the earth's atmosphere and for the Johnson noise in an electrical circuit.

14-4 Thermodynamic probability.

We now set ourselves the problem of determining how many microstates correspond to a given macrostate, and if there is any particular macrostate for which this number is a maximum. The number of microstates corresponding to any given macrostate is called the *thermodynamic probability* of the macrostate and is represented by W. In general, W is a very large number.

Let us take a simple example. Suppose there are just two cells in phase space, i and j, and four phase points, a, b, c, and d. Let N_i and N_j represent the number of phase points in the respective cells. The possible macrostates are

N_i	4	3	2	1	0
N_j	0	1	2	3	4

and we see that there are five altogether. To each of these macrostates there corresponds, in general, a different number of microstates. The microstates corresponding to the particular macrostate, $N_i = 3$, $N_j = 1$, are shown in Fig. 14-2(a) and we see that there are four, so for this macrostate $W = 4$.

Changing the order of the phase points *within a particular cell* is not considered to change the microstate. That is, the microstate in Fig. 14-2(b) is the same as the first of those tabulated in Fig. 14-2(a).

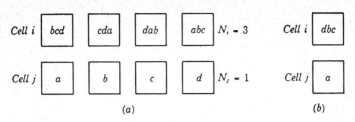

FIG. 14-2.

The number of microstates corresponding to a given macrostate can be computed by writing down the number of different arrangements or permutations of the phase points in the macrostate, exclusive of permutations which merely interchange the order of points within a particular cell. The number of different ways in which N things can be arranged in sequence, or the number of permutations, is $N!$ There are N choices for the first, $(N - 1)$ for the second, $(N - 2)$ for the third, and so on up to 1 for the last. Thus the number of permutations of the four letters a, b, c, d, is $4! = 24$. This does not give the number of microstates in the example above, however, because it includes all the possible permutations of the three points in cell i, of which there are $3! = 6$. We must divide the total number of permutations, 24, by those that only permute the points within cell i, which gives $24/6 = 4$, in agreement with the result obtained by counting.

In the general case of N phase points, and where in general permutations within more than one cell are possible, the number of microstates corresponding to a given macrostate, or the thermodynamic probability of the macrostate, is

$$W = \frac{N!}{N_1! \, N_2! \, N_3! \cdots},$$

or, introducing the symbol Π for the product of the terms following it (corresponding to Σ for their sum),

$$W = \frac{N!}{\Pi N_i!}. \tag{14-2}$$

If a cell is empty, $N_i = 0$ for that cell, and if Eq. (14-2) is to give the right answer, we must have $0! = 1$. This may be considered the definition of $0!$ but it also follows from the general definition of $x!$ as a special case of the gamma function of x.

Returning to the above example of four phase points and two cells, we find for the thermodynamic probabilities of the five macrostates:

$$W(N_i = 4, \quad N_j = 0) = \frac{4!}{4! \, 0!} = 1,$$

$$W(N_i = 3, \quad N_j = 1) = \frac{4!}{3! \, 1!} = 4,$$

$$W(N_i = 2, \quad N_j = 2) = \frac{4!}{2! \, 2!} = 6,$$

$$W(N_i = 1, \quad N_j = 3) = \frac{4!}{1! \, 3!} = 4,$$

$$W(N_i = 0, \quad N_j = 4) = \frac{4!}{0! \, 4!} = 1.$$

To verify the calculations above, the reader should tabulate the microstates corresponding to the macrostate $N_i = 2$, $N_j = 2$. Note, as would be expected, that the macrostate of maximum probability is that with two points in each cell.

There are altogether 16 possible microstates corresponding to the five macrostates. If the phase points a, b, c, and d are continuously shifting around so that one microstate after the other turns up, and all microstates turn up with equal frequency, the first and fifth macrostates will each be observed 1/16th of the time, the second and fourth each 1/4th of the time, and the third 3/8ths of the time.

We now return to the problem of evaluating W for a gas, where the number N and all the N_i's as well are very large. The factorial of a large number can be found with sufficient precision from Stirling's approximation, which we now derive.

The natural logarithm of factorial x is

$$\ln (x!) = \ln 2 + \ln 3 + \cdots + \ln x.$$

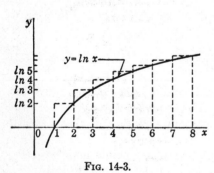

FIG. 14-3.

This is *exactly* equal to the area under the step curve shown by dotted lines in Fig. 14-3, between $x = 1$ and $x = x$, since each rectangle is of unit width and the height of the first is $\ln 2$, that of the second is $\ln 3$, etc. This area is *approximately* equal to the area under the smooth curve $y = \ln x$ between the same limits, provided x is large. For small values of x, the step curve differs appreciably from the smooth curve, but the latter becomes more and more nearly horizontal as x increases. Hence approximately, for large x,

$$\ln (x!) = \int_1^x \ln x\, dx.$$

Integration by parts gives

$$\ln (x!) = x \ln x - x + 1,$$

and if x is large we may neglect the 1, so finally

$$\ln (x!) = x \ln x - x. \qquad (14\text{-}3)$$

This is Stirling's approximation.

An exact analysis leads to the following infinite series.

$$x! = \sqrt{2\pi x}\, (x/e)^x \left[1 + \frac{1}{12x} + \frac{1}{288x^2} - \frac{139}{51840x^3} + \cdots \right]. \qquad (14\text{-}4)$$

If all terms in the series except the first are neglected, we obtain

$$\ln (x!) = \tfrac{1}{2} \ln 2\pi + \tfrac{1}{2} \ln x + x \ln x - x. \qquad (14\text{-}5)$$

If x is very large compared with unity, the first two terms of this expression are negligible also, and we get Eq. (14-3).

Taking logarithms of both sides of Eq. (14-2) and making use of Stirling's approximation, we get

$$\ln W = \ln (N!) - \Sigma \ln (N_i!)$$

$$= N \ln N - N - \Sigma N_i \ln N_i + \Sigma N_i$$

$$= N \ln N - \Sigma N_i \ln N_i, \qquad (14\text{-}6)$$

since $\Sigma N_i = N$.

Now as time goes on and the phase points in the cells of phase space shift around, the numbers N_i will change. If the system is in a state of maximum thermodynamic probability W^0, the first variation of W^0 arising from variations in the N_i's is zero. We shall use the symbol δ to represent a small change arising from the continual motion of the points in phase space. If the probability W^0 is a maximum its logarithm is a maximum also, so the condition for a maximum probability is

$$\delta \ln W^0 = -\Sigma N_i \delta \ln N_i - \Sigma \ln N_i \delta N_i = 0.$$

But

$$\Sigma N_i \delta \ln N_i = \Sigma N_i \frac{1}{N_i} \delta N_i = 0,$$

since the total number of particles is constant.   Hence

$$\Sigma \ln N_i \delta N_i = 0. \tag{14-7}$$

Writing out the first few terms, this is equivalent to

$$\ln N_1 \delta N_1 + \ln N_2 \delta N_2 + \ln N_3 \delta N_3 + \cdots = 0. \tag{14-8}$$

The quantities δN_1, δN_2, etc., are the small increases or decreases in the numbers N_1, N_2, etc., as a result of molecular motions or collisions. If these were all independent, the coefficient of each would have to vanish separately, as explained in Sec. 12-1.   But the δN_i's are not independent, because the total number of particles is constant, and any increases in the populations of some cells must be just balanced by decreases in the populations of others.   That is,

$$\delta N = \Sigma \delta N_i = \delta N_1 + \delta N_2 + \delta N_3 + \cdots = 0. \tag{14-9}$$

This is one *condition equation* imposed on the δN_i's.   But there is another one also.   The system under consideration is presumed to be isolated, so that its internal energy U remains constant.   Therefore any shifts in the populations of the cells that take some phase points into cells of greater energy must be balanced by shifts that take other points into cells of lower energy.   Let w_i represent the energy of a molecule when its phase point lies in the ith cell.   The quantity w_i depends, in general, on all of the coordinates of the cell.   The total energy of all the N_i particles whose phase points lie in the ith cell is $w_i N_i$, and the internal energy U of the system is therefore

$$U = \Sigma w_i N_i. \tag{14-10}$$

The change in internal energy, when the number of points in the ith cell changes by δN_i, is $w_i \delta N_i$, and since the total internal energy remains constant the sum of all these changes must be zero.   Hence

$$\delta U = \Sigma w_i \delta N_i = w_1 \delta N_1 + w_2 \delta N_2 + w_3 \delta N_3 + \cdots = 0. \tag{14-11}$$

This is a second condition equation imposed on the δN_i's.

We now use Lagrange's method of undetermined multipliers, described in Sec. 12-1.   Multiply Eq. (14-9) by a constant which for convenience we write as $-\ln \alpha$, multiply Eq. (14-11) by a constant β, and add to Eq. (14-7).   This gives

$$\Sigma(\ln N_i - \ln \alpha + \beta w_i)\delta N_i = 0.$$

Since the δN_i's are now in effect independent, the coefficient of each must vanish, so for any value of i,

$$\ln N_i - \ln \alpha + \beta w_i = 0,$$

or

$$N_i = \alpha \exp(-\beta w_i). \tag{14-12}$$

For comparison with the results of other statistical theories to be developed later, we note at this point that by defining a quantity A as $A \equiv 1/\alpha$, we may write this equation as

$$N_i = \frac{1}{A \exp(\beta w_i)}. \tag{14-13}$$

An expression for α can now be obtained from the requirement that the sum of all the N_i's must equal the total number of particles, N.

$$\Sigma N_i = N = \alpha \Sigma \exp(-\beta w_i). \tag{14-14}$$

The sum $\Sigma \exp(-\beta w_i)$ plays an important role in statistical theory. It is called the *partition function* or *sum of state* and is represented by the letter Z (German, *Zustandssumme*).

$$Z = \Sigma \exp(-\beta w_i). \tag{14-15}$$

The partition function depends on β, and on the way in which the energy w_i varies from cell to cell. Since the latter is different in different problems, no general expression can be written for Z other than that above; it must be evaluated for each special case. However, from Eq. (14-14), we can express α in terms of Z.

$$\alpha = N/Z.$$

The number of particles in the ith cell, in the state of maximum thermodynamic probability, is therefore

$$N_i = \frac{N}{Z} \exp(-\beta w_i). \tag{14-16}$$

14-5 Entropy and probability. Equation (14-15) provides an expression for the number of phase points N_i in the ith cell of phase space, for the macrostate of maximum probability. This, presumably, is the state toward which an isolated system will tend. But from the thermodynamic viewpoint the equilibrium state of a closed system is the state of maximum entropy. If the system is not in equilibrium then changes take place within the system until the state of maximum entropy has been attained.

Thus in the equilibrium state both the entropy and the thermodynamic probability have their maximum values, which leads us to expect some correlation between them. We might assume the entropy proportional to the probability, but it turns out that to obtain agreement between the thermodynamic and statistical definitions we should take the entropy as proportional to the logarithm of the thermodynamic probability. Of course if the probability is a maximum its logarithm is a maximum also. We therefore set

$$S = k \ln W, \qquad (14\text{-}17)$$

where k is a proportionality constant that we shall identify later. (It turns out to be none other than the Boltzmann constant.)

Statistical mechanics therefore interprets the increase of entropy in a closed system as a consequence of the natural trend of a system from a less probable to a more probable state.

It is often helpful to phrase the concept of probability in other terms, such as the "mixed-upness" or the "disorder" of a system. The greater the disorder, the greater the thermodynamic probability and the greater the entropy. The greatest degree of order of the phase points of a gas in phase space results if all are in a single cell, that is, if all are in a very small volume in ordinary space and all are traveling with the same velocity. The thermodynamic probability W of such a state has its minimum value of unity and the entropy $k \ln W$ is zero. The more the particles spread out in ordinary space, and the more their velocities spread out in velocity space, the greater the disorder and the greater the entropy.

Consider a vessel divided into two equal compartments by a partition, with equal numbers of molecules of two different gases on opposite sides of the partition. Such a system has a certain degree of order in that all molecules of one gas are on one side of the partition and all those of the other gas on the other side. If the partition is now removed the gases diffuse into each other. Eventually, both kinds of molecules are uniformly distributed throughout the total volume. The original order has disappeared and the disorder of the system, or its mixed-upness, has increased. But the entropy has increased also, since the volume occupied by each gas has doubled (at constant temperature, if the gases are ideal).

In a reversible adiabatic expansion of a gas, the volume increases but the temperature decreases. The entropy remains constant, however, so the disorder remains constant. The increase in disorder resulting from the increase in volume is compensated by a decrease in disorder resulting from a smaller velocity spread at the lower temperature.

According to the laws of thermodynamics, only those processes can take place in a closed system for which the entropy of the system increases or, in the limit, remains constant.   Any process in which the entropy would decrease is prohibited.   We see that in the light of the statistical interpretation of entropy this dogmatic statement must be modified. Consider a system in a state of maximum probability or maximum entropy. This state is not a static one because of the continuous shifting around of the phase points in phase space.   Occasionally, a state will result for which the probability, and hence the entropy, is less than its maximum value. Small changes are more likely than large ones, but large ones are not impossible, only highly improbable.   We shall consider this question in more detail in the chapter on Fluctuations.

Let us now return to Eq. (14-17), $S = k \ln W$.   From Eqs. (14-6) and (14-16),

$$\ln W = N \ln N - \Sigma N_i \ln N_i$$
$$= N \ln N - \Sigma N_i (\ln N - \ln Z - \beta w_i)$$
$$= N \ln N - \ln N \Sigma N_i + \ln Z \Sigma N_i + \beta \Sigma w_i N_i.$$

But $\Sigma N_i = N$ and $\Sigma w_i N_i$ equals the internal energy U.   Therefore

$$S = k \ln W = Nk \ln Z + k\beta U. \tag{14-18}$$

Up to this point, the concept of temperature has not appeared in our development of statistical theory.   It can now be introduced as follows. The principles of thermodynamics lead to the relation (see Sec. 9-5)

$$\left(\frac{\partial U}{\partial S}\right)_v = T, \quad \text{or} \quad \left(\frac{\partial S}{\partial U}\right)_v = \frac{1}{T}. \tag{14-19}$$

From Eq. (14-18),

$$\left(\frac{\partial S}{\partial U}\right)_v = \frac{Nk}{Z}\left(\frac{\partial Z}{\partial \beta}\right)_v \left(\frac{\partial \beta}{\partial U}\right)_v + k\beta + kU\left(\frac{\partial \beta}{\partial U}\right)_v,$$

and from the definitions of U, Z, and N_i,

$$\left(\frac{\partial Z}{\partial \beta}\right)_v = -\Sigma w_i \exp(-\beta w_i) = -\frac{UZ}{N}.$$

Hence the first and last terms cancel in the preceding equation and

$$\left(\frac{\partial S}{\partial U}\right)_v = k\beta. \tag{14-20}$$

The assumed relation between S and W will therefore lead to the same value for $(\partial S/\partial U)_v$ as that given by thermodynamics if

$$k\beta = 1/T, \quad \text{or} \quad \beta = 1/kT. \tag{14-21}$$

The constant β is now determined, except that we have not yet shown that k is the Boltzmann constant.

The number of points in the ith cell can now be expressed in terms of T.

$$N_i = \frac{N}{Z} \exp\left(-w_i/kT\right), \tag{14-22}$$

where the partition function Z, from Eq. (14-15), is

$$Z = \Sigma \exp\left(-w_i/kT\right). \tag{14-23}$$

The internal energy U of the system is

$$U = \Sigma w_i N_i = \frac{N}{Z}\Sigma w_i \exp\left(-w_i/kT\right).$$

Now the derivative of Z with respect to T is

$$\frac{dZ}{dT} = \frac{1}{kT^2} \Sigma w_i \exp\left(-w_i/kT\right).$$

Hence, from the two preceding equations,

$$U = \frac{NkT^2}{Z}\frac{dZ}{dT} = NkT^2\frac{d(\ln Z)}{dT}. \tag{14-24}$$

Also, from Eq. (14-18),

$$S = Nk \ln Z + \frac{U}{T}. \tag{14-25}$$

The Helmholtz function, $F = U - TS$, is given by

$$F = -NkT \ln Z. \tag{14-26}$$

Thus we see that once the partition function Z has been evaluated, all thermodynamic properties of the system can be calculated. Note that while only *differences* in internal energy and entropy can be defined in thermodynamics, statistical methods provide expressions for both of these quantities with no undetermined constants.

As an example, consider a system of N particles and a phase space of n cells. Suppose that the energy of a particle has the same value w in all cells so that $w_1 = w_2 = \cdots = w_n = w$. Then

$$Z = \sum_{i=1}^{n} \exp\left(-w_i/kT\right) = n \exp\left(-w/kT\right).$$

From Eq. (14-22),

$$N_i = \frac{N}{n \exp\left(-w/kT\right)} \exp\left(-w/kT\right) = \frac{N}{n}.$$

The particles are therefore distributed uniformly among the cells, as would be expected.

The internal energy U, from Eq. (14-24), is

$$U = NkT^2 \frac{d(\ln Z)}{dT} = NkT^2 \frac{d(\ln n - w/kT)}{dT} = Nw,$$

which is obvious since the energy of each of the N particles is w.

The entropy S, from Eq. (14-25), is

$$S = Nk\left(\ln n - \frac{w}{kT}\right) + \frac{Nw}{T} = Nk \ln n.$$

In this simple example the distribution of particles between cells, the internal energy, and the entropy are all constants independent of the temperature.

Consider next a system of N particles and a phase space of just three cells, 1, 2, and 3. Let $w_1 = 0$, $w_2 = w$, and $w_3 = 2w$. The partition function is

$$Z = \sum \exp\left(-w_i/kT\right)$$
$$= 1 + \exp\left(-w/kT\right) + \exp\left(-2w/kT\right).$$

The ratio w/k has the dimensions of temperature. It is called the *characteristic temperature* and is represented by Θ. In terms of Θ,

$$Z = 1 + \exp\left(-\Theta/T\right) + \exp\left(-2\Theta/T\right).$$

The numbers of particles in the respective cells are

$$N_1 = \frac{N}{1 + \exp\left(-\Theta/T\right) + \exp\left(-2\Theta/T\right)},$$

$$N_2 = \frac{N}{1 + \exp\left(-\Theta/T\right) + \exp\left(\Theta/T\right)},$$

$$N_3 = \frac{N}{1 + \exp\left(\Theta/T\right) + \exp\left(2\Theta/T\right)}.$$

At temperatures that are very small compared with the characteristic temperature, both Θ/T and $2\Theta/T$ are very large compared with 1, $\exp\left(-\Theta/T\right)$ and $\exp\left(-2\Theta/T\right)$ are very small, and $\exp\left(\Theta/T\right)$ and $\exp\left(2\Theta/T\right)$ are very large. Then N_1 is very nearly equal to N, and N_2 and N_3 are very small. That is, nearly all the particles are in cell 1.

At temperatures that are large compared with the characteristic temperature, Θ/T and $2\Theta/T$ are very much less than 1, all exponential terms are nearly unity, and N_1, N_2, and N_3 are all nearly equal to $N/3$.

When $\Theta/T = 1$, or when $T = \Theta$, $N_1 = 0.67N$, $N_2 = 0.24N$, and $N_3 = 0.09N$. Thus as the temperature is raised from a value where $T \ll \Theta$ (or where $kT \ll w$), the numbers of particles in the cells of higher energy increase, but even at very high temperatures, where $T \gg \Theta$, one-third of the particles remain in a state of zero energy. It is seen that "high" and "low" temperatures have a meaning only insofar as T is large or small compared with the characteristic temperature Θ, or as the product kT is large or small compared with the energy w.

The internal energy of the system is

$$U = \frac{NkT^2}{Z}\frac{dZ}{dT}$$

$$= Nw\,\frac{\exp\,(-\Theta/T) + 2\exp\,(-2\Theta/T)}{1 + \exp\,(-\Theta/T) + \exp\,(-2\Theta/T)}.$$

The entropy S is

$$S = Nk \ln Z + \frac{U}{T}$$

$$= Nk\{\ln\,[1 + \exp\,(-\Theta/T) + \exp\,(-2\Theta/T)]$$

$$+ \frac{\Theta}{T}\frac{\exp\,(-\Theta/T) + 2\exp\,(-2\Theta/T)}{1 + \exp\,(-\Theta/T) + \exp\,(-2\Theta/T)}.\}$$

At very low temperatures (the reader should verify these results) both U and S approach zero. At very high temperatures U approaches Nw and S approaches $Nk \ln 3$.

Problems

1. The 52 cards of a deck are dealt into four hands by tossing the cards into a box containing 4 compartments.   Any one card is equally likely to land in any one compartment.   (a) How many microstates are there in the 13-13-13-13 macrostate?   This is the number of·possible deals at bridge.   (b) What are the relative probabilities of the macrostates

$$12\text{-}13\text{-}14\text{-}13, \quad 12\text{-}14\text{-}10\text{-}16, \quad 16\text{-}22\text{-}10\text{-}4,$$

compared with the 13-13-13-13 macrostate?

2. Compute $\ln (10!)$ from Eqs. (14-3) and (14-5), and find the percent difference between each approximation and the exact value.

3. Suppose there are three cells in phase space: 1, 2, and 3.   Let $N = 30$, $N_1 = N_2 = N_3 = 10$, and $w_1 = 2$ joules, $w_2 = 4$ joules, $w_3 = 6$ joules.   If $\delta N_3 = -2$, find δN_1 and δN_2 such that $\delta N = 0$ and $\delta U = 0$.

4. Consider a system of 10^6 particles and a phase space of 5×10^5 cells, in which the energy w_i is the same for all cells.   What is the thermodynamic probability of (a) the most probable distribution, (b) the least probable distribution?

5. (a) The most probable distribution of a large number of particles among cells of equal energy is a uniform one.   Let W^0 represent the thermodynamic probability of such a distribution, with N_i particles in each cell, and W the probability of a distribution in which cell #1 has dN extra particles and cell #2 has dN too few.   Compute $\ln (W/W^0)$.   [Write out the first few terms in the sum in Eq. (14-6) for each distribution.   Use the approximation $\ln (1 + x) = x$, when $x \ll 1$.]

(b) Calculate the relative probability that in air at standard conditions a given cubic centimeter shall contain 1% more molecules than the average, and that another cubic centimeter shall contain 1% less.

(c) What is the difference in entropy between the uniform and nonuniform distributions described above?

(d) For what value of dN is W equal to $W^0/2$?

6. (a) In the second example at the end of Section 14-5, where $w_1 = 0$, $w_2 = w$, and $w_3 = 2w$, construct graphs of the dimensionless ratios N_1/N, N_2/N, N_3/N, U/Nw, and S/Nk, as functions of the dimensionless ratio T/Θ, over the range from $T = 0$ to $T = 4\Theta$.   (b) Compute the heat capacity C of the system, dU/dT, and plot C/Nk as a function of T/Θ.

CHAPTER 15

APPLICATIONS OF THE BOLTZMANN STATISTICS

15-1 The monatomic ideal gas. Consider a monatomic gas consisting of N molecules, each of mass m, in an enclosure of volume V. Each molecule is characterized by its position coordinates x, y, z, and its velocity coordinates v_x, v_y, and v_z. The energy w of a molecule is the sum of its potential and kinetic energy. If the molecules exert no forces on one another there is no mutual potential energy between them. For the present we neglect any effect of a gravitational force field (see the next Section). The potential energy is then a constant in all cells of phase space whose coordinates x, y, z, lie within the space occupied by the gas, and we shall consider this constant to be zero. The fact that the walls of the container are impenetrable to molecules can be taken into account by considering the potential energy to be infinite in all cells for which x, y, z lie outside the container. Then in all such cells $w = \infty$ and $\exp(-w/kT) = 0$. The number of molecules in such cells is then zero, and the cells contribute nothing to the partition function.

If the molecules can be considered point masses the kinetic energy is translational only. For cell i, whose velocity coordinates are v_x, v_y, v_z, the kinetic energy is $\frac{1}{2}m(v_x^2 + v_y^2 + v_z^2) = \frac{1}{2}mv_i^2$. Then for any cell in the space occupied by the gas

$$w_i = \tfrac{1}{2}mv_i^2$$

and for any cell outside this space

$$w_i = \infty.$$

The partition function is therefore

$$Z = \Sigma \exp(-mv_i^2/2kT),$$

where the sum now extends only over those cells in the space occupied by the gas. We evaluate this sum by the following artifice. Divide phase space into cells of equal volume $H = dx\,dy\,dz\,dv_x\,dv_y\,dv_z$, and multiply the preceding equation by the product of the six differentials and divide it by H. The sum can then be replaced by an integral.

$$Z = \frac{1}{H} \int\int\int\int\int\int \exp(-mv^2/2kT)\,dx\,dy\,dz\,dv_x\,dv_y\,dv_z$$

$$= \frac{1}{H} \iiint dx\,dy\,dz \int_{-\infty}^{\infty} \exp\left(-mv_x^2/2kT\right)dv_x$$

$$\int_{-\infty}^{\infty} \exp\left(-mv_y^2/2kT\right)dv_y \int_{-\infty}^{\infty} \exp\left(-mv_z^2/2kT\right)dv_z.$$

The triple integral over x, y, and z is simply the total volume V occupied by the gas. Each of the single integrals, from Table 12-1, is $(2\pi kT/m)^{1/2}$. Hence

$$Z = \frac{V}{H}\,(2\pi kT/m)^{3/2}. \tag{15-1}$$

Then from Eq. (14-22),

$$N_i = \frac{NH}{V}\,(m/2\pi kT)^{3/2}\exp\left(-mv^2/2kT\right),$$

or

$$d^6N = \frac{N}{V}\,(m/2\pi kT)^{3/2}\exp\left(-mv^2/2kT\right)dx\,dy\,dz\,dv_x\,dv_y\,dv_z, \tag{15-2}$$

where we have written the left side as d^6N to accord with the differential notation on the right.

The distribution in ordinary space is now obtained by integrating Eq. (15-2) over all values of v_x, v_y, and v_z. This gives

$$d^3N = \frac{N}{V}\,(m/2\pi kT)^{3/2}(2\pi kT/m)^{3/2}dx\,dy\,dz$$

or

$$\frac{d^3N}{dx\,dy\,dz} = \frac{N}{V}.$$

That is, the number of molecules per unit volume of ordinary space is a constant, independent of position, and equal to the total number of molecules N divided by the total volume V. In other words, the molecules are distributed uniformly throughout the space occupied by the gas.

To find the distribution in velocity space we integrate Eq. (15-2) over x, y, and z, the limits being chosen so as to include the space occupied by the gas. This integral is just the total volume V, so

$$d^3N = N(m/2\pi kT)^{3/2}\exp\left(-mv^2/2kT\right)dv_x\,dv_y\,dv_z.$$

Comparison with Eq. (12-29) shows that this is precisely the velocity distribution function obtained from kinetic theory, provided we identify k with the Boltzmann constant.

The equation of state can be obtained from the Helmholtz function $F = -NkT \ln Z$ and the thermodynamic relation

$$p = - \left(\frac{\partial F}{\partial V} \right)_T.$$

We have

$$F = -NkT \left(\ln V - \ln H + \frac{3}{2} \ln \frac{2\pi kT}{m} \right)$$

and hence

$$p = \frac{NkT}{V} = \frac{nRT}{V},$$

the familiar equation of state of an ideal gas.

The entropy S is

$$S = Nk \ln Z + U/T$$

$$= Nk \left(\ln V + \tfrac{3}{2} \ln 2\pi kT - \ln H - \tfrac{3}{2} \ln m \right) + \tfrac{3}{2} Nk$$

$$= Nk \left(\ln V + \tfrac{3}{2} \ln T + A \right)$$

$$= nR \left(\ln V + \tfrac{3}{2} \ln T + A \right),$$

and

$$s = R \ln V + \tfrac{3}{2} R \ln T + RA, \tag{15-3}$$

where A stands for the sum of all terms that do not depend on T or V and s is the molar specific entropy, S/n. Comparison with Eq. (9-27) shows the two expressions for s to be identical as far as the dependence on temperature and volume is concerned. (Note that $v/v_0 = V/V_0$, and that $c_v = 3R/2$.) Whether the constant term is identical with the constant in Eq. (9-27) we leave unanswered for the present, returning to this question in Section 16-3, where we obtain another expression for s.

The energy U of the gas is

$$U = NkT^2 \frac{d(\ln Z)}{dT}.$$

But

$$\ln Z = \ln V - \ln H + \frac{3}{2} \ln \frac{2\pi k}{m} + \frac{3}{2} \ln T,$$

so

$$U = \frac{3}{2} NkT = \frac{3}{2} nRT,$$

and

$$u = \frac{U}{n} = \frac{3}{2} RT.$$

The molar specific heat capacity at constant volume is

$$c_v = \left(\frac{\partial u}{\partial T}\right)_v = \frac{3}{2} R,$$

in agreement with the result derived from kinetic theory and the equipartition principle.

15-2 The barometric equation. In the preceding section the energy
of a molecule was considered to be wholly kinetic. Now let us consider
the effect of a force field, as illustrated by the vertical distribution of molecules in the earth's atmosphere. Take the origin of space coordinates at
the earth's surface with the Z-axis vertically upward, and consider a column
of air of horizontal cross section A and uniform temperature T. (Near the
earth's surface the temperature decreases with increasing elevation but
it is fairly constant in the stratosphere.) A molecule in a cell whose vertical
coordinate is z then has a potential energy mgz in addition to its kinetic
energy $mv^2/2$, so

$$w = mgz + mv^2/2.$$

The partition function is now

$$Z = \frac{1}{H} \int\int dxdy \int \exp\,(-mgz/kT)dz$$

$$\int\int\int \exp\,(-mv^2/2kT)dv_x dv_y dv_z. \quad (15\text{-}4)$$

The double integral over x and y gives the horizontal cross section A. The
integral over z, between the limits $z = 0$ and $z = \infty$, gives kT/mg. The
triple integral equals $(2\pi kT/m)^{3/2}$. Hence

$$Z = \frac{A}{H}\frac{kT}{mg}\,(2\pi kT/m)^{3/2}.$$

Replacing H by the product of the six differentials and using Eq.
(14-22), we find

$$d^6N = \frac{Nmg}{AkT}\,(m/2\pi kT)^{3/2} \exp\,[-(mgz + mv^2/2)/kT]dxdydzdv_x dv_y dv_z. \quad (15\text{-}5)$$

To obtain the distribution in z, integrate over all variables except z.
The result is

$$dN_z = \frac{Nmg}{kT} \exp\,(-mgz/kT)dz, \qquad (15\text{-}6)$$

where dN_z is the number of molecules in a thin layer of cross section A and thickness dz, at an elevation z. For two such layers of equal thickness, at heights z_1 and z_2, the relative numbers of molecules is

$$\frac{dN_2}{dN_1} = \exp\left[-mg(z_2 - z_1)/kT\right]. \tag{15-7}$$

The French physicist Jean Perrin, in 1909, used the relation above for one of the earliest precision determinations of Avogadro's number N_0. Instead of counting the molecules in the earth's atmosphere he used particles of microscopic size suspended in a liquid of slightly smaller density, thus reducing the effective value of "g." By counting the numbers of particles at various levels of the suspension, he was able both to verify the predicted form of the distribution function (i.e., an exponential decrease with height) and to obtain a value of N_0 of the correct order of magnitude. It will be recalled that $k \equiv R/N_0$, where R is the universal gas constant. All of the quantities in Eq. (15-6) except k can be measured directly, so the equation can be used to calculate k. Then N_0 can be found, since R is known from experiment. Perrin concluded that the value of N_0 lay between 6.5 and 7.2×10^{26}, compared with the present best figure of 6.0251×10^{26} molecules/kgm-mole.

To return to the earth's atmosphere. Integrating Eq. (15-5) over v_x, v_y, and v_z gives the distribution in ordinary space.

$$\frac{d^3N}{dx\,dy\,dz} = \frac{Nmg}{AkT} \exp\left(-mgz/kT\right).$$

The left side of this equation is the number of molecules per unit volume, n. But $p = nkT$, so the pressure at a height z is

$$p = \frac{Nmg}{A} \exp\left(-mgz/kT\right).$$

When $z = 0$, $p = p_0$, the pressure at the earth's surface. Hence

$$p_0 = Nmg/A,$$

which is evidently correct, since Nmg is the total weight of all molecules in the column. We can therefore write

$$p = p_0 \exp\left(-mgz/kT\right). \tag{15-8}$$

This equation is known as the *law of atmospheres*. It can also be derived directly from the principles of hydrostatics and the equation of state of an ideal gas.

It is left as a problem to show that at any height z the distribution in velocity has the same form as in the absence of a gravitational field. That is, the distributions in ordinary space and velocity space are independent as long as the expression for the energy w can be written as a sum of terms, one of which contains only the space coordinates and the other only the velocity coordinates.

15-3 The principle of equipartition of energy. It will be recalled that the principle of equipartition of energy was introduced in Chapter 12 merely as an inference that might be drawn from some of the results of the kinetic theory of an ideal gas. We now show how this principle follows from the Boltzmann statistics, and what are its limitations.

The energy w of a molecule is, in general, a function of all the coordinates of the cell in phase space in which the phase point of the molecule is located. Let z represent any arbitrary coordinate and w_z the energy associated with that coordinate. If the distribution in phase space can be represented by a continuous function of the coordinates, as in the preceding sections, the distribution in the coordinate z can be obtained by setting up the general expression for the distribution function Z, and integrating over all coordinates except z. [See, for example, the method of deriving Eq. (15-6).] The result will have the form

$$dN_z = A \exp(-w_z/kT)dz,$$

where A is a constant independent of z. The total number of particles, N, is

$$N = \int dN_z = A \int \exp(-w_z/kT)dz$$

and the total energy U_z associated with the coordinate z is

$$U_z = \int w_z dN_z = A \int w_z \exp(-w_z/kT)dz.$$

The mean energy $\overline{w}_z$ of a single particle, associated with the coordinate z, is

$$\overline{w}_z = U_z/N.$$

Now if the energy w_z is a *quadratic* function of z, that is, if it has the form $w_z = az^2$, where a is a constant, and if the limits of z are from 0 to ∞ or from $-\infty$ to ∞, then from Table 12-1,

$$\overline{w}_z = \frac{\int az^2 \exp\left(-az^2/kT\right)dz}{\int \exp\left(-az^2/kT\right)dz} = \tfrac{1}{2}\,kT.$$

That is, for every coordinate for which the conditions above are fulfilled, the mean energy per particle, in an assembly of particles in thermodynamic equilibrium at a temperature T, is $\tfrac{1}{2}kT$. This is the general statement of the equipartition principle. The conditions above *are* fulfilled for the translational velocity coordinates v_x, v_y, and v_z, since the energy associated with, say, v_x, is $\tfrac{1}{2}mv_x^2$ and the range of each is from $-\infty$ to ∞. They are also fulfilled for the displacement x of a simple harmonic oscillator, since the potential energy associated with x is $\tfrac{1}{2}Kx^2$, K being the force constant. They are *not* fulfilled for the vertical coordinate z of a gas in a gravitational field, where the potential energy mgz is a *linear* function of z; the mean gravitational potential energy is not $\tfrac{1}{2}kT$. Neither are they fulfilled for the energy associated with molecular rotation, vibration, and electronic excitation, because of the quantized character of these energies, which can take on certain discrete values only and cannot be expressed as a continuous function of some coordinate. The energy associated with them is not a simple linear function of the temperature.

15-4 Specific heat capacity of a diatomic gas.

The theory of a monatomic ideal gas as given in Section 12-8 led to a value of c_v equal to $3R/2$. This is in good agreement with experiment for monatomic gases over a wide range of temperatures. We consider next a gas whose molecules are polyatomic. If the energy of a molecule does not depend on the space coordinates x, y, and z of its center of mass, and if there is no mutual potential energy between molecules, the partition function will be directly proportional to V as in Eq. (15-1) for a monatomic gas. The Helmholtz function $F = -NkT \ln Z$ then has the same dependence on V as for a monatomic gas, and the gas has the same equation of state, $p = nRT/V$. The specific heat capacity, however, will differ from that of a monatomic gas because a polyatomic molecule can have an "internal energy" of its own, made up of energy of rotation, vibration, and electronic excitation. When heat flows into a polyatomic gas, only a portion of it is available for increasing the average translational kinetic energy of the molecules, the remainder going into an increase in molecular internal energy. Since the temperature is proportional to the mean translational kinetic energy, the rise in temperature for a given heat inflow is smaller in a polyatomic than in a monatomic gas and the specific heat capacity is correspondingly larger.

We consider first the classical theory of the specific heat capacity of a diatomic gas, picturing the molecules as dumbbell-like structures composed of two atoms (treated as point masses) having a finite separation. Associated with each of the three translational degrees of freedom of the center of mass is a mean energy $\frac{1}{2}kT$, just as for a monatomic gas. Since the kinetic energy of rotation is proportional to the square of the angular velocity, the principle of equipartition applies to rotation also with an energy $\frac{1}{2}kT$ for each rotational degree of freedom. But if the atoms are point masses, rotation about the line joining them has no significance and there are only two rotational degrees of freedom, about two mutually perpendicular axes in a plane at right angles to the line joining the atoms. Finally, considering the molecules as simple harmonic oscillators, the mean energy associated with vibration is kT ($\frac{1}{2}kT$ for kinetic energy, $\frac{1}{2}kT$ for potential energy). The mean energy of a molecule is therefore $\frac{3}{2}kT$ for translation, kT for rotation, and kT for vibration. The total internal energy U of an assembly of N molecules is

$$U = U_{\text{trans}} + U_{\text{rot}} + U_{\text{vib}}$$

$$= \tfrac{3}{2}NkT + NkT + NkT$$

$$= \tfrac{3}{2}nRT + nRT + nRT.$$

The molal specific internal energy is

$$u = \frac{U}{n} = \frac{3}{2}RT + RT + RT,$$

and hence

$$c_v = \left(\frac{\partial u}{\partial T}\right)_v = \frac{3}{2}R + R + R = \frac{7}{2}R. \tag{15-9}$$

$$= (c_v)_{\text{trans}} + (c_v)_{\text{rot}} + (c_v)_{\text{vib}}.$$

The theory above is not in good agreement with experiment. Figure 15-1 is a graph of experimental values of c_v/R for hydrogen as a function of temperature. At very low temperatures c_v/R is equal to 3/2, the value for a *monatomic* gas. As the temperature is increased c_v increases, and over a considerable range near room temperature c_v/R is about 5/2, which is the theoretical value if either the energy of rotation or vibration, but not both, is added to the energy of translation. Only at very high temperatures does c_v/R approach 7/2, the value predicted by Eq. (15-9).

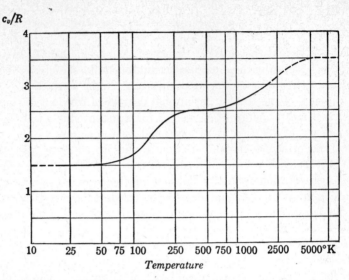

FIG. 15-1.   Experimental values of c_v/R for hydrogen as a function of temperature, plotted on a logarithmic scale.

The first explanation of the variation of c_v with temperature was given by Einstein in 1907, making use of the concept of quantization of energy that had been proposed shortly before by Planck to account for the energy distribution in the spectrum of the radiation emitted by a blackbody. The principles of quantum mechanics restrict the energy of a rotating or vibrating molecule to some one of a set of discrete values. Hence the energy cannot be expressed as a continuous function of the coordinates specifying the state of the molecule, and the phase points representing an assembly of molecules are not distributed continuously in phase space. The conditions leading to the equipartition principle are not fulfilled, therefore, and this principle does not apply.

According to quantum mechanics, the energy of a rotating molecule can have only some one of a set of values given by

$$w_{\text{rot}} = n(n + 1)\frac{h^2}{8\pi^2 I},\qquad(15\text{-}10)$$

while the possible vibrational energies are

$$w_{\text{vib}} = (n + \tfrac{1}{2})hf.\qquad(15\text{-}11)$$

In these equations, n is an integer or zero, h is a universal constant called Planck's constant and equal to 6.62377×10^{-34} joule-sec, I is the moment of inertia of the molecule about its center of mass, and f is the vibrational frequency. The derivation of the equations above is given in any standard text on quantum mechanics.

To find the way in which the molecules are distributed among the possible energy states, we must first evaluate the partition functions for rotation and for vibration. The latter problem is simpler so we shall consider it first.

$$Z_{\text{vib}} = \Sigma \exp\left(-w_{\text{vib}}/kT\right) = \sum_{n=0}^{n=\infty} \exp -[(n + \tfrac{1}{2})\Theta_{\text{vib}}/T], \quad (15\text{-}12)$$

where Θ_{vib} is an abbreviation for hf/k and has the dimensions of a temperature. It is called the *characteristic temperature for vibration*. The vibrational frequencies f of diatomic molecules lie in the infrared region of the electromagnetic spectrum. By studying the emission or absorption spectra

TABLE 15-1.

CHARACTERISTIC TEMPERATURES FOR VIBRATION AND ROTATION OF DIATOMIC MOLECULES

Substance	Θ_{vib}, °K	Θ_{rot}, °K
H_2	6140	85.5
OH	5360	27.5
HCl	4300	15.3
CH	4100	20.7
CO	3120	2.77
NO	2740	2.47
O_2	2260	2.09
Cl_2	810	0.347
Br_2	470	0.117
Na_2	230	0.224
K_2	140	0.081

in the infrared one can determine f and hence the characteristic temperature Θ_{vib}. A few values are given in Table 15-1.

Since the energy w_{vib} is not a continuous function of a coordinate, the sum in Eq. (15-12) must be evaluated directly and we cannot use the artifice of introducing the volume H of a cell in phase space and replacing the sum by an integral. Equation (15-12) can be written

$$Z = \exp\left(-\Theta_{vib}/2T\right)[1 + \exp\left(-\Theta_{vib}/T\right) + \exp\left(-2\Theta_{vib}/T\right) + \cdots]$$

$$= \exp\left(-\Theta_{vib}/2T\right)\{1 + \exp\left(-\Theta_{vib}/T\right) + [\exp\left(-\Theta_{vib}/T\right)]^2 + \cdots\}.$$

But

$$1 + x + x^2 + \cdots = \frac{1}{1 - x},$$

and hence

$$Z_{vib} = \frac{\exp\left(-\Theta_{vib}/2T\right)}{1 - \exp\left(-\Theta_{vib}/T\right)}.$$

Then from Eq. (14-22), the number of particles in any energy state is

$$N_i = N\frac{1 - \exp\left(-\Theta_{vib}/T\right)}{\exp\left(-\Theta_{vib}/2T\right)} \exp\left[-(n + \tfrac{1}{2})\Theta_{vib}/T\right]$$

$$= N \exp\left(-n\Theta_{vib}/T\right)[1 - \exp\left(-\Theta_{vib}/T\right)].$$

Letting $n = 0, 1, 2, \cdots$, we find

$$N_0 = N[1 - \exp\left(-\Theta_{vib}/T\right)],$$

$$N_1 = N \exp\left(-\Theta_{vib}/T\right)[1 - \exp\left(-\Theta_{vib}/T\right)],$$

$$N_2 = N \exp\left(-2\Theta_{vib}/T\right)[1 - \exp\left(-\Theta_{vib}/T\right)],$$

etc.

At very low temperatures, where $T \ll \Theta_{vib}$, all of the exponential terms approach zero. Hence at $T = 0°$ K, $N_0 = N$ and $N_1 = N_2 = \cdots = 0$. That is, all of the molecules are in the lowest vibrational energy state at $0°$ K. Since the energy of this state is not zero but equals $\tfrac{1}{2}hf$, the total vibrational energy U_{vib} is *not* zero at absolute zero but equals $\tfrac{1}{2}Nhf$. Thus absolute zero is not the temperature at which the vibrational energy becomes zero but rather that at which the molecules are in the lowest possible energy state.

At any temperature above absolute zero all the energy states are occupied to some extent. The total energy at any temperature is given by

$$U = \Sigma w_i N_i,$$

or it can be found from Eq. (14-24). By either method we find

$$U = Nk\Theta_{vib}\left[\frac{1}{2} + \frac{1}{\exp(\Theta_{vib}/T) - 1}\right]. \qquad (15\text{-}13)$$

The mean energy $\bar{w}$ of a single oscillator is then

$$\bar{w} = \frac{U}{N} = k\Theta_{vib}\left[\frac{1}{2} + \frac{1}{\exp(\Theta_{vib}/T) - 1}\right]. \qquad (15\text{-}14)$$

Thus the mean energy of an oscillator in quantum mechanics is a much more complicated function of temperature than the value kT predicted by classical mechanics. At very low temperatures where $T \ll \Theta_{vib}$, the exponential term is very large and

$$\bar{w} \approx k\Theta_{vib}/2 \approx \tfrac{1}{2}hf,$$

as previously shown. At very high temperatures where $T \gg \Theta_{vib}$, the exponential term is small and can be approximated by

$$\exp(\Theta_{vib}/T) \approx 1 + (\Theta_{vib}/T).$$

Then

$$\frac{1}{\exp(\Theta_{vib}/T) - 1} \approx \frac{T}{\Theta_{vib}}.$$

Since by hypothesis this is very large, the term $\tfrac{1}{2}$ in Eq. (15-14) can be neglected and

$$\bar{w} \approx kT.$$

That is, at very high temperatures, quantum and classical mechanics both give the same value for the mean energy of one of an assembly of oscillators in thermal equilibrium.

Replacing Nk by nR in Eq. (15-13), and dividing through by n, we obtain the molar vibrational energy u_{vib}. The specific heat capacity for vibration is then

$$(c_v)_{vib} = \left(\frac{\partial u_{vib}}{\partial T}\right)_v = R\left(\frac{\Theta_{vib}}{T}\right)^2 \frac{\exp(\Theta_{vib}/T)}{[\exp(\Theta_{vib}/T) - 1]^2}. \qquad (15\text{-}15)$$

When $T \ll \Theta_{vib}$, $(c_v)_{vib}$ approaches zero, and when $T \gg \Theta_{vib}$ it approaches R, the classical value.

The curves in Fig. 15-2 are graphs of the dimensionless ratios $u_{vib}/R\Theta_{vib}$ and $(c_v)_{vib}/R$, as functions of the dimensionless ratio T/Θ_{vib}. The second, of course, is proportional to the slope of the first. Classically, $u = RT$, or $u/R\Theta_{vib} = T/\Theta_{vib}$. The dotted line is a graph of $u/R\Theta_{vib}$ as a function of T/Θ_{vib}. Its slope, equal to unity, is proportional to the classical specific heat capacity. The figure shows how the quantum expressions approach the classical expressions at temperatures large compared with the characteristic temperature.

We next consider molecular rotations. For reasons that are too involved to describe in detail here, evaluation of the partition function for rotation is much more complicated mathematically than for vibration. We can, however, point out one important aspect of the problem. The partition function contains terms of the form

$$\exp\left[-n(n+1)h^2/8\pi^2 IkT\right]$$
$$= \exp\left[-n(n+1)\Theta_{rot}/T\right], \quad (15\text{-}16)$$

where the characteristic temperature for rotation, Θ_{rot}, is defined as

$$\Theta_{rot} = \frac{h^2}{8\pi^2 Ik}.$$

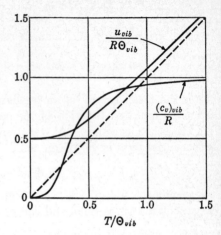

FIG. 15-2.   Vibrational energy and specific heat of a harmonic oscillator.

As for vibrations, the moment of inertia I of a rotating molecule, and hence the characteristic temperature Θ_{rot}, can be determined from a study of its optical spectrum. A few values are given in Table 15-1. These characteristic temperatures are all much lower than those for vibration. The largest is that of hydrogen, as might be expected since Θ_{rot} is inversely proportional to the moment of inertia I and this should be smaller for hydrogen than for any other molecule. Molecules containing one hydrogen atom form another group, with characteristic temperatures in the neighborhood of 20° K, and all others have characteristic temperatures of the order of a few degrees or less. Hence except at very low temperatures the actual temperature is much greater than the characteristic temperature for rotation and, as in all other instances when this is the case, quantum mechanics gives the same answer as classical mechanics. That is, except at very low temperatures, the mean rotational energy per molecule is equal to the classical value kT and the rotational part of c_v equals R.

We can now understand in a general way the features of the graph in Fig. 15-1. Up to a temperature of about 50° K, practically all of the molecules are in their lowest energy states of rotation and vibration. Any heat flowing into the gas serves only to increase the translational kinetic energy, and the specific heat capacity is the same as that of a monatomic gas, $3R/2$. In the temperature range from about 50° to about 250°, the rotational states of higher energy begin to be populated (for hydrogen, $\Theta_{rot} = 86°$) and above 250° the molecules behave like classical rotators.

Starting at about 500°, some molecules begin to move to states of higher vibrational energy and c_v approaches the limiting classical value of $7R/2$.

Many of the important features of the general theory have been ignored in the (relatively) simple treatment of the problem given here. Some of these are: (a) the difference between the behavior of molecules such as H_2, whose atoms are alike, and those such as NO composed of unlike atoms; (b) the degeneracy of the rotational energy levels as a result of space quantization; (c) the energy associated with electronic excitation at high temperatures; (d) the coupling between rotational and vibrational states; and (e) the fact that the vibrations are not precisely simple harmonic. However, the exact theory is apparently so firmly established that specific heat capacities of gases can be computed theoretically, from optical measurements, more accurately than they can be measured experimentally by the techniques of calorimetry.

15-5 Specific heat capacity of solids. The classical theory of the specific heat capacity of a solid assumes that its molecules, when displaced from their equilibrium positions, are acted on by a linear restoring force and oscillate about these positions with simple harmonic motion. With increasing temperature the amplitude, and hence the energy, of the oscillatory motion increases. The specific heat capacity at constant volume is a measure of the energy that must be supplied to increase the energy of these molecular vibrations. Since both the kinetic and potential energies of a harmonic oscillator are quadratic functions of the respective coordinates, the equipartition principle applies and the mean total energy is kT ($\frac{1}{2}kT$ for kinetic energy, $\frac{1}{2}kT$ for potential). But since the molecules of a solid are free to oscillate in three dimensions and are not restricted to move on a straight line, a mean energy $3kT$ is assigned to each. The total energy U of an assembly of N molecules in thermal equilibrium at a temperature T is therefore

$$U = 3NkT = 3nRT.$$

The internal energy per mole is

$$u = \frac{U}{n} = 3RT,$$

and therefore

$$c_v = \left(\frac{\partial u}{\partial T}\right)_v = 3R.$$

Figure 4-3 shows experimental values of c_p and c_v for copper down to 0° K, the last fraction of a degree, of course, being extrapolated. At high temperatures c_v is very nearly equal to the classical value $3R$, but it decreases to zero at $0°$ K. These curves are typical of all substances, although the temperature range over which the decrease from $3R$ takes place varies widely from one substance to another.

The first explanation of the decrease in c_v at low temperatures was given by Einstein, using the same reasoning as that given in the preceding section for a linear oscillator, except that a factor 3 is introduced because the molecules are free to move in three dimensions. Thus the Einstein expression for the specific heat capacity of a solid is

$$c_v = 3R \left(\frac{\Theta_E}{T}\right)^2 \frac{\exp(\Theta_E/T)}{[\exp(\Theta_E/T) - 1]^2}, \tag{15-17}$$

where Θ_E, the characteristic Einstein temperature, is defined as

$$\Theta_E = hf/k,$$

f being the frequency of molecular vibration. A graph of c_v vs. T has the same form as that of c_v in Fig. 15-2. Although its general shape is like that of the experimental curve in Fig. 4-3, it is not possible to find a value of Θ_E which gives good agreement at both high and low temperatures. In particular, if a value of Θ_E is selected which gives good agreement at high temperatures, the experimental values at low temperatures are considerably larger than the theoretical.

The simple Einstein theory assumes that the molecules all oscillate with the same frequency f. Nernst and Lindemann found that the agreement between theory and experiment could be improved by assuming that the molecules of a solid could oscillate at two frequencies, f and $2f$, and this idea was extended by Debye, who considered that the thermal vibrations of the individual molecules could be replaced by a set of stationary elastic waves having a continuous range of frequencies up to a certain maximum value f_{max} corresponding to a wavelength of the order of intermolecular distances. The Debye theory is more complicated mathematically than that of Einstein and we shall only state the result, which is

$$c_v = 3R \frac{3}{x_0^3} \int_0^{x_0} \frac{x^4 e^x}{(e^x - 1)^2} \, dx, \tag{15-18}$$

where

$$x = hf/kT, \quad x_0 = hf_{max}/kT,$$

f_{max} being the maximum frequency referred to above. The characteristic Debye temperature Θ_D is defined as

$$\Theta_D = hf_{max}/k.$$

At high temperatures, $x \ll 1$ and, approximately, $e^x = 1 + x$. In the numerator of the integrand in Eq. (15-18), we can replace e^x by 1. The integral then reduces to $x_0^3/3$ and hence at high temperatures the Debye theory, like the classical theory, gives $c_v = 3R$.

At low temperatures, $x_0 \gg 1$ and the upper limit of the integral in Eq. (15-18) can be taken as ∞. The definite integral thus obtained equals $4\pi^4/15$, and hence at low temperatures

$$c_v = 3R \frac{4\pi^4}{5} \frac{T^3}{\Theta_D^3} . \quad (15\text{-}19)$$

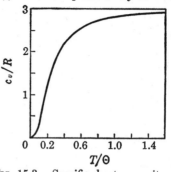

FIG. 15-3. Specific heat capacity of a solid as a function of temperature, as given by Debye's theory.

Thus at low temperatures the Debye theory predicts that c_v decreases with T^3, whereas the Einstein theory gives an exponential decrease. By a proper choice of Θ_D a much better fit can be obtained with experimental values than for the Einstein equation, but the theory is far from complete and the details are still a part of the unfinished business of theoretical physics.

Figure 15-3 is a graph of c_v/R as a function of T/Θ, according to the Debye theory. Its resemblance to Fig. 4-3 is evident.

15-6 Theory of paramagnetism. The reader will recall that the theory of both dia- and paramagnetism starts by assuming that a molecule contains one or more electrons revolving in circular orbits and spinning about their own axes, so that the molecule is a system with both a magnetic moment and an angular momentum. The effect of an external magnetic field is to cause the magnetic moment vector to precess around the magnetic induction vector, and this precessional motion always gives rise to a diamagnetic effect. The torque exerted by the magnetic field cannot, of itself, produce the alignment of molecular magnetic moments with the external field which would result in a paramagnetic effect, even though the potential energy is a minimum when these vectors are parallel. It is only by collisions between molecules and a resulting redistribution of energy that alignment can be brought about, but even then not all molecules line up in the direction of minimum magnetic potential energy, any more than all molecules in the earth's atmosphere settle down in a state of minimum gravitational potential energy. However, although molecular collisions are necessary for any alignment at all to take place, they also work in the opposite direction to destroy any regular arrangement and replace it by a random one.   Qualitatively, it would be expected that the higher the temperature and the more violent the random thermal motion in a gas, the more difficult it would be for the molecules to keep lined up with the field.   In other words, one would expect the magnetization M to increase with increasing magnetic intensity H, at constant temperature, and to *decrease* with increasing temperature and a constant value of H.

The first precise experimental measurements were made by Pierre Curie about 1895.   He found that for many substances, in the ranges of magnetic intensity and temperature covered by his experiments, the magnetization was directly proportional to H and inversely proportional to T. That is,

$$M = C \frac{H}{T},$$

where C is a proportionality constant called the *Curie constant*.   If the Curie law were obeyed at all values of H and T, the magnetization would increase indefinitely with increasing H and with decreasing T, which obviously cannot be the case, since M must approach a maximum or saturation value when all molecular magnets are aligned parallel to the magnetizing field.

The elementary theory of paramagnetism, which we shall next develop, is restricted to systems in which interactions between molecules can be ignored, so that it is essentially a theory of a paramagnetic gas.   However, the results hold quite well for many liquids and solids, the inference being that in such substances the interactions are very small.

Consider a sample of gas, each of whose molecules has a permanent magnetic moment μ, in an external magnetic field of flux density B.   The energy of a molecular magnet depends on the angle θ between its magnetic moment and the external field.   The torque acting on a magnet of magnetic moment μ at any angle θ is

$$\tau = \mu B \sin \theta,$$

and the work necessary to turn it through an angle $d\theta$, or the change in magnetic potential energy, is

$$dw = \tau d\theta = \mu B \sin \theta d\theta.$$

Integrating this expression, we get

$$w = -\mu B \cos \theta,$$

if w is set equal to zero when $\theta = 90°$, or when the magnetic moment is perpendicular to the field.   Since the magnetic energy does not involve the velocity of the center of mass, the position, or any coordinates specifying the molecular internal energy, we can consider the magnetic energy alone. For brevity, let $u = -\cos \theta$ and let $x = \mu B/kT$. The partition function Z is then

$$Z = \Sigma \exp\left(-\mu Bu/kT\right) = \Sigma \exp\left(-xu\right). \qquad (15\text{-}20)$$

According to classical theory, a molecular magnet can assume any angle relative to the magnetic field and its magnetic energy is therefore a continuous function of the angle θ or of u. Hence, to evaluate the partition function classically, we let* $du = H$, multiply Eq. (15-20) by du and divide by H, and replace the sum by an integral.

$$Z = \frac{1}{H} \int_{-1}^{+1} \exp\left(-xu\right) du,$$

where the limits -1 and $+1$ for the variable u correspond to the limits of θ between 0 and π. The integral is

$$Z = \frac{1}{H} \frac{2 \sinh x}{x}.$$

Then from Eq. (14-22), replacing H by du, the number of molecules per unit volume, dn_u, whose magnetic moments make an angle θ with the direction of the field is

$$dn_u = \frac{nx}{2 \sinh x} \exp\left(-xu\right) du,$$

where n is the total number of molecules per unit volume.

Each of these molecules has a component of magnetic moment, parallel to the field, of $\mu \cos \theta = -\mu u$, so the magnetization M of the system, or the magnetic moment per unit volume, is

$$M = \int -\mu u \, dn_u$$

$$= -\frac{n\mu x}{2 \sinh x} \int_{-1}^{+1} u \exp\left(-xu\right) du$$

$$= n\mu \left(\coth x - \frac{1}{x}\right) \qquad (15\text{-}21)$$

$$= n\mu \left(\coth \frac{\mu B}{kT} - \frac{kT}{\mu B}\right). \qquad (15\text{-}22)$$

---

* On this page, H represents a volume element in phase space and should not be confused with the magnetic intensity.

The preceding theory was first developed by Langevin in !905, and the function

$$L(x) = \coth x - \frac{1}{x}$$

is called the *Langevin function*.

Let us investigate the limiting values of Eq. (15-22) in the two extreme cases, (1) in strong fields and low temperatures where $x(=\mu B/kT)$ is very large, and (2) in weak fields and high temperatures where x is very small. When $x \gg 1$, $\coth x \approx 1$ and $1/x$ is negligible, so in this range

$$M = n\mu. \tag{15-23}$$

But this is simply the saturation magnetization which would result if all the molecules were aligned parallel to the field.

In weak fields and at high temperatures, $x \ll 1$ and we can use the approximate expression for the hyperbolic cotangent of a small angle,

$$\coth x \approx \frac{1}{x} + \frac{x}{3}.$$

This gives

$$M = \frac{n\mu^2 B}{3kT} = \left(\frac{n\mu^2\mu_0}{3k}\right)\frac{H}{T}, \tag{15-24}$$

since the magnetization is so small in all paramagnetic materials that for all practical purposes we can set $B = \mu_0 H$. But this is just Curie's law, with the Curie constant C equal to

$$C = \frac{n\mu^2\mu_0}{3k}. \tag{15-25}$$

That is, the Langevin theory leads to Curie's law in weak fields and at high temperatures but predicts that the substance approaches saturation at sufficiently strong fields and low temperatures. The curve in Fig. 15-4 is a graph of the Langevin function, and the straight line is its tangent at $x = 0$ where it reduces to Curie's law.

In a region where Curie's law is obeyed, Eq. (15-25) can be used to compute the molecular magnetic moment μ on the basis of the Lange-

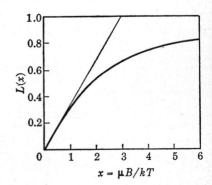

FIG. 15-4.   Graph of the Langevin function, $L(x) = \coth x - (1/x)$.

vin theory.   The values obtained are of the order of magnitude of a few Bohr magnetons.   (A Bohr magneton, μ_B, is the magnetic moment of an electron revolving in the first Bohr orbit of atomic hydrogen, and it also equals the magnetic moment of an electron arising from the electron's spin or rotation about its own axis.   In mks units, $\mu_B = 0.9274 \times 10^{-23}$ amp-m².)   Thus for oxygen gas, which is paramagnetic and obeys Curie's law down to very low temperatures, $\mu \approx 3\mu_B$.   We can now estimate the extent to which the molecular magnets in oxygen are aligned by an external field.   If Curie's law is obeyed, the ratio of the actual magnetization M to that at saturation, $M_{sat} = n\mu$, is

$$\frac{M}{M_{sat}} = \frac{n\mu^2 B/3kT}{n\mu} = \frac{1}{3}\frac{\mu B}{kT} = \frac{1}{3}x.$$

Let $B = 2$ w/m² (20,000 gauss), $T = 300°$ K, and $\mu = 3\mu_B$.   Then

$$x = \frac{3 \times 0.93 \times 10^{-23} \times 2}{1.38 \times 10^{-23} \times 300} = 13.5 \times 10^{-3},$$

$$\frac{M}{M_{sat}} = 4.5 \times 10^{-3}.$$

Under the conditions assumed, x is very much less than unity, so that the Langevin theory reduces to Curie's law, and we see that even a strong magnetic field is capable of producing only a relatively small alignment, equivalent to that which would result if one or two molecules per thousand were exactly parallel to the field while the others remained oriented at random.   In other words, at a temperature of 300° K, the disorienting effect of thermal motions far outweighs the aligning influence of the field.

The principles of quantum mechanics lead to two modifications of the classical theory of paramagnetism.   First, these principles provide a definite expression for the effective magnetic moment of a molecule, determined by the number and arrangement of its electrons.   Second, the magnetic moment of a molecule may not have any arbitrary direction but only some one of a few definite directions.   This latter effect is known as *space quantization*.

Since this is not a text on quantum mechanics, we shall not attempt to give the complete theory but will illustrate the method of attack by the simple example, first worked out by Lenz, of a gas in which the magnetic moments of the molecules can have only two directions, either parallel or antiparallel to the external field.   That the atoms of silver vapor actually take on only one or the other of these two directions was demonstrated in a famous experiment performed by Stern and Gerlach and shown, in principle, in Fig. 15-5.   A beam of silver atoms from an oven (not shown)

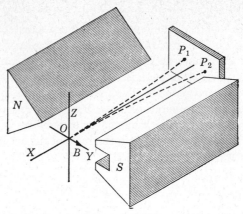

Fig. 15-5. Principle of Stern-Gerlach experiment. A beam of silver atoms traveling along the X-axis is split into two beams in an inhomogeneous magnetic field as a result of space quantization.

enters a magnetic field at point O, traveling along the X-axis. The general direction of the field B is parallel to the Y-axis, but because of the shape of the pole-pieces N and S the flux density decreases from the N-pole toward the S-pole. The magnetic moments of the atoms become aligned either parallel or antiparallel to the B-vector. Because of the gradient of the flux density, those atoms whose moments are parallel to B are deflected toward the N-pole of the field magnet while the others are deflected toward the S-pole. The beam is therefore split as indicated by the dotted lines, and deposits on a plate beyond the magnets in the two spots P_1 and P_2.

We now compute the numbers of molecules per unit volume aligned parallel and antiparallel to the field. The energy of a molecule whose magnetic moment μ is parallel to the field is

$$w_1 = -\mu B,$$

and if the magnetic moment is antiparallel to the field the energy is

$$w_2 = \mu B.$$

Since there are only two possible energy states, the partition function (considering the magnetic energy only) is simply

$$Z = e^x + e^{-x} = 2 \cosh x,$$

where $x = \mu B/kT$.

The numbers of molecules per unit volume in the two states are

$$n_1 = \frac{n}{2} \frac{e^x}{\cosh x},$$

$$n_2 = \frac{n}{2} \frac{e^{-x}}{\cosh x}.$$

The total magnetization parallel to B is $n_1\mu$ and that antiparallel to B is $n_2\mu$. The net magnetization M in the direction of B is

$$M = n_1\mu - n_2\mu = (n_1 - n_2)\mu$$

$$= n\mu \frac{e^x - e^{-x}}{2 \cosh x} = n\mu \frac{2 \sinh x}{2 \cosh x}$$

$$= n\mu \tanh x$$

$$= n\mu \tanh \frac{\mu B}{kT}, \qquad (15\text{-}26)$$

which should be compared with Eq. (15-22). When $\mu B/kT \gg 1$, $\tanh \mu B/kT \approx 1$ and the magnetization approaches a saturation value of $n\mu$. When $\mu B/kT$ is small, $\tanh \mu B/kT \approx \mu B/kT$ and, since B is very nearly equal to $\mu_0 H$,

$$M = \frac{n\mu^2\mu_0}{k} \frac{H}{T}. \qquad (15\text{-}27)$$

Thus we are again led to Curie's law in the region of weak fields and high temperatures, the Curie constant C now being given by

$$C = \frac{n\mu^2\mu_0}{k}, \qquad (15\text{-}28)$$

which differs by a factor of $\frac{1}{3}$ from the classical expression, Eq. (15-25). A graph of Eq. (15-26) has the same general form as that of the Langevin function but its initial slope is three times as great.

The really interesting aspects of the experimental and theoretical study of paramagnetism are those having to do with the behavior of paramagnetic materials in *strong* fields and *low* temperatures, and when the interactions between molecules can *not* be neglected. This is an active field of current research, but to pursue the matter further would take us far beyond the scope of this book.

Problems

1. (a) Find the partition function for a two-dimensional monatomic gas, i.e., one whose molecules can move freely in a plane but are confined within an area A. (b) Find the equation of state of the gas from its Helmholtz function. (See Problem 11, Chapter 11.)

2. When a gas is whirled in a centrifuge its molecules can be considered to be acted on by a radially outward centrifugal force of magnitude $m\omega^2 r$. Find an expression for the density of the gas as a function of r.

3. (a) Derive the law of atmospheres from the principles of hydrostatics and the equation of state of an ideal gas. (b) Find the variation of pressure with elevation in an adiabatic atmosphere, i.e., one in which pv^γ is constant, rather than pv.

4. Show that the velocity distribution in an isothermal atmosphere has the same form as in the absence of a gravitational field.

5. Find the mean gravitational potential energy of a molecule in an isothermal atmosphere.

6. Find the specific heat capacity at constant area for a two-dimensional monatomic ideal gas. (See Problem 1 above.)

7. Consider 1000 diatomic molecules at a temperature equal to $\Theta_{vib}/2$. Find the number in each of the three lowest vibrational energy states.

8. The characteristic Debye temperature for diamond is $1843°$ K and the characteristic Einstein temperature is $1450°$ K. The experimental value of c_v for diamond, at a temperature of $207°$ K, is 2.68×10^3 joules/kilomole-deg. Calculate c_v at $207°$ K from the Einstein and Debye equations and compare with experiment.

9. (a) From Fig. 4-3, find the characteristic Einstein temperature Θ_E for copper such that the Einstein equation for c_v agrees with experiment at a temperature of $100°$ K. (b) Using this value of Θ_E, calculate c_v at $20°$ K and $1200°$ K and compare with the experimental values.

10. Gadolinium sulfate, $Gd_2(SO_4)_3 8H_2O$, obeys the Langevin theory down to temperatures of a few degrees Kelvin. The molecular magnetic moment μ is 7.2×10^{-23} amp-m^2. (a) Find the value of $x = \mu B/kT$ at a temperature of $2°$ K in a field of flux density 2 w/m^2. (b) Find the ratio M/M_{sat} under these conditions.

11. Oxygen is a paramagnetic gas, the susceptibility M/H at $293°$ K and atmospheric pressure being 1.80×10^{-6}. (a) Compute the Curie constant C for oxygen. (b) Use this value of C to find the magnetic moment μ of an oxygen molecule. Compare with the Bohr magneton, $\mu_B = 0.93 \times 10^{-23}$ amp-m^2.

12. According to quantum theory and in agreement with the results of the Stern-Gerlach experiment, when atoms of silver vapor, which have a magnetic moment μ_B, are in a magnetic field, the molecules align themselves either parallel or antiparallel to the field, and in no other orientation. Find the relative number of atoms of silver vapor aligned parallel and antiparallel to a magnetic field of flux density 0.1 w/m^2, at a temperature of $1000°$ K.

CHAPTER 16

QUANTUM STATISTICS

16-1 Difficulties with the Maxwell-Boltzmann statistics. Many lines of evidence indicate that within a metallic conductor there are free electrons, confined within the volume of the metal much as the molecules of a gas are confined in a containing vessel. When the Maxwell-Boltzmann statistics is applied to an electron gas, a number of discrepancies arise between theory and observation. We have already mentioned one, namely, the fact that the electrons do not appear to share at all in the thermal energy of a conductor. That is, the observed molar specific heat capacity of a metal (at elevated temperatures) is $3R$, equal to that of the metal lattice alone, while according to the Maxwell-Boltzmann statistics the free electrons (a monatomic gas) should make a contribution of $3R/2$ to the heat capacity. Another discrepancy is that the predicted velocity distribution of photoelectrons does not agree with experimental results.

When the Maxwell-Boltzmann statistics is applied to a photon gas, that is, to a batch of electromagnetic radiant energy, another difficulty arises. The energy of a photon is proportional to its frequency, so the statistical analysis that leads to the energy distribution function also gives the distribution in frequency (or wave length) of a photon gas. The result obtained from the Maxwell-Boltzmann statistics predicts a continuously increasing number of photons per unit range of frequency as the frequency increases, whereas the actual distribution, as given by the well-known law of Planck, exhibits a maximum and falls off asymptotically to zero on either side of the maximum.

All of these difficulties have been resolved by the quantum statistics. The essential difference between the newer and older theories lies in the method of defining a microstate and of counting the number of microstates associated with a particular macrostate. Quantum statistics actually includes the Maxwell-Boltzmann statistics as a limiting case, going over in form to the latter when the density of phase points in phase space is very small.

16-2 The Bose-Einstein statistics. In setting up the quantum statistics, we again make use of a six-dimensional phase space. Along three of the axes we plot the rectangular coordinates x, y, z, of ordinary space. Instead of plotting the velocity components along the other three axes, it is necessary to use the three rectangular components of momentum. If m is the mass of a particle moving with velocity v, its momentum p is

$$p = mv,$$

and the rectangular components of momentum are

$$p_x = mv_x, \quad p_y = mv_y, \quad p_z = mv_z.$$

The coordinates of a point in this space are then x, y, z, p_x, p_y, p_z, and a volume element is a six-dimensional rectangular parallepiped of volume

$$H = dx\,dy\,dz\,dp_x\,dp_y\,dp_z.$$

According to classical mechanics, the position and momentum of a particle can be specified to any desired degree of precision and can therefore be represented by a geometrical point in phase space. One of the basic principles of quantum mechanics, however, is that there is a limit both to the experimental precision with which the position and momentum of a particle can be simultaneously determined, and to the precision with which these quantities can or should be specified mathematically. This law of nature, justified by the correctness of the conclusions drawn from it, is called the *Heisenberg uncertainty principle*. It can be formulated in several different ways, but for our present purposes the principle states that the coordinates of a particle in phase space can be specified only to the extent that the point representing the position and momentum of the particle lies *somewhere* within an element of phase space of volume h^3, where h is Planck's constant, 6.6237×10^{-34} joule-sec. The existence of this constant is intimately connected with the whole of quantum theory. We cannot at this point go into the question of the experimental methods for determining its magnitude. That h^3 has the dimensions of a volume in phase space is easy to see, however, since

$$(\text{joule-sec})^3 = (\text{newton-meter-sec})^3$$

$$= (\text{meter})^3 \times (\text{newton-sec})^3.$$

The newton-second is the *mks* unit of impulse, equal to that of momentum, so the units of h^3 are those of $(\text{length})^3 \times (\text{momentum})^3$.

Let us speak of an element of volume h^3 as a *compartment*, to distinguish it from a *cell* of volume H. The volume H is arbitrary, subject only to the restriction that dx, dy, dz are small compared with the linear dimensions of the system and dp_x, dp_y, and dp_z are small compared with the range of momenta of the particles. Even with this restriction H can be made very much larger than h^3, and we superpose on the subdivision of phase space into cells of volume H, a still finer subdivision into compartments of volume h^3. The number of compartments per cell, n, is therefore equal to H/h^3, and we shall take the cells sufficiently large so that the number of compartments is great enough to allow the use of Stirling's approximation for $n!$.

As before, let N_i represent the number of phase points in the i'th cell. The observable properties of a system, in any type of statistics, are determined by the macrostate of the system, i.e., by the numbers N_i. The thermodynamic probability W of a macrostate is also defined as the number of microstates corresponding to it. In the Maxwell-Boltzmann statistics the number of microstates is defined as the number of permutations of a given macrostate. For example, if molecules a and b exchange cells in phase space, as in Fig. 14-2(a), the macrostate of the system is unaltered but the microstate is considered to be different. To say that it is different implies that molecules a and b are different and can in some way be distinguished from one another. An essential feature of the quantum statistics is that one recognizes the fact that it is meaningless to identify individual molecules, and hence it is incorrect to set up a method of counting microstates which is based, even by implication, on the assumption that a molecule has an identity. That is, it has no meaning to speak of molecules a and b as exchanging cells in phase space. We must therefore devise a new method of defining a microstate.

Let us take the same simple example we used in Sec. 14-4, that of four phase points and two cells, i and j, and consider the particular macrostate $N_i = 3$, $N_j = 1$. Reference to Sec. 14-4 and Fig. 14-2 will recall that according to the Maxwell-Boltzmann statistics there are four microstates corresponding to this macrostate, so that $W = 4$.

Since molecules cannot be distinguished, let us represent them by dots instead of letters. If it were not for the subdivision of cells into smaller compartments, Fig. 16-1(a) would be the only way of setting up the macrostate, but with such a subdivision we see that there are a number of different ways. At this point, however, we must stop to consider an additional restriction that may be imposed on the phase points. This is the *Pauli exclusion principle*. It applies to electrons, but not to the molecules of a gas or to photons. We shall discuss this principle in more detail later; for the present it is enough to say that as applied to electrons it limits the number of phase points in any compartment to not more than two. The statistics of particles obeying the Pauli exclusion principle was developed first by Fermi and Dirac, and later extended by Sommerfeld, and we return to it in Sec. 16-5. In this section we shall consider only particles to which the exclusion principle does not apply, and for which there may be any number of phase points in a compartment. The theory

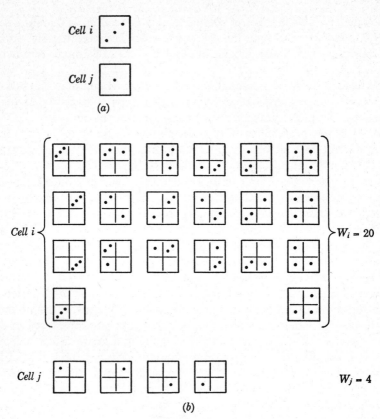

FIG. 16-1. Different ways of arranging phase points within a cell of phase space, in the Bose-Einstein statistics.

was developed independently by Einstein and by Bose, and is called the *Bose-Einstein statistics.*

We now return to a consideration of the microstates illustrated in Fig. 16-1. Let us assume there are four compartments per cell. Fig. 16-1(b) shows the cells i and j divided into four compartments each, and without making any use of the identities of the particles we see that there are 20 different ways of arranging the three phase points in cell i, and four ways of arranging the single point in cell j. We can therefore assign a thermodynamic probability to *each cell*, equal to the number of possible ways of arranging the phase points within that cell. This could not be done in the Maxwell-Boltzmann statistics, where microstates were considered different only when a given particle was shifted from one cell to another. If W_i and W_j represent the probabilities for the respective cells, then in this example

$$W_i = 20, \quad W_j = 4.$$

For any one of the arrangements in cell i we can have any one of those in cell j, so the total possible number of arrangements, which we now call the thermodynamic probability of the macrostate, is

$$W = W_i W_j = 20 \times 4 = 80.$$

This contrasts with $W = 4$ on the basis of the Maxwell-Boltzmann statistics.

In general, when there are any number of cells,

$$W = \Pi W_i, \tag{16-1}$$

where the product extends over all cells of phase space.

We now derive the expression for W in terms of the N_i's. Suppose the compartments in the ith cell are numbered 1, 2, 3, $\cdots$ up to n, and the phase points are lettered a, b, c, $\cdots$ up to N_i. Although the phase points are not considered to have an identity, we assign letters to them temporarily as an aid in explaining how the thermodynamic probability is computed. In some one arrangement of the phase points in cell i we might have points a and b in compartment 1, c in compartment 2, compartment 3 might be empty, while compartment 4 contained points d, e, f, etc. This state can be represented by the mixed sequence of letters and numbers

$$\boxed{1 \; a \; b} \qquad \boxed{2 \; c} \qquad \boxed{3} \qquad \boxed{4 \; d \; e \; f} \quad \cdots, \tag{16-2}$$

where the letters following a number designate the phase points in the compartment of that number. If the numbers and letters are arranged in all possible sequences each sequence will represent a microstate, provided the sequence begins with a number. There are therefore n ways in which the sequences can begin, one for each of the n compartments, and in each of these the remaining $(n + N_i - 1)$ numbers and letters can be arranged in any order. The number of different ways in which x things can be arranged in sequence is $x!$, so the number of different sequences that begin with a number is

$$n(n + N_i - 1)!. \tag{16-3}$$

Now although each sequence represents a microstate, many of them represent the same microstate. For example, arranging the blocks in (16-2) in a different sequence, such as

$$\boxed{3} \quad \boxed{1\ a\ b} \quad \boxed{4\ d\ e\ f} \quad \boxed{2\ c} \quad \cdots,$$

does not change the microstate, since the same compartments contain the same particles. There are n such blocks in the sequence, one for each compartment, so the number of different sequences of blocks is $n!$ and we must divide (16-3) by $n!$ to avoid counting the same microstate more than once.

Also, since the molecules are actually indistinguishable, a different sequence of letters such as

$$\boxed{1\ c\ a} \quad \boxed{2\ e} \quad \boxed{3} \quad \boxed{4\ d\ b\ f} \quad \cdots$$

represents the same microstate as (16-2), because any given compartment contains the same *number* of phase points. The N_i letters can be arranged in sequence in $N_i!$ different ways, so (16-3) must also be divided by $N_i!$. Hence the number of microstates for the i'th cell is

$$W_i = \frac{n(n + N_i - 1)!}{n!\,N_i!},$$

which is more conveniently written as

$$W_i = \frac{(n + N_i - 1)!}{(n - 1)!\,N_i!}, \tag{16-4}$$

since

$$n! = n(n - 1)!$$

Applying the formula above to the case illustrated in Fig. 16-1(b), where $n = 4$, $N_i = 3$, $N_j = 1$, we get

$$W_i = \frac{(4 + 3 - 1)!}{(4 - 1)!\,3!} = \frac{6!}{3!\,3!} = 20,$$

$$W_j = \frac{(4 + 1 - 1)!}{(4 - 1)!\,1!} = \frac{4!}{3!\,1!} = 4,$$

which agrees with the result obtained by counting.

For each microstate of cell i we may have any one of the microstates of cell j. The total number of microstates, including all cells, or the thermodynamic probability W, is

$$W = \Pi W_i = \Pi \frac{(n + N_i - 1)!}{(n - 1)! N_i!}. \tag{16-5}$$

As before, we set the entropy S of the system equal to $k \ln W$, and find the distribution that makes S or $\ln W$ a maximum. From the preceding equation,

$$\ln W = \Sigma[\ln (n + N_i - 1)! - \ln (n - 1)! - \ln N_i!],$$

and using the Stirling approximation,

$$\ln W = \Sigma[(N_i + n) \ln (N_i + n) - n \ln n - N_i \ln N_i], \tag{16-6}$$

where 1 has been neglected compared with n and N_i.

The change in $\ln W$ as a result of the changes in the N_i's, which we set equal to zero for the state of maximum thermodynamic probability, is

$$\delta \ln W = \sum \left[\ln \frac{n + N_i^0}{N_i^0} \right] \delta N_i = 0. \tag{16-7}$$

If the number of particles and the total energy are constant, we have the condition equations

$$\delta N = \Sigma \delta N_i = 0, \quad \delta U = \Sigma w_i \delta N_i = 0.$$

Multiplying the first by $-\ln B$ and the second by $-\beta$, and adding to Eq. (16-7), gives

$$\sum \left[\ln \frac{n + N_i^0}{N_i^0} - \ln B - \beta w_i \right] \delta N_i = 0,$$

and since in effect the δN_i's are now independent,

$$\ln \frac{n + N_i^0}{N_i^0} = \ln B + \beta w_i,$$

$$\boxed{\frac{N_i^0}{n} = \frac{1}{B \exp (\beta w_i) - 1}.} \tag{16-8}$$

This is the Bose-Einstein distribution function. Comparison with Eq. (14-12) shows it to be similar to the Maxwell-Boltzmann function except that on the left we have the number of phase points per compartment in the ith cell, while on the right there is a -1 in the denominator.

The multiplier β is found as before by setting $dU = TdS = k\,d\ln W$, and equals $1/kT$ as in the Maxwell-Boltzmann statistics. The quantity B can be determined, in principle at least, from the condition that $\Sigma N_i = N$. The actual evaluation of B, however, is not as straightforward as in the classical statistics. We shall consider only two special cases, one where $B >> 1$, the other where $B = 1$. These are discussed in the next two sections.

16-3 The Maxwell-Boltzmann statistics.

Let us consider a system in which the number of phase points in a cell, N_i, is very much smaller than the number of compartments, n. If such a system exists, the left side of Eq. (16-8) is very much less than unity and hence the denominator on the right side is much greater than unity. The term -1 in the denominator can then be neglected, and for such a system

$$\frac{N_i^0}{n} = \frac{1}{B\exp(w_i/kT)}$$

Note that this has the same form as Eq. (14-13) if we replace A in that equation by B/n. Let us write it as

$$N_i^0 = n\alpha \exp(-w_i/kT),\qquad(16\text{-}9)$$

where $\alpha \equiv 1/B$.

We can now determine α from the condition $\Sigma N_i = N$, replacing the sum by an integral as before. The number n is

$$n = \frac{H}{h^3} = \frac{1}{h^3}\,dxdydzdp_xdp_ydp_z$$

$$= \frac{m^3}{h^3}\,dxdydzdv_xdv_ydv_z.$$

Now insert this expression for n in Eq. (16-9), replace N_i^0 by d^6N, w_i by $mv^2/2$, and integrate over all values of x, y, and z. The result is

$$d^3N = \frac{\alpha m^3 V}{h^3}\exp(-mv^2/2kT)dv_xdv_ydv_z.\qquad(16\text{-}10)$$

Integrating again over all values of v_x, v_y, and v_z, we get

$$N = \frac{\alpha V}{h^3}(2\pi mkT)^{3/2},$$

and hence

$$\alpha = \frac{Nh^3}{V}(2\pi mkT)^{-3/2}.\qquad(16\text{-}11)$$

Finally, inserting this expression for α in Eq. (16-10), we obtain

$$d^3N = N(m/2\pi kT)^{3/2} \exp\left(-mv^2/2kT\right)dv_x dv_y dv_z,$$

which is seen to be the Maxwell-Boltzmann velocity distribution function. The new statistics therefore leads to the same distribution function as the old, provided the assumption that N_i/n is very much less than unity is true. To see if this is the case for a molecular gas, let us compute its value from Eq. (16-9), taking as an example helium at standard conditions. Since we have a Maxwell velocity distribution, the energies of the molecules are grouped around the mean energy $3kT/2$, so the quantity w/kT is of the order of unity and so is $\exp(-w/kT)$. To compute α, we have, for a gas at standard conditions, $N/V \approx 3 \times 10^{25}$ molecules/m^3, and for helium, $m \approx 6.7 \times 10^{-27}$ kgm. Inserting the values of h, k, and T in Eq. (16-11) we get

$$\alpha \approx 4 \times 10^{-6},$$

which is certainly much less than unity. However, as the temperature is lowered the number of molecules per unit volume increases and T decreases. Both of these effects make α larger, and provided the gas can be cooled to very low temperatures without condensing, the Maxwell-Boltzmann statistics may cease to be applicable.

Although the new statistics leads to the same velocity distribution as the old, for an ordinary gas, it does not give the same expression for the entropy. Combining the expression $S = k \ln W$ with those derived above for W, N_i, β and α, we find

$$S = R\left[\tfrac{5}{2} - \ln N_0 h^3 + \tfrac{3}{2} \ln (2\pi mk)\right] + \tfrac{3}{2} R \ln T + R \ln V. \quad (16\text{-}12)$$

The quantity A in Eq. (15-3), derived from the older statistics, contained among other things the volume H of a cell in phase space. This quantity is entirely arbitrary, except that it must be a small part of phase space, and hence the entropy is not uniquely determined. In Eq. (16-12), on the other hand, there are no arbitrary or undetermined constants. This brings up the question as to whether Eq. (16-12) can ever be verified experimentally, since apart from this equation we have developed no other explicit expression for the entropy of a gas. Thermodynamic reasoning, of course, defines only entropy *differences*. The absolute value of the entropy of a system is a matter of the greatest importance in physical chemistry but we shall be unable to go into more detail here. Suffice it to say that there are other methods of determining absolute values of entropy, and the equation above does seem to hold, within the limits of experimental accuracy.

16-4 Statistics of a photon gas. Suppose that an evacuated cylinder provided with a piston has perfectly reflecting internal walls and contains a small speck of matter whose surface is ideally black (see Sec. 7-6). The radiant energy in the cylinder can be considered as a "gas" whose particles are photons. The number of photons is not necessarily constant, however, since photons can be emitted and absorbed by the speck of matter. Hence we can omit the requirement that $\delta N = 0$ and retain only the condition that $\delta U = 0$. The result is that, in effect, $B = 1$ for a photon gas and the distribution function in Eq. (16-8) becomes

$$\frac{N_i^0}{n} = \frac{1}{\exp{(w_i/kT)} - 1}. \tag{16-13}$$

The energy of a photon of frequency f is

$$w = hf,$$

and its momentum is

$$p = \frac{hf}{c} = \frac{w}{c}.$$

Now replace n by $\dfrac{2}{h^3} dx\,dy\,dz\,dp_x\,dp_y\,dp_z$, N_i^0 by d^6N, and integrate over x, y, and z to obtain the distribution in momentum space. (The factor 2 in the expression for n is equivalent to doubling the number of compartments per cell, or the number of phase points per compartment, and is inserted in order to get the right answer. The justification is that there are both right-handed and left-handed photons, i.e., light can be either right or left circularly polarized.) The result is:

$$d^3N = \frac{2V}{h^3} \frac{1}{\exp{(pc/kT)} - 1} dp_x\,dp_y\,dp_z.$$

The distribution function is spherically symmetrical, since it contains only p, so the number of representative points in a thin spherical shell in momentum space, of radius p and thickness dp, is

$$dN_p = \frac{2V}{h^3} \frac{4\pi p^2}{\exp{(pc/kT)} - 1} dp.$$

Finally, expressing the distribution in terms of frequency rather than momentum, through the relations

$$p = \frac{h}{c} f, \qquad dp = \frac{h}{c} df,$$

we get

$$dN_f = \frac{8\pi V}{c^3} \frac{f^2}{\exp{(hf/kT)} - 1} df.$$

The number of photons per unit volume of ordinary space is dN_f/V, and since the energy of a photon of frequency f is hf, the energy per unit volume, or the energy density, within a frequency range (or bandwidth) df, is

$$\frac{hf}{V} dN_f = \frac{8\pi h}{c^3} \frac{f^3}{\exp{(hf/kT)} - 1} df. \tag{16-14}$$

This equation agrees exactly with Planck's formula for the density of radiant energy in an enclosure whose walls are at a temperature T. It was originally proposed by Planck as a purely empirical equation to fit the experimental data of Lummer and Pringsheim. Planck attempted to derive the equation from the classical laws of electromagnetic radiation, and his failure to do so forced him to invent the quantum theory. Planck's original derivation was quite different from that above. He considered the processes of emission and absorption by individual atoms, an approach that is related to the statistical method in much the same way that the kinetic theory derivation of the equation of state of an ideal gas is related to its derivation by the methods of statistics.

16-5 The Fermi-Dirac statistics. We now return to the statistics of an electron gas, a system to which the Pauli exclusion principle applies. As before, let N_i represent the number of phase points in the i'th cell. In neither the Maxwell-Boltzmann nor the Bose-Einstein statistics was there an *a priori* restriction on the magnitude of any N_i, but there is a very definite restriction in the Fermi-Dirac statistics. The exclusion principle, as it applies to an electron gas, asserts that there can be no more than two phase points in each of the compartments of volume h^3. The same principle governs the arrangement of electrons in an atom, where it states that no two electrons in the same atom can have the same set of quantum numbers. The coordinates of a compartment in phase space correspond to quantum numbers. The reason there can be two points in a compartment is that the electrons which the points represent have oppositely directed spins. The maximum number of representative points in a cell is therefore twice the number of compartments. (Of course the actual number may be less than this if not all compartments are occupied.) Let us therefore imagine that each compartment is divided in two and that there can be no more than one point in each half. The number of half-compartments in each cell, n, is therefore

$$n = 2\frac{H}{h^3},$$

and the maximum number of points in each cell is n.

For brevity, we shall use the term "compartment" for these half-compartments.

Let us again take as a specific example a system with just two cells, i and j, each divided into four compartments, and consider the macrostate $N_i = 3$, $N_j = 1$. Fig. 16-2 shows the cells i and j, and we see that if there cannot be more than one point per compartment there are four different ways of arranging the three phase points in cell i, and four ways of arranging the single point in cell j. Defining as in Sec. 16-2 a thermodynamic probability for each cell, we have

$$W_i = 4, \quad W_j = 4.$$

For any one of the arrangements in cell i we can have any one of those in cell j, so the total number of possible arrangements, or the thermodynamic probability of the macrostate, is

$$W = W_iW_j = 4 \times 4 = 16.$$

This contrasts with $W = 4$ for the same macrostate for the Maxwell-Boltzmann, and $W = 80$ for the Bose-Einstein statistics.

In general, when there are any number of cells,

$$W = \Pi W_i.$$

The derivation of the expression for any W_i is simpler than for the Bose-Einstein statistics. Of the n compartments of a cell, N_i are occupied and $(n - N_i)$ are empty. The problem therefore consists of counting the number of ways in which n compartments can be divided into two groups, with the occupied compartments in one group and the empty compartments in the other.

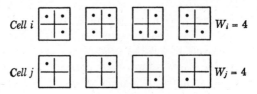

FIG. 16-2. Different ways of arranging phase points within a cell of phase space, in the Fermi-Dirac statistics.

In Sec. 14-4 we discussed the number of ways in which N *particles* could be distributed among the *cells* of phase space, with N_1 particles in cell 1, N_2 in cell 2, and so on.   This number was shown to be

$$\frac{N!}{N_1!\,N_2!\,N_3!\,\cdots} = \frac{N!}{\Pi N_i!}.$$

In general, the equation above gives the number of ways in which N things can be arranged in groups, the numbers N_1, N_2, etc., representing the number in each group.   In the Maxwell-Boltzmann statistics the "things" to be arranged are the phase points, the number of "groups" equals the number of cells in phase space, and the number of ways of arranging the "things" is taken as the thermodynamic probability of a macrostate.

Here we have a similar but somewhat simpler problem.   The thermodynamic probability for a given cell is defined as the number of different ways the *compartments* can be divided into just *two* groups, with the occupied compartments in one group and the unoccupied in the other. That is, the "things" to be arranged are now the compartments of a cell, rather than the phase points.   The total number of things is n, the number of compartments.   The number of occupied compartments equals the number of phase points in the cell, N_i, and the number of empty compartments is $n - N_i$.   Hence the number of different ways of dividing the compartments into occupied and unoccupied groups, or the thermodynamic probability W_i, is

$$W_i = \frac{n!}{N_i!(n - N_i)!}. \tag{16-15}$$

In our simple example, $N_i = 3$, $N_j = 1$, $n = 4$.   Hence

$$W_i = \frac{4!}{3!\,1!} = 4, \qquad W_j = \frac{4!}{1!\,3!} = 4,$$

which agrees with the result obtained by counting.

The general expression for the thermodynamic probability of a given macrostate, in the Fermi-Dirac statistics, is therefore

$$W = \Pi \frac{n!}{N_i!(n - N_i)!}. \tag{16-16}$$

Next, as in any type of statistics, we assume that entropy is proportional to the logarithm of the thermodynamic probability and that the equilibrium state of maximum entropy is also that for which $\ln W$ is a maximum or $\delta \ln W = 0$.   From Eq. (16-16),

$$\ln W = \Sigma[\ln n! - \ln N_i! - \ln (n - N_i)!].$$ (16-17)

Since the cells are large enough so that n and N_i are large numbers, we can use Stirling's approximation.

$$\ln W = \Sigma[n \ln n - N_i \ln N_i - n \ln (n - N_i) + N_i \ln (n - N_i)].$$

Let W^0 represent the maximum probability, and N_i^0 the corresponding number of points in the i'th cell. Then, since n is a constant,

$$\delta \ln W = \sum \ln \frac{n - N_i^0}{N_i^0} \delta N_i = 0.$$ (16-18)

These variations in the N_i's, due to the random motions of the electrons, are subject to the conditions that the total number of electrons and the total energy remain constant. We therefore have the condition equations:

$$\delta N = \Sigma \delta N_i = 0,$$

$$\delta U = \Sigma w_i \delta N_i = 0.$$

Multiply the first condition equation by $-\ln B$, the second by $-\beta$, and add to Eq. (16-18). This gives

$$\sum \left[\ln \frac{n - N_i^0}{N_i^0} - \ln B - \beta w_i \right] \delta N_i = 0,$$

and since in effect the δN_i's are now independent,

$$\ln \frac{n - N_i^0}{N_i^0} = \ln B + \beta w_i,$$

$$\boxed{\frac{N_i^0}{n} = \frac{1}{B \exp (\beta w_i) + 1}.}$$ (16-19)

This is the Fermi-Dirac distribution function for the state of maximum thermodynamic probability. It should be compared with the corresponding equation derived by the Maxwell-Boltzmann statistics,

$$\frac{N_i^0}{n} = \frac{1}{B \exp (\beta w_i)},$$

and by the Bose-Einstein statistics,

$$\frac{N_i^0}{n} = \frac{1}{B \exp (\beta w_i) - 1}.$$

The next step is to evaluate the quantities B and β. To determine β, we again make use of the thermodynamic relation that for a system in equilibrium, in a process at constant volume,

$$dU = TdS.$$

The result is the same, namely,

$$\beta = \frac{1}{kT}.$$

The quantity B is determined, as in any statistics, from the fact that $\Sigma N_i = N$, the total number of particles. To evaluate ΣN_i, we approximate the discontinuous distribution of phase points by a continuous function and replace the sum by an integral. In Eq. (16-19), replace n by

$$n = \frac{2H}{h^3} = \frac{2}{h^3} \, dxdydzdp_xdp_ydp_z,$$

and change the notation from N_i^0 to d^6N and from w_i to w. Then

$$d^6N = \frac{2}{h^3} \frac{1}{B \exp (w/kT) + 1} \, dx \cdots dp_z.$$

Now integrate over x, y, and z. In the absence of a force field these quantities appear only in the differentials, and the integral over these variables is the total volume of the system, V.

$$d^3N = \frac{2V}{h^3} \frac{1}{B \exp (w/kT) + 1} \, dp_xdp_ydp_z. \qquad (16\text{-}20)$$

We now have the distribution function in three-dimensional momentum space. The next step is to express w in terms of p, or vice versa, and set the integral of d^3N over all values of p (or w) equal to N.

If $B \exp (w/kT) >> 1$, the 1 in the denominator can be neglected and, as with the Bose-Einstein statistics, we obtain the Maxwell-Boltzmann statistics as a limiting case, presenting nothing new of interest. For an electron gas, however, this approximation cannot be made, and B must be evaluated from Eq. (16-20).

The expression for B, when B is small, was first derived by Sommerfeld. The calculation is long and complicated and we shall only state the result. For reasons which will be evident later, let us write

$$B = \exp (-w_m/kT),$$

so that Eq. (16-20) becomes

$$d^3N = \frac{2V}{h^3} \frac{1}{\exp\left[(w - w_m)/kT\right] + 1} \, dp_x dp_y dp_z. \qquad (16\text{-}21)$$

$$= \rho \, dp_x dp_y dp_z.$$

When $T = 0°$ K, this distribution function reduces to a very simple one. Let w_{mo} represent the value of w_m when $T = 0°$ K. For a cell in momentum space for which w is less than w_{mo}, the term in square brackets in Eq. (16-21) is $-\infty$, and since $\exp(-\infty) = 0$, it follows that

$$\rho_0 = \frac{2V}{h^3} \qquad (T = 0° \text{ K}, \, w < w_{mo}). \qquad (16\text{-}22)$$

In other words, at absolute zero the density of representative points in momentum space is constant and equal to $2V/h^3$, in all cells for which $w < w_{mo}$.

On the other hand, if w is greater than w_{mo} and $T = 0°$ K, the term in square brackets is $+\infty$, and since $\exp(+\infty) = \infty$, the density in momentum space is zero in all cells for which $w > w_{mo}$.

$$\rho_0 = 0 \qquad (T = 0° \text{ K}, \, w > w_{mo}).$$

The physical significance of w_{mo}, then, is *the maximum energy of the electrons at absolute zero*, which is the reason for the choice of this symbol. The energy w and the momentum p are related by the equation

$$\frac{1}{2} mv^2 = w = \frac{p^2}{2m}, \qquad p^2 = 2mw.$$

To the maximum energy w_{mo} there corresponds a maximum momentum p_{mo}, given by

$$p_{mo} = (2mw_{mo})^{1/2},$$

and, in geometrical language, we can say that at absolute zero momentum space is uniformly populated within a sphere of radius p_{mo} and that there are no phase points outside this sphere. The process of integrating the density over all of momentum space therefore reduces to the multiplication of the constant density ρ_0 by the volume of a sphere of radius p_{mo}, and this product equals the total number of electrons, N.

$$\frac{2V}{h^3} \times \frac{4}{3} \pi p_{mo}^3 = N,$$

from which we find that

$$p_{mo} = \left(\frac{3Nh^3}{8\pi V}\right)^{1/3},$$

and

$$w_{mo} = \frac{h^2}{8m} \left(\frac{3N}{\pi V}\right)^{2/3}. \qquad (16\text{-}23)$$

We next estimate the magnitude of w_{mo}, from Eq. (16-23). The constant h is Planck's constant, 6.62×10^{-34} joule-sec, and m is the electron mass, 9×10^{-31} kgm. The number of electrons per unit volume cannot be measured directly. The most reasonable assumption, since the atoms are all alike, is that each atom contributes the same (integral) number of electrons to the electron gas. We would also expect this number to be small, probably 1 for monovalent atoms, 2 for divalent, etc. There is good indirect evidence that this assumption is correct. If we make our calculations for silver and assume one electron per atom, then $\frac{N}{V} = 5.86$ $\times 10^{28}$ free electrons/m^3, and from Eq. (16-23),

$$w_{mo} = \frac{(6.62 \times 10^{-34})^2}{2 \times 9 \times 10^{-31}} \left(\frac{3 \times 5.86 \times 10^{28}}{8\pi}\right)^{2/3}$$

$$= 9.0 \times 10^{-19} \text{ joule}$$

$$= 5.6 \text{ electron-volts.}$$

This is the maximum kinetic energy of the free electrons at absolute zero. The average energy $\bar{w}$ at absolute zero (see Sec. 16-7) is 3/5 of the maximum, so

$$\bar{w} = (3/5)(5.6) = 3.46 \text{ ev} = 5.75 \times 10^{-19} \text{ joule.}$$

According to the Maxwell-Boltzmann statistics, the average kinetic energy of the molecules of a gas is $3kT/2$ and is zero at absolute zero. The temperature at which $3kT/2 = 5.75 \times 10^{-19}$ joule is $27,800°$ K. Hence if the new statistics is correct, and there is ample evidence that it is, the concept of absolute zero as a state in which all molecular (or electronic) motion has ceased is far from the truth. The mean kinetic energy of the electrons in a metal, even at absolute zero, is much greater than that of the molecules of an ordinary gas even at a temperature of thousands of degrees.

Let us now return to the evaluation of w_m, at a temperature other than $0°$ K. The result obtained by Sommerfeld is

$$w_m = w_{mo} \left\{1 - \frac{\pi^2}{12}\left(\frac{kT}{w_{mo}}\right)^2 + \cdots\right\}. \qquad (16\text{-}24)$$

When $T = 0°$ K, this reduces, of course, to w_{mo}. Even at elevated temperatures the difference between w_m and w_{mo} is small, since the term kT is only a few tenths of an electron-volt, while w_{mo} is of the order of 2 to 10 electron-volts. Hence, in evaluating the distribution function ρ in Eq. (16-21), even at temperatures as high as several thousand degrees Kelvin, we make but a slight error in substituting w_{mo} for w_m.

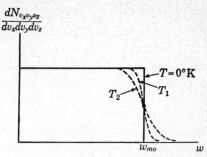

FIG. 16-3. Distribution in momentum space in the Fermi-Dirac statistics, at $T = 0°$ K (full line) and at two higher temperatures T_1 and T_2.

Fig. 16-3 is a graph of the distribution function, plotted as a function of w. The ordinate of the curve is the number of representative points per unit "volume" of momentum space. The solid line is the distribution at $T = 0°$ K. The density is constant at all points for which $w < w_{mo}$ (or $p < p_{mo}$) and is zero beyond this value. The dotted lines are the distributions at higher temperatures, T_1 and T_2. If $T \neq 0$, the function falls off asymptotically to zero as the energy increases, and there is no sharp upper limit to the energy or momentum. That is, w_m does *not* represent the maximum energy at a temperature T in the way that w_{mo} represents the maximum energy at $T = 0°$ K. Notice also that only the more energetic electrons are affected by a rise in temperature.

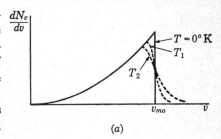

(a)

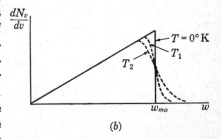

(b)

16-6 Velocity, speed, and energy distribution functions. To obtain the *velocity* distribution function from Eq. (16-21), we need only replace dp_x by $d(mv_x) = mdv_x$, etc. This gives

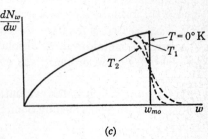

(c)

FIG. 16-4. Energy distribution function in the Fermi-Dirac statistics.

$$d^3N_{v_x v_y v_z} = \frac{2m^3 V}{h^3} \frac{1}{\exp\left[(w - w_m)/kT\right] + 1} \, dv_x dv_y dv_z. \qquad (16\text{-}25)$$

Of course w may be written out explicitly as

$$w = \tfrac{1}{2}m(v_x^2 + v_y^2 + v_z^2)$$

to obtain an expression involving velocity components only. The coefficient of the volume element $dv_x dv_y dv_z$ in Eq. (16-25) is the number of representative points per unit volume or the density in velocity space.

The *speed* distribution function is most readily derived from the fact that the distribution is spherically symmetrical, and hence the number of representative points in a thin shell in velocity space of radius v equals the product of the density in velocity space at this radius, and the volume of the shell, $4\pi v^2 dv$. The density is a function of v only, since $w = \tfrac{1}{2}mv^2$. Therefore

$$dN_v = \frac{8\pi m^3 V}{h^3} \frac{v^2}{\exp\left[(\tfrac{1}{2}mv^2 - w_m)/kT\right] + 1} \, dv \qquad (16\text{-}26)$$

$$= \frac{16\pi m^2 V}{h^3} \frac{w}{\exp\left[(w - w_m)/kT\right] + 1} \, dv. \qquad (16\text{-}27)$$

At 0° K,

$$\frac{dN_v}{dv} = \frac{8\pi m^3 V}{h^3} v^2 \qquad\qquad (v < v_{mo}),$$

$$= \frac{16\pi m^2 V}{h^3} w \qquad\qquad (w < w_{mo}),$$

$$= 0 \qquad\qquad (v > v_{mo}, \; w > w_{mo}).$$

The speed distribution function is plotted in Fig. 16-4(a) as a function of v, and in Fig. 16-4(b) as a function of w, at $T = 0°$ K and at two higher temperatures.

The *energy* distribution function follows from the relations

$$w = \frac{1}{2}mv^2, \quad v^2 = \frac{2w}{m}, \quad dv = (2wm)^{-1/2} \, dw.$$

Inserting these expressions for v^2 and dv in Eq. (16-27), we get

$$dN_w = \frac{4\pi V}{h^3}(2m)^{3/2} \frac{w^{1/2}}{\exp\left[(w - w_m)/kT\right] + 1} \, dw. \qquad (16\text{-}28)$$

The coefficient of dw, or the energy distribution function, is plotted in Fig. 16-4(c) as a function of w.

To find the distribution in *any one velocity component*, say v_x, we return to Eq. (16-25) and integrate over all values of v_y and v_z. Then

$$dN_{v_x} = \frac{2m^3V}{h^3} \left[\int_{-\infty}^{+\infty} \int_{-\infty}^{+\infty} \frac{1}{\exp\left[(w - w_m)/kT\right] + 1} \, dv_y dv_z \right] dv_x,$$

where

$$w = \tfrac{1}{2}m(v_x^2 + v_y^2 + v_z^2).$$

To evaluate the integral, let us consider v_y and v_z as variables in a rectangular coordinate system. Then $dv_y dv_z$ is an element of area and the double integral is the surface integral of a function of v_y and v_z over the entire v_y-v_z plane. Now transform to polar coordinates, r and θ, as in Fig. 16-5. Then

$$v_y^2 + v_z^2 = r^2,$$

and an element of area is

$$dv_x dv_y = r\,dr\,d\theta.$$

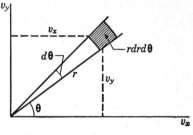

FIG. 16-5.

Hence

$$dN_{v_x} = \frac{2m^3V}{h^3} \left[\int_0^\infty \int_0^{2\pi} \frac{r\,dr\,d\theta}{\exp\left\{[\tfrac{1}{2}m(r^2 + v_x^2) - w_m]/kT\right\} + 1} \right] dv_x.$$

Now

$$\frac{\tfrac{1}{2}m(r^2 + v_x^2) - w_m}{kT} = \frac{mr^2}{2kT} + \frac{\tfrac{1}{2}mv_x^2 - w_m}{kT}.$$

Let

$$\frac{mr^2}{2kT} = x, \quad r\,dr = \frac{kT}{m}\,dx, \quad \exp\left[(\tfrac{1}{2}mv_x^2 - w_m)/kT\right] = a.$$

Then

$$dN_{v_x} = \frac{2m^3V}{h^3} \frac{kT}{m} \left[\int_0^\infty \int_0^{2\pi} \frac{dx\,d\theta}{ae^x + 1} \right] dv_x.$$

The integral over θ is simply 2π, and

$$\int_0^\infty \frac{dx}{ae^x + 1} = -\ln\left(a + e^{-x}\right)\Big]_0^\infty = \ln\left(1 + \frac{1}{a}\right).$$

Finally,

$$dN_{v_x} = \frac{4\pi V m^2 kT}{h^3} \ln \{\exp [(w_m - \tfrac{1}{2}mv_x^2)/kT] + 1\} dv_x, \quad (16\text{-}29)$$

or, since $w_x = \tfrac{1}{2}mv_x^2$,

$$dN_{v_x} = \frac{4\pi V m^2 kT}{h^3} \ln \{\exp [(w_m - w_x)/kT] + 1\} dv_x. \quad (16\text{-}30)$$

To see what form this expression takes at 0° K, we note that T appears both in the coefficient of the logarithmic term and in the denominator of the exponential term, so that $dN_{v_x} = 0 \times \infty$ when $T = 0$. Therefore let T be some finite but very small number. Then if $w_x < w_m$, the exponential term is large and we may neglect the 1. But

$$\ln [\exp (x)] = x,$$

so when T is very small

$$dN_{v_x} = \frac{4\pi V m^2}{h^3} (w_m - w_x) dv_x, \quad (16\text{-}31)$$

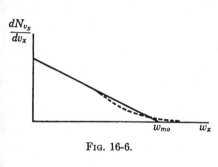

$\dfrac{dN_{v_x}}{dv_x}$

w_{mo}　　w_x

FIG. 16-6.

and since T has dropped out, this is the distribution function at $T = 0°$ K. It decreases linearly with w_x, as in Fig. 16-6, with a very gradual tailing off at higher temperatures.

16-7 Specific heat of the electron gas. We next give one example to justify the hypotheses introduced in setting up the Fermi-Dirac statistics. One of the outstanding failures of the Maxwell-Boltzmann statistics, as mentioned in Sec. 16-1, was its prediction that the specific heat capacity of a metal should be much greater than the Dulong-Petit value of $3R$. That is, if there is equipartition of energy between the atoms and the free electrons, the electrons should contribute an amount $3R/2$ per mole to the specific heat, like any monatomic gas. We can now see that although the Fermi-Dirac statistics attributes a much greater energy to the electrons than does the older theory, the *change* in energy with temperature is very small, and it is only the change in energy that influences the heat capacity. The average energy $\overline{w}$ of an electron is defined in the usual way as

$$\overline{w} = \frac{\displaystyle\int_0^\infty w\, dN_w}{\displaystyle\int_0^\infty dN_w}.$$

At absolute zero, the upper limit of the integral can be taken as w_{mo}, since at this temperature there are no electrons with energies greater than w_{mo}. For $w < w_{mo}$, and at $T = 0°$ K, we have from Eq. (16-28),

$$dN_w = \frac{4\pi V}{h^3} (2m)^{3/2} w^{1/2} dw.$$

Hence

$$\overline{w}_o = \frac{\displaystyle\int_0^{w_{mo}} w^{3/2} dw}{\displaystyle\int_0^{w_{mo}} w^{1/2} dw} = \tfrac{3}{5} w_{mo},$$

and the average energy at absolute zero equals 3/5 of the maximum energy.

The average energy at any temperature T is obtained in the same way, using the series expansion for w_m as a function of T and integrating from 0 to ∞. Details will be omitted, but the result is

$$\overline{w} = \frac{3}{5} w_{mo} \left[1 + \frac{5\pi^2}{12} \left(\frac{kT}{w_{mo}} \right)^2 + \cdots \right]. \tag{16-32}$$

The total internal energy U of N electrons is

$$U = N\overline{w},$$

and the heat capacity at constant volume is

$$C_v = \frac{dU}{dT} = N \frac{d\overline{w}}{dT} = \frac{N\pi^2 k^2}{2w_{mo}} T.$$

If N equals Avogadro's number, then $Nk = R$ and C_v becomes the molar specific heat capacity c_v.

$$c_v = \frac{\pi^2 kT}{2w_{mo}} R. \tag{16-33}$$

The Maxwell-Boltzmann statistics predicts a value

$$c_v = \tfrac{3}{2} R,$$

independent of temperature, while the predicted Fermi-Dirac value is proportional to the temperature. The numerical value of $\pi^2 k/2w_{mo}$ for silver is

$$\frac{\pi^2 k}{2w_{mo}} = \frac{\pi^2 \times 1.38 \times 10^{-23}}{2 \times 9 \times 10^{-19}} = 7.6 \times 10^{-5} \text{ deg}^{-1}.$$

Hence at a temperature of 300° K the coefficient of R in Eq. (16-33) is only 0.023, compared with 3/2 or 1.50. The contribution of the electrons to the specific heat is therefore extremely small, in agreement with experiment.

16-8 Thermionic emission. Electrons within a conductor, coming up to the surface of the conductor with sufficient energy, can escape through the surface. This phenomenon is called *thermionic emission*. The emitted electrons can be drawn to a collecting electrode at a positive potential with respect to the emitting surface. If the potential difference between collecting electrode and emitter is great enough, all of the emitted electrons will be collected. The corresponding current density at the surface of the emitter is called the *saturation current density*, J_{sat}, and we now show how this can be computed.

Let the X-axis be taken normal to the surface, and consider first those electrons with a particular velocity component v_x. In a time interval dt, all such electrons within a distance $v_x dt$ of the surface will reach it. For a surface of area A, then, the number of electrons arriving at the surface in time dt with a velocity component v_x equals the number with this velocity component that are contained in a volume $V = A v_x dt$. Substituting this value of V in Eq. (16-30), dividing both sides by $A dt$, and multiplying by the electron charge e, we get the charge per unit time and per unit area, or the current density dJ_{v_x}, resulting from electrons with velocity v_x.

$$dJ_{v_x} = \frac{4\pi mekT}{h^3} \ln \left\{ \exp\left[(w_m - w_x)/kT \right] + 1 \right\} dw_x, \qquad (16\text{-}34)$$

where $v_x dv_x$ has been replaced by dw_x/m.

There exists at the surface of all conductors a so-called *potential barrier*, that is, a narrow region in which there is an electric field directed so as to slow down an electron approaching the surface from within. This must be the case, or otherwise all electrons reaching the surface would escape. Only those electrons with sufficiently great energies can surmount the potential barrier, escape through the surface, and contribute to the emission current. Electrons with smaller energies will be turned back. Let w_B be the minimum kinetic energy, normal to the surface, that an electron must have to surmount the potential barrier. The saturation current density is then obtained by integrating Eq. (16-34) from w_B to infinity.

$$J_{sat} = \frac{4\pi mekT}{h^3} \int_{w_B}^{\infty} \ln \left\{ \exp\left[(w_m - w_x)/kT \right] + 1 \right\} dw_x. \qquad (16\text{-}35)$$

In the integration range, w_x is always greater than w_B. Further-more, w_B must be considerably greater than w_m, since at ordinary temperatures the electrons in a metal do not spontaneously leak out. Hence $(w_m - w_x)/kT$, in the integration range, is a large negative number, the exponential term is small, and using the approximation $\ln(1 + x) = x$, Eq. (16-35) becomes

$$J_{sat} = AT^2 \exp(-\phi/kT), \tag{16-36}$$

where $A = 4\pi mek^2/h^3$ and $\phi = w_B - w_m$.

Equation (16-36) is the Dushman equation for thermionic emission. It is similar in form to an equation derived earlier by Richardson, based on the assumption that the electrons in a metal obey the Boltzmann rather than the Fermi-Dirac statistics. (See Problem 10 at the end of the chapter.)

A text on Electronics should be consulted for a detailed discussion of the agreement between experiment and theory. It must suffice here to state that the theory does predict the observed functional dependence of J_{sat} on the temperature T, and that from the experiments one can deduce the height w_B of the potential barrier, which turns out to be a few volts greater than the energy w_m.

Problems

1. Compute on the basis of the Fermi-Dirac statistics, for 4 phase points and 2 cells, and with $n = 4$, the thermodynamic probabilities of the macrostates $N_i = 4$, $N_j = 0$; $N_i = 2$, $N_j = 2$; $N_i = 1$, $N_j = 3$; $N_i = 0$, $N_j = 4$. Which macrostate has the greatest probability?

2. Calculate the mean speed, the rms speed, and the mean reciprocal speed, in terms of the maximum speed, for an electron gas at $0°$ K.

3. (a) Evaluate w_{mo} for tungsten, assuming two free electrons per tungsten atom. (b) Show that for tungsten at $3000°$ K, w_m differs from w_{mo} by less than one-tenth of one percent.

4. Plot the Fermi-Dirac speed distribution function for the free electrons in tungsten, (a) at $0°$ K, and (b) at $3000°$ K. Let $w_{mo} = 9.0$ ev.

5. (a) Calculate the electronic contribution to the molar specific heat capacity of tungsten, in terms of R. (b) What fraction is this of the molar heat capacity $3R$? Let $w_{mo} = 9.0$ ev.

6. (a) Find the number of electrons per unit time and per unit area, crossing a surface within a metal at $0°$ K in either direction. (b) What is the corresponding current density, in amp/cm²?

7. In an electron gas as well as in a molecular gas, $p = 2U/3V$. Find the pressure of the electron gas in silver at $0°$ K.

8. In order to escape from the surface of a metal, an electron must have a velocity component normal to the surface such that the kinetic energy associated with this component is greater than a certain value w_B. What fraction of the electrons in tungsten at a temperature of $2900°$ K have a *total* kinetic energy greater than $w_B = 13.5$ ev? Let $w_{mo} = 9.0$ ev. [See Table 12-2 for values of $erf(x)$.]

9. Derive Eq. (16-31) directly from the distribution in velocity space at $0°$ K.

10. Derive the Richardson equation for thermionic emission,

$$J_{sat} = A'T^{\frac{1}{2}} \exp\left(-\phi'/kT\right),$$

on the assumption that the electrons in a metal behave like a monatomic ideal gas obeying the Boltzmann statistics.

CHAPTER 17

FLUCTUATIONS

17-1 Density fluctuations in a gas.* A necessary consequence of the random motion of the molecules of a gas is that the number of molecules per unit volume, in any volume element, is not at every instant equal to its average value but instead fluctuates about this average. The theory of density fluctuations in a gas was first developed by Smoluchowski in 1908, and was followed by another treatment in 1914. The argument as we give it here is not entirely rigorous but in principle it is correct.

We have seen that the Boltzmann statistics applied to molecules in a gravitational field leads to Eq. (15-6),

$$dN_z = \frac{Nmg}{kT} \exp\left(-mgz/kT\right)dz,$$

where dN_z is the number of molecules in a vertical column between the elevations z and $z + dz$, and mgz is the potential energy of a molecule at the elevation z. This equation is of the form

$$dN_x = \alpha \exp\left(-\phi/kT\right)dx, \tag{17-1}$$

where ϕ represents the potential energy associated with some coordinate x, and α is a constant independent of x. The more general statistical theory mentioned in the footnote on page 277, instead of considering a large number of *molecules*, considers a large number of identical *systems*, each containing many molecules. This approach leads to an equation having precisely the form above except that dN_x represents the number of *systems* having the potential energy ϕ associated with some coordinate x. Each system is assumed to be in contact with a heat reservoir which maintains the system at a constant temperature T.

To apply the preceding equation to the problem of density fluctuations in a gas, we consider a very large volume of the gas, subdivided in imagination into a large number N of smaller volume elements or systems. The remainder of the gas serves as the heat reservoir for any one system. Each system contains a large number of molecules, n. (Because of a

---

* A comprehensive review of the literature bearing on the subject matter of this chapter, together with an extensive bibliography, will be found in an article by R. Bowling Barnes and S. Silverman in the *Reviews of Modern Physics*, Vol. 6, (1934), p. 162.

letter shortage we now use n for the number of molecules per system rather than for the number per unit volume.) For example, we might consider a volume of 10 liters or 10,000 cm^3 of a gas, and think of this as subdivided into volume elements or systems of one mm^3 each. Then $N = 10^7$ systems, and at standard conditions $n = 3 \times 10^{16}$ molecules/system.

We imagine each system of molecules enclosed within a perfectly flexible, heat-conducting sac, so that there is no exchange of molecules between systems. Then as a result of random molecular motions, the molecules of any one system will at times occupy a volume somewhat less than the normal volume V_0, and at other times they will occupy a volume somewhat greater than normal. At any one instant there will be fluctuations in density from system to system, throughout the body of the gas, or if we follow any one system as time goes on, its density will fluctuate with time.

Since we wish to obtain an expression for the number of systems, each of normal volume V_0, which as a consequence of fluctuations have an actual volume between V and $V + dV$, we let $x = V$ in Eq. (17-1) and write

$$dN_V = \alpha \exp(-\phi/kT)dV. \qquad (17\text{-}2)$$

The next step is to obtain an expression for the potential energy ϕ. We consider the potential energy of a system to be zero when it has the volume V_0 and pressure p_0 appropriate to a perfectly uniform distribution of molecules throughout the main body of the gas. The potential energy in any other state, of volume V and pressure p, is the work done on the system to bring it from the uniform state to this state. We assume that during the change the remainder of the gas exerts on the system the pressure p_0. Then if p is the pressure exerted by the molecules of the system at any instant, the net external pressure is $p_0 - p$ and the work done on the system while its volume changes from V_0 to V, or the potential energy ϕ, is

$$\phi = \int_{V_0}^{V} (p_0 - p)dV = -\int_{V_0}^{V} (p - p_0)dV. \qquad (17\text{-}3)$$

The pressure p is some function of the volume V, and without making any special assumptions as to the equation of state of the gas, we can always use a Taylor's series to express the pressure p as follows:

$$p = p_0 + \left(\frac{\partial p}{\partial V}\right)_0 (V - V_0) + \left(\frac{\partial^2 p}{\partial V^2}\right)_0 \frac{(V - V_0)^2}{2!}$$
$$+ \left(\frac{\partial^3 p}{\partial V^3}\right)_0 \frac{(V - V_0)^3}{3!} + \cdots, \qquad (17\text{-}4)$$

where the derivatives are to be evaluated at constant temperature and at the volume V_0. The number of terms to be retained in the series depends on the nature of the gas.

We consider first the special case of an ideal gas. Since $pV = nkT$,

$$\left(\frac{\partial p}{\partial V}\right)_0 = -\frac{1}{V_0^2} nkT,$$

$$\left(\frac{\partial^2 p}{\partial V^2}\right)_0 = \frac{2}{V_0^3} nkT, \text{ etc.,}$$

and since from the nature of the problem the fluctuations are small and $(V - V_0) \ll V_0$, it follows from Eq. (17-4) that the terms containing the second and higher derivatives are very small compared with that containing the first derivative. Then we can write

$$p - p_0 = -nkT \frac{V - V_0}{V_0^2}$$

$$= -\frac{nkT}{V_0} \frac{V - V_0}{V_0}$$

$$= -p_0 \frac{\Delta V}{V_0}. \tag{17-5}$$

The fractional change in volume, $\Delta V/V_0$, was called by Smoluchowski the *condensation* (Verdichtung) δ.

$$\delta = \frac{\Delta V}{V_0} = \frac{V - V_0}{V_0} = \frac{V}{V_0} - 1. \tag{17-6}$$

Hence

$$d\delta = \frac{1}{V_0} dV,$$

and using Eq. (17-5) we can write Eq. (17-3) in the form

$$\phi = \int_0^\delta p_0 V_0 \delta d\delta$$

$$= \frac{p_0 V_0 \delta^2}{2} = \frac{nkT\delta^2}{2}, \tag{17-7}$$

and hence

$$\frac{\phi}{kT} = \frac{n\delta^2}{2}. \tag{17-8}$$

Equation (17-2) therefore becomes, for an ideal gas,

$$dN_\delta = V_0 \, \alpha \exp(-n\delta^2/2) d\delta. \tag{17-9}$$

The constant α can now be determined from the requirement that the integral of dN_δ over all possible values of δ must equal the total number of systems, N. Now δ is always a small quantity, but suppose it is as large as $\pm 1\%$ or $\pm 10^{-2}$. Then $\delta^2 = 10^{-4}$. Also, suppose we consider a system so small that it contains only 2×10^6 molecules (in general, n is much larger than this). Then $n\delta^2/2 = 2 \times 10^6 \times 10^{-4}/2 = 100$ and $\exp(-n\delta^2/2) = \exp(-100)$. Hence the exponential term is already so small when $\delta = \pm 10^{-2}$ that we may without appreciable error take the limits of integration from $-\infty$ to $+\infty$. Then

$$N = \int dN_\delta = V_0 \alpha \int_{-\infty}^{\infty} \exp(-n\delta^2/2)d\delta$$

$$= V_0 \alpha \sqrt{\frac{2\pi}{n}},$$

and

$$V_0 \alpha = N\sqrt{\frac{n}{2\pi}}.$$

Then from Eq. (17-9),

$$\frac{dN}{N} = \sqrt{\frac{n}{2\pi}} \exp(-n\delta^2/2)d\delta. \tag{17-10}$$

The ratio dN/N can be considered either as the fractional number of systems for which the condensation, at any instant, lies between δ and $\delta + d\delta$, or as the fraction of time spent by any one system in this state. Note that the number of systems in which the condensation at any instant has the value δ decreases exponentially both with n and with δ^2.

The mean condensation $\bar{\delta}$ is of course zero, as would be expected, since the distribution is an even function of δ. Let us therefore calculate the root-mean-square condensation, $\sqrt{\bar{\delta^2}} = \delta_{\text{rms}}$.

$$\delta_{\text{rms}} = \left[\frac{\int_{-\infty}^{\infty} \delta^2 \exp(-n\delta^2/2)d\delta}{\int_{-\infty}^{\infty} \exp(-n\delta^2/2)d\delta} \right]^{1/2} = \frac{1}{\sqrt{n}}. \tag{17-11}$$

The rms condensation is therefore equal to the reciprocal of the square root of the number of particles in the system. For example, in a volume containing 10^{16} molecules (approximately 1 mm³ at standard conditions)

$$\delta_{\text{rms}} = \frac{1}{\sqrt{10^{16}}} = 10^{-8}.$$

Since $\delta = \Delta V/V_0$, the rms fluctuation in volume (or density), in a volume of this size, is only one part in one hundred million. On the other hand, a volume having linear dimensions of the order of a wavelength of light (say 600 mμ = 6 $\times$ 10^{-7} m) contains about 6 $\times$ 10^6 molecules, and in such a volume $\delta \approx$ 5 $\times$ 10^{-4} or 0.05%. Smoluchowski showed that fluctuations of this order of magnitude resulted in variations of the index of refraction throughout a gas, of sufficient amount to cause appreciable scattering of light passing through the gas. In fact, Smoluchowski derived the same formula for light scattering that had been obtained by Rayleigh from a consideration of the polarizability of air molecules. It will be recalled that the Rayleigh formula predicts a scattering inversely proportional to the 4th power of the wavelength, and that hence blue light is scattered more than red, which accounts for the blue of the sky. Measurements of the scattering of sunlight by the earth's atmosphere, made at very high altitudes where the amount of dust is small, have been used to compute the value of k and thus, knowing R, to find Avogadro's number N_0. The remarkably precise value of 6.05 $\times$ 10^{26} was obtained by Fowler in 1914, from observations on Mt. Wilson in California.

Using Eq. (17-11), we can write Eq. (17-10) as

$$dN/N = \frac{1}{\delta_{\text{rms}}\sqrt{2\pi}} \exp\left(-\delta^2/2\delta_{\text{rms}}^2\right)d\delta, \qquad (17\text{-}12)$$

or, if we define a dimensionless quantity x by the equation

$$x = \delta/\delta_{\text{rms}},$$

$$dN/N = (1/\sqrt{2\pi}) \exp\left(-x^2/2\right)dx.$$

Figure 17-1 is a graph in which the dimensionless ratio $(dN/N)/dx$ is plotted as a function of x. The curve is said to represent a *normal* or *Gaussian* distribution, and it is typical of all types of random fluctuations. It has the same mathematical form as the Maxwell-Boltzmann velocity distribution function, which can be considered to represent the fluctuations (in velocity) of a system consisting of just one molecule. However, because of the factor n in the exponential term in Eq. (17-10),

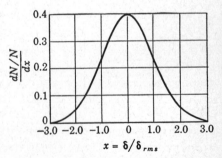

Fig. 17-1. Normal or Gaussian distribution of random fluctuations. $x = \delta/\delta_{\text{rms}}$, $y = (dN/N)/dx = 1/\sqrt{2\pi} \exp\left(-x^2/2\right)$.

the fluctuations in a system containing n molecules are extremely small compared with those of a single molecule.

Let us now compute the mean potential energy of a system, resulting from fluctuations in density. We obtained for the potential energy ϕ the expression

$$\phi = \frac{nkT}{2}\,\delta^2.$$

Hence the mean potential energy, $\bar{\phi}$, equals the product of $nkT/2$ and the mean square condensation, $\overline{\delta^2}$. But from Eq. (17-11),

$$\overline{\delta^2} = \frac{1}{n},$$

so

$$\bar{\phi} = \frac{nkT}{2} \times \frac{1}{n} = \tfrac{1}{2}\,kT. \tag{17-13}$$

This is another illustration of the equipartition principle. (Note that ϕ depends on δ^2.) The number of particles, n, does not appear in the expression for $\bar{\phi}$. The mean potential energy of any volume element of an ideal gas, due to fluctuations, is $\tfrac{1}{2}kT$.

The phenomenon of light scattering is especially pronounced in a substance at or near its critical point, resulting in a milky or opalescent appearance. This effect had been observed for many years but its cause was not known until the theory was given by Smoluchowski. For a substance at its critical point, we cannot of course assume that the equation of state of an ideal gas is obeyed, and so we must return to the general series expansion for the pressure p, Eq. (17-4). Since at the critical point

$$\frac{\partial p}{\partial V} = \frac{\partial^2 p}{\partial V^2} = 0,$$

the first nonvanishing derivative is $\partial^3 p/\partial V^3$, and Eq. (17-3) becomes

$$\phi = -\int_{V_c}^{V}\left(\frac{\partial^3 p}{\partial V^3}\right)_c \frac{(V - V_c)^3}{3!}\,dV, \tag{17-14}$$

where we have replaced V_0 by the critical volume V_c. To proceed further we must know p as a function of V, so let us assume that van der Waals' equation is obeyed. Then

$$p = \frac{RT}{v - b} - \frac{a}{v^2}, \quad V = \frac{n}{N_0}\,v,$$

and

$$\left(\frac{\partial^3 p}{\partial V^3}\right)_c = -\frac{a}{81b^5}\left(\frac{N_0}{n}\right)^3 = -\frac{27}{8}\frac{RT_c}{v_c^4}\left(\frac{N_0}{n}\right)^3. \tag{17-15}$$

Again introducing the condensation δ, we find on evaluating Eq. (17-14) that

$$\frac{\phi}{kT_c} = \frac{9}{64} n\delta^4,$$

so

$$dN = \alpha \exp(-9n\delta^4/64)d\delta, \qquad (17\text{-}16)$$

as contrasted with Eq. (17-9) for an ideal gas. Note that the fluctuations now depend on the 4th power of the condensation, rather than on the square.

The constant α is evaluated,* as before, from the requirement that $\int dN = N$, and we find

$$\frac{dN}{N} = \frac{\sqrt[4]{9n/64}}{2\Gamma(5/4)} \exp(-9n\delta^4/64)d\delta. \qquad (17\text{-}17)$$

Again the mean condensation is zero, while the root-mean-square value, evaluated in the usual way, is

$$\delta_{\text{rms}} = \frac{0.95}{\sqrt[4]{n}}. \qquad (17\text{-}18)$$

Since the fluctuations now vary inversely with the 4th root of n, rather than with the square root, they can be relatively large even for relatively large values of n. For example, at the critical point of ethyl ether, in a volume of linear dimensions of the order of the wavelength of visible light, there are about 4×10^8 molecules and the rms density fluctuation is of the order of 1.5%. It is these relatively large density fluctuations which account for the opalescence observed at the critical point.

17-2 Theory of Brownian motion. The considerations in the preceding section hold also for colloidal suspensions (a colloidal particle is not fundamentally different from a molecule according to statistical ideas) and since such particles can be observed directly with a microscope it is possible by direct counting to measure fluctuations in their concentration. In such measurements n is a very small number (it was a very large number in the preceding examples) which calls for certain modifications in the Smoluchowski formula which we need not go into here, since the principles are the same. Table 17-1 gives a series of observations made by Svedberg in 1912 of the number of colloidal particles within a certain small volume of a colloidal suspension. The number was observed 36 times per minute

---

* Use the relation

$$\int_0^\infty \exp(-x^n)\,dx = \Gamma\left(\frac{1}{n}+1\right).$$

TABLE 17-1

Number of particles	Number of times observed
0	15
1	36
2	24
3	14
4	8
5	2
6	1
7	0
8	0

and the existence of fluctuations is evident. The average number of particles is 1.74, and large fluctuations evidently occur less frequently than small ones. Svedberg found an excellent quantitative agreement between the theory and observation.

To say that a particle in suspension carries out an irregular motion as a result of collisions by the molecules around it is only another way of expressing the cause of fluctuations in concentration. Without such a motion, fluctuations in concentration would be impossible.

As a matter of fact, this zigzag to-and-fro motion of suspended particles has been known for a long time. It was observed in 1827 by the English botanist Brown and is named after him, *Brownian motion*. The theory of this remarkable phenomenon, on the other hand, was developed only comparatively recently. At first, the explanation of this continuous movement was sought either in inhomogeneities of temperature in the surrounding fluid or in other external influences. The systematic researches of Wiener and Gouy first made it evident that the explanation must be sought in the collisions with molecules of the surrounding fluid. In 1906, Einstein and Smoluchowski both derived essentially the same formula from kinetic theory considerations (although by entirely different methods) and this formula has been completely verified by the experiments of Perrin, Svedberg, Seddig, and others.

We now give the derivation of the Einstein formula as it was worked out by Langevin in 1908. This method of attack leads us most quickly to our goal, although it does not give the deeper insight into the details of the phenomenon that is provided by the theories of Einstein and Smoluchowski.

Langevin proceeded from the assumption that the force on a suspended particle of mass m could be considered of two kinds, of which the first is a "frictional" force proportional to the velocity, while all other external influences of the surrounding fluid can be combined in the second. It cannot be denied that this subdivision is somewhat artificial, since the so-called friction force also arises from collisions with neighboring molecules, as explained in Section 13-3. This division is therefore a mixture of two points of view, i.e., the statistical-atomic, and the continuous fluid viewpoint of ordinary hydrodynamics. Nevertheless, the result shows that the division is justified.

For the motion of a particle in any specified but arbitrary direction, which we take as the x-direction, we have, according to Langevin, an equation of the form

$$m\ddot{x} = -f\dot{x} + X.$$ (17-19)

Here $(-f\dot{x})$ designates the x-component of the friction force and X is the combined effect of all other influences. When this equation is multiplied through by x, we get

$$m\ddot{x}x = -f\dot{x}x + Xx.$$ (17-20)

Now

$$\dot{x}x = \frac{1}{2}\frac{d(x^2)}{dt},$$

and

$$\ddot{x}x = \frac{1}{2}\frac{d}{dt}\left[\frac{d(x^2)}{dt}\right] - \dot{x}^2.$$

Hence Eq. (17-20) becomes

$$\frac{m}{2}\frac{d}{dt}\left[\frac{d(x^2)}{dt}\right] - m\dot{x}^2 = -\frac{f}{2}\frac{d(x^2)}{dt} + Xx.$$ (17-21)

We form such an equation for each particle which is suspended in the fluid, and take the mean of these expressions for all particles.

$$\frac{m}{2}\frac{\overline{d}}{dt}\left[\frac{d(x^2)}{dt}\right] - \overline{m\dot{x}^2} = -\frac{f}{2}\frac{\overline{d(x^2)}}{dt} + \overline{Xx}.$$ (17-22)

Let us now assume (strictly, a special proof is required) that the mean value $\overline{Xx}$ vanishes, because the force X varies in a completely irregular manner. Further. according to the equipartition theorem,

$$\overline{m\dot{x}^2} = kT,$$

so that we obtain finally, since $\dfrac{\overline{d(x^2)}}{dt} = \dfrac{d}{dt}\,\overline{(x^2)}$,

$$\frac{m}{2}\frac{d}{dt}\left[\frac{d\overline{(x^2)}}{dt}\right] + \frac{1}{2}f\frac{d\overline{(x^2)}}{dt} = kT.$$ (17-23)

For brevity, let

$$\frac{d\overline{(x^2)}}{dt} = u.$$

Then Eq. (17-23) can be written

$$\frac{m}{2}\frac{du}{dt} + \frac{1}{2}fu = kT,$$

which is a differential equation for determining u. The general solution is

$$u = kT\frac{2}{f} + C \exp(-ft/m),$$

where C is an integration constant. Now because of the small value of m the quotient f/m is a very large number, so that the exponential term has no influence after the first extremely small time interval and

$$u = \frac{d\overline{(x^2)}}{dt} = kT\frac{2}{f}. \tag{17-24}$$

After integration from $t = 0$ to $t = \tau$, this gives

$$\overline{x^2} - \overline{x_0^2} = kT\frac{2}{f}\tau.$$

If we now set $x_0 = 0$ when $t = 0$, and because of its small value write $\overline{\Delta x^2}$ instead of $\overline{x^2}$, then

$$\overline{\Delta x^2} = kT\frac{2}{f}\tau. \tag{17-25}$$

The quantity $\overline{\Delta x^2}$ has the following meaning. A particle is observed at time 0 and time τ. During this time interval it has undergone a displacement Δs, whose projection on the x-axis is Δx. The same particle is observed at later times, always separated by the same interval τ, i.e., at times 2τ, 3τ, $\cdots$, and Δx is determined for each interval. These values are squared and their mean is computed, thus giving $\overline{\Delta x^2}$. The displacements thus observed are in no sense the actual path of the particle, nor is $\Delta x/\tau$ the x-component of its velocity. For example, in a time interval $\tau = 1$ sec (actually much too short a time interval for the observations; in the experiments of Perrin described below τ equaled 30 sec), the particle makes millions of collisions and what we see are simply its initial and final positions, which we connect by a straight line, while the true path is a confused zigzag of linear segments. What we observe is already a greatly simplified "path," an example of which is given in Fig. 17-2. If one imagines each of the linear elements in this figure to be composed of millions of straight lines one will begin to approximate the actual path. It is impossible to analyze this complicated motion in all of its details and we must therefore be satisfied to observe, in a certain time interval τ, the corresponding magnitude of Δx and to form $\overline{\Delta x^2}$, which is only loosely related to the true path.

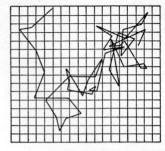

FIG. 17-2.

An expression for the factor f is now introduced from hydrodynamics, a procedure which is naturally open to the same objections as the original division of the forces into a friction force $-f\dot{x}$ and an irregular force X. But once we have admitted this possibility, then it is only natural to call on ordinary hydrodynamics for the determination of f. The physical significance of f is a force per unit of velocity. But Stokes' law gives for the viscous force F on a sphere of radius R, moving with velocity v in a fluid of viscosity η, the expression

$$F = 6\pi\eta Rv.$$

Therefore

$$f = \frac{F}{v} = 6\pi\eta R.$$

Combining this equation with Eq. (17-25) gives finally

$$\sqrt{\overline{\Delta x^2}} = \sqrt{kT}\, \frac{\sqrt{\tau}}{\sqrt{3\pi\eta R}}. \qquad (17\text{-}26)$$

This is the Einstein formula (and, with a slight change in the numerical coefficient, that of Smoluchowski also), the experimental proof of which we now consider. If the formula is satisfied we have a convincing proof of the existence of molecules, and since Brownian motion is brought about by molecular collisions, this is of the greatest importance for the verification of the molecular-kinetic theory.

One sees first from the formula (an extremely surprising result) that $\sqrt{\overline{\Delta x^2}}$ does not depend at all on the mass of the particle. Nevertheless this prediction of the theory was shown by Perrin to be satisfied to high precision. In his experiments the masses of the particles observed varied in the ratio $1:15{,}000$, nevertheless his results, within the limits of experimental error, all gave the same value for the Boltzmann constant k (or for Avogadro's number $N_0 = R/k$). The measurements were made in the following way.

The instantaneous position of a particle was determined at equal time intervals τ by a rectangular network in the ocular of a compound microscope, and was plotted on a sheet of rectangular coordinate paper. Two successive positions determine a value of Δs, or rather, of the horizontal projection of Δs (since only the latter can be determined by a microscope). From each Δs the projection is taken in a specified direction, to give Δx.

From his best measurements, Perrin found for N_0 the value 6.85×10^{26} molecules/kilomole. In the light of later measurements this value is undoubtedly too large. Westgren, using the same methods, obtained 6.04 to 6.05×10^{26}, which is probably correct to within 1%.

The results of Perrin, Svedberg, and Westgren all agree in proving that $\sqrt{\overline{\Delta x^2}}$ is proportional to $\sqrt{\tau}$ and inversely proportional to $\sqrt{\eta}$. The temperature effect is not large, since $\sqrt{\overline{\Delta x^2}}$ is proportional to $\sqrt{T}$, but since the viscosity η decreases rapidly with increasing temperature, the pure temperature effect is outweighed by the large decrease in viscosity. The work of Perrin and Svedberg is a brilliant quantitative confirmation of the Einstein-Smoluchowski equation and with it of the kinetic theory.

One remark of fundamental significance should be made here. The diffusion of a nonuniform colloidal suspension is obviously only possible because the individual particles execute Brownian motion. Diffusion, Brownian motion, and fluctuations in concentration are therefore all a single phenomenon. In macroscopic observations we speak of diffusion, in substantial, of Brownian motion, and in local, of fluctuations in concentration. Here the terms "substantial" and "local" are used in the same sense as in hydrodynamics. In a "substantial" consideration we follow a particle of the fluid in its motion; in a "local," we consider a volume fixed in space, into which particles come and out of which they wander.

17-3 Brownian motion of a galvanometer.

The moving system of a D'Arsonval galvanometer consists of a coil of wire and a mirror, suspended by a fine fiber and capable of rotation about a vertical axis. Random collisions of air molecules with the suspended system produce torques which are not equal and opposite at all instants. The result is that the angular position of the system is continuously fluctuating and the system exhibits an unsteady zero, another example of Brownian motion.

Corresponding to the viscous friction force on a particle in suspension, we have air damping or electromagnetic damping of the galvanometer, but the motion differs from that of a particle in that an elastic restoring torque develops when the mirror is displaced from its true equilibrium position, while no such restoring force acts on a suspended particle. We can, however, immediately write down the expression for the rms displacement or angular velocity, since the elastic potential energy $\frac{1}{2}K\theta^2$ and the rotational kinetic energy $\frac{1}{2}I\omega^2$ are both proportional to the squares of their respective coordinates, and the mean energy associated with each is $\frac{1}{2}kT$.

$$\frac{1}{2}I\overline{\omega^2} = \frac{1}{2}kT,$$

$$\frac{1}{2}K\overline{\theta^2} = \frac{1}{2}kT.$$

From the second equation, the root-mean-square angular displacement is

$$\theta_{\text{rms}} = \sqrt{\overline{\theta^2}} = \sqrt{\frac{kT}{K}}. \tag{17-27}$$

The torque constant K for a fine quartz fiber is of the order of 10^{-6} dyne-cm/radian or 10^{-13} n-m/radian, so that at a temperature of 300° K,

$$\theta_{\text{rms}} = \sqrt{\frac{1.38 \times 10^{-23} \times 300}{10^{-13}}}$$

$$\approx 2 \times 10^{-4} \text{ radian.}$$

If the light source and scale are at a distance of 1 meter from the mirror, this corresponds to a root-mean-square fluctuation of the light spot of 4×10^{-4} m or 0.4 mm. Note that the smaller the torque constant K and the more sensitive the galvanometer, the larger are the statistical fluctuations of its zero point.

A measurement of θ_{rms} for a galvanometer system of known torque constant evidently provides still another method of determining k or N_0. Such a study was made by Kappler, who found $N_0 = 6.0 \times 10^{26}$ molecules/kilomole.

In order to detect a current with a galvanometer, we must be reasonably sure that an observed deflection is not just a stray kick due to Brownian motion. Since the random deflections follow a Gaussian distribution like that in Fig. 17-1, the fractional number greater than any arbitrary assigned value can be computed. It turns out that only one out of 16,000 is greater than 4 times the rms deflection, so we may take $4\theta_{\text{rms}}$ as an arbitrary limit and feel very sure that any observed deflection greater than this is not due to chance.

The general expression for the minimum detectable current can be expressed in terms of galvanometer constants as follows. Let the coil have N turns of area A, and swing in a magnetic field of flux density B.

The deflecting torque M_d when the current is i, assuming the plane of the coil parallel to the magnetic field, is

$$M_d = NiAB = (N\Phi)i,$$

where we have replaced AB by Φ, the total flux intercepted by the coil when normal to the field.

The restoring torque at an angular deflection θ is

$$M_r = K\theta.$$

In the equilibrium position these are equal, so

$$\theta = \frac{N\Phi}{K} i. \qquad (17\text{-}28)$$

The natural period of oscillation, τ_0, is

$$\tau_0 = 2\pi\sqrt{\frac{I}{K}}. \qquad (17\text{-}29)$$

It can be shown that the critical external damping resistance (CXDR) R_c is given by

$$R_c = \frac{N^2\Phi^2\tau_0}{4\pi I}, \qquad (17\text{-}30)$$

and we shall assume the instrument shunted by this resistance.

To find the minimum current i_{min} that can be detected with adequate certainty, we set θ in Eq. (17-28) equal to $4\theta_{rms}$.

$$\frac{N\Phi}{K} i_{min} = 4\theta_{rms}.$$

Using Eqs. (17-27), (17-29), and (17-30), this becomes

$$i_{min} = 4\sqrt{\frac{\pi kT}{R_c\tau_0}}. \qquad (17\text{-}31)$$

The corresponding minimum voltage v_{min} is

$$v_{min} = 4\sqrt{\frac{\pi kTR_c}{\tau_0}}. \qquad (17\text{-}32)$$

At a temperature of 300° K,

$$i_{min} = 4.4 \times 10^{-10}\sqrt{\frac{1}{R_c\tau_0}},$$

$$v_{min} = 4.4 \times 10^{-10}\sqrt{\frac{R_c}{\tau_0}}.$$

Thus if $\tau_0 = 16$ sec and $R_c = 100$ ohms,

$$i_{min} \approx 10^{-11} \text{ amp}, \quad v_{min} \approx 10^{-9} \text{ volt}.$$

Thus, although the statistical fluctuations increase inversely with $\sqrt{K}$, the minimum detectable current can be decreased by using a long period instrument, since the natural period τ_0 is inversely proportional to $\sqrt{K}$. The limit is set by the mechanical stability of an extremely fine fiber and the patience of the observer.

The reader has probably wondered why the Brownian fluctuations of a galvanometer system cannot be removed by suspending the mirror in a vacuum, thus eliminating the fluctuating torques produced by molecular collisions. Apart from the fact that even at the low pressure produced by the best pumping systems there still remains a tremendous number of molecules per unit volume, we see that such a procedure would not produce the result desired. Let us first consider the effect of reducing the pressure. If the galvanometer system is in thermal equilibrium with a heat reservoir at temperature T (the galvanometer case) it must have a mean rotational kinetic energy of $\frac{1}{2}kT$. If the system, initially at rest, receives an angular impulse from a molecular collision, it starts to oscillate at its natural frequency and continues to do so until it is disturbed by the next following impulse. When the density of the surrounding gas is relatively high these impulses come in such rapid succession that the natural oscillation is scarcely detectable. As the pressure is lowered, the intervals between collisions become longer and the motion tends more and more toward that of an isolated system. The rms amplitude, however, remains the same. This effect is illustrated in Fig. 17-3, where the upper curve is a trace of the oscillations at atmospheric pressure, and the lower curve is a trace of the oscillations at a pressure of 10^{-4} mm of mercury.

Even if the colliding *molecules* could be completely eliminated, there would still be a flow of radiant energy between the system and its surroundings. But radiant energy is carried by light quanta or photons, which

FIG. 17-3.

have energy and momentum and whose emission and absorption are statistical phenomena. The emission or absorption of a photon produces a change in angular momentum of the system, and the rms energy of oscillation is still $\frac{1}{2}kT$. Reduction of the temperature, however, does reduce the amplitude of the fluctuations, which approach zero as the temperature approaches 0° K. But although the oscillations of a *freely swinging* galvanometer can be reduced in this way, there are fluctuations of charge in any external circuit to which the galvanometer is connected and if the temperature of the external circuit is T, the rms energy of the galvanometer is still $\frac{1}{2}kT$ even if the temperature of the galvanometer itself is 0° K. We show this as follows.

Since the electricity in a conductor is atomistic in nature, i.e., it consists of discrete charged particles, then as a result of the random motions of these particles the quantity of charge crossing any section of the conductor in one direction does not always equal that crossing in the other direction. In other words, random currents exist in any conductor, with which we can associate random emf's. Such effects are responsible for "thermal noise" or Johnson noise in an amplifier, as well as for the existence of a lower limit to the current that can be detected by a galvanometer.

We consider the case of a single wire in the form of a closed loop, having a resistance R and self-inductance L. Capacitive effects can be neglected. We assume that the random electronic motion is equivalent to a fluctuating emf $\mathcal{E}$ in the circuit. Then at any instant

$$L\frac{di}{dt} + Ri = \mathcal{E},$$

or, if q represents the net charge crossing any section of the circuit,

$$L\frac{d^2q}{dt^2} + R\frac{dq}{dt} = \mathcal{E}.$$

This equation has exactly the same form as that for the displacement of a particle in Brownian motion,

$$m\frac{d^2x}{dt^2} + f\frac{dx}{dt} = X,$$

and we can follow the same mathematical procedure. Multiply through by q, set the mean magnetic energy $\frac{1}{2}L\overline{i^2}$ equal to $\frac{1}{2}kT$, and assume that because of the random nature of $\mathcal{E}$ the mean value $\overline{\mathcal{E}q} = 0$. The result is

$$\overline{q^2} = \frac{2kT}{R}\,\tau. \qquad (17\text{-}33)$$

(We shall use the symbol q instead of Δq.)

Again, the significance of $\overline{q^2}$ must be kept in mind. For each of a number of equal time intervals τ we find the net charge q that has crossed the section during this interval, then we square these, and finally take their average value. Equation (17-33) states that the average thus found is proportional to the time interval and to the temperature, and inversely proportional to the resistance. Note that the self-inductance L drops out, as did the mass m in Brownian motion, showing that the shape of the circuit has no effect (except that the time interval τ must be much larger than the time constant L/R).

The average current $\bar{i}$ during any one of the time intervals is

$$\bar{i} = \frac{q}{\tau},$$

where q is the charge crossing during that interval. These average currents are of course different for different intervals. The square of the average current in any one interval is

$$(\bar{i})^2 = \frac{q^2}{\tau^2},$$

and the average of these average squares over a large number of intervals is

$$\overline{(\bar{i})^2} = \frac{\overline{q^2}}{\tau^2}.$$

But from Eq. (17-33),

$$\overline{q^2} = \frac{2kT}{R}\,\tau,$$

so

$$\sqrt{\overline{(\bar{i})^2}} = \sqrt{\frac{2kT}{R\tau}}. \tag{17-34}$$

Except for the numerical factor, the right side of this equation has exactly the same form as that of Eq. (17-31) if we let $\tau = \tau_0$, the natural period of the galvanometer, and $R = R_c$. That is, the natural fluctuations of the electrons in the external circuit set the same lower limit to the current that can be detected by a galvanometer as do the oscillations of the galvanometer mirror, provided both are at the same temperature.

Of course the significance of $\sqrt{\overline{(\bar{i})^2}}$ in Eq. (17-34) is not exactly the same as that of i in Eq. (17-31), since they are obtained by different averaging processes. The original literature should be consulted for further discussion of this point.

17-4 The small-shot effect.   The thermionic current in a vacuum tube is not a smooth flow of electricity, but is subject to fluctuations caused by the random emission of electrons from the cathode.   These fluctuations were discovered by Schottky and were called by him the Schrot or small-shot effect ("bird-shot" might have been a better English translation). When the current in the tube is amplified and sent through a speaker the fluctuations make themselves evident as a continuous sound or noise of indefinite frequency.   (The shot effect should not be confused with another phenomenon also discovered by Schottky and called the Schottky effect, which has to do with the reduction of the work function of a thermionic cathode by an accelerating field.)

The mathematical analysis of the problem is very similar to that of the fluctuations of density in an ideal gas, given in Section 17-1, where we showed that

$$\delta_{\text{rms}} = \frac{1}{\sqrt{n}},$$

n being the number of particles in a volume V_0, and δ being defined as $\Delta V/V_0$.

If in Section 17-1 we had considered a volume V_0 fixed in size, and had computed the fluctuations in the number of particles within it, we would have found by the same method

$$\delta_{\text{rms}} = \frac{1}{\sqrt{n_0}},$$

where δ is now defined as

$$\delta = \frac{\Delta n}{n_0},$$

and n_0 is the normal number of particles in the volume V_0.   From the definition above,

$$\delta_{\text{rms}} = \frac{(\Delta n)_{\text{rms}}}{n_0},$$

and combining with the preceding equation, we get

$$(\Delta n)_{\text{rms}} = \sqrt{n_0}. \tag{17-35}$$

That is, the rms fluctuation in n equals the square root of n_0.   The same relation applies to the fluctuations in thermionic emission.   Let i_0 be the average emission current.   The charge q_0 carried in time τ is

$$q_0 = i_0\tau,$$

and the number of electrons n_0 is

$$n_0 = \frac{q_0}{e} = \frac{i_0 \tau}{e}.$$

The time τ must be long enough so that n_0 is a large number.

The rms fluctuation in n is

$$(\Delta n)_{\text{rms}} = \sqrt{n_0} = \sqrt{\frac{i_0 \tau}{e}},$$

and the corresponding fluctuation in current is

$$(\Delta i)_{\text{rms}} = \frac{e(\Delta n)_{\text{rms}}}{\tau} = \sqrt{\frac{i_0 e}{\tau}}. \tag{17-36}$$

Note that the larger the charge of an individual electron, the greater the fluctuations in current. It is only because the charge e is so small that these fluctuations are not ordinarily observed. Equation (17-36) also provides another relation from which the electron charge e can be determined experimentally, by a technique quite different from the Millikan experiment. The time interval τ is the time constant of the measuring circuit. Hull and Williams obtained in this way the value

$$e = 1.585 \times 10^{-19} \text{ coul,}$$

in excellent agreement with the present accepted value.

Under ordinary conditions of use, the thermionic current in a vacuum tube is space charge limited and the shot effect is masked by space charge effects. The predominant source of thermal noise in a well-designed amplifier is the emf developed in the grid resistors by Brownian fluctuations and discussed in the following section.

17-5 Johnson noise. We conclude this chapter with a brief discussion of the "spectrum analysis" of thermal noise, that is, the amount of energy in any specified frequency range or bandwidth. The problem was studied experimentally by Johnson and theoretically by Nyquist. Although the theoretical approach seems somewhat artificial, there is good agreement between theory and experiment.

Consider the simple circuit of Fig. 17-4, a transmission line of zero resistance, self-inductance and capacitance per unit length of L and C respectively, and terminated at each end by a pure resistance equal to the characteristic impedance, $R = \sqrt{L/C}$. Because of the

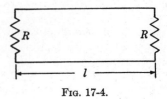

Fig. 17-4.

fluctuations of the charge within it, each resistor can be considered as an A.C. generator transmitting power to the other. All of the power is absorbed and none reflected, since the line is terminated by its characteristic impedance.

At some instant after the steady state has been reached let the line be isolated from the resistors and the ends either left open or shorted. The waves traveling along the line are now completely reflected at the ends, the energy in the line is trapped, and the system can be considered as a set of standing waves. If the length of the line is l and the velocity of propagation is v, the wavelength of the longest standing wave is $2l$ and its frequency f_0 is $v/2l$. The frequencies of the other standing waves are $2f_0$, $3f_0$, $\cdots$, nf_0, where n is an integer. Each of these standing waves can be considered as a degree of freedom of the system, and each has associated with it an energy kT ($\frac{1}{2}kT$ for magnetic energy, $\frac{1}{2}kT$ for electrostatic energy).

Now consider the band of frequencies between a frequency $f_2 = nf_0$ and $f_1 = mf_0$, where n and m are integers and $n > m$. The number of modes of vibration N in this band is $n - m$.

$$N = n - m.$$

Multiplying and dividing the right side by f_0, we get

$$N = \frac{nf_0 - mf_0}{f_0} = \frac{f_2 - f_1}{f_0}.$$

Since the energy associated with each mode is kT, the total energy W in this band is

$$W = NkT = \frac{kT}{f_0}(f_2 - f_1).$$

In the original circuit, where the line was terminated by its characteristic impedance, the expression above gives the amount of energy delivered to the line by the two resistors during the time of transit l/v. Hence the power output P of each resistor in this band is

$$P = \frac{1}{2}\frac{W}{l/v} = \frac{kTv}{2f_0 l}(f_2 - f_1),$$

and, since $f_0 = v/2l$, we have finally

$$P = kT(f_2 - f_1). \tag{17-37}$$

The power is proportional to the temperature and to the bandwidth $f_2 - f_1$, but does not depend on the location of the band. That is, under the conditions assumed, the power in a bandwidth of 1000 cycles/sec between 1000 and 2000 cycles/sec, equals that in the band between 15,000 and 16,000 cycles/sec. In other words, we have a uniform noise spectrum.

The equivalent mean square current in the circuit can be obtained by setting $P = R\bar{i^2}$, which gives

$$\bar{i^2} = \frac{kT}{R} (f_2 - f_1).$$ (17-38)

The equivalent mean square emf is

$$\bar{\mathcal{E}^2} = \bar{i^2} (2R)^2 = 4RkT(f_2 - f_1).$$ (17-39)

For example, the rms Johnson emf developed in a grid resistor of 100,000 ohms at a temperature of 300° K, in the bandwidth between 100 and 15,000 cycles/sec, is

$$\mathcal{E}_{rms} = \sqrt{4RkT(f_2 - f_1)}$$

$$= \sqrt{4 \times 10^5 \times 1.38 \times 10^{-23} \times 300 \times (15000 - 100)}$$

$$\approx 5 \times 10^{-6}\text{v} = 5\mu\text{v}.$$

It is obvious that the three equations, (17-37), (17-38), and (17-39), cannot be entirely correct because the total bandwidth is infinitely great, which would lead to an infinite rms current. We have neglected the fact that the impedance of any actual circuit element is a function of frequency. That is, it is not correct to consider the element as a pure resistance at all frequencies. The mean square thermal emf *generated* in any element, in a narrow frequency range between f and $f + df$, is, from Eq. (17-39),

$$d(\bar{\mathcal{E}^2}) = 4RkTdf,$$

where in general R is a function of f. If Z is the impedance of the element in which the current is *measured*, the mean square current $d(\bar{i^2})$ in this frequency range is

$$d(\bar{i^2}) = \frac{d(\bar{\mathcal{E}^2})}{Z^2} = \frac{4RkT}{Z^2} df,$$

and the integral of this expression over all values of f does not lead to an infinite current. Assume for simplicity that R is the same for both elements and is independent of f, and that $Z^2 = R^2 + 4\pi^2L^2f^2$. Then the mean square current in the entire frequency range from zero to infinity is

$$\bar{i^2} = \int d(\bar{i^2}) = 4RkT \int_0^\infty \frac{1}{R^2 + 4\pi^2L^2f^2} df = \frac{kT}{L},$$

and

$$\tfrac{1}{2} L\overline{i^2} = \tfrac{1}{2} kT.$$

The total energy of the circuit is therefore finite and equal to $\tfrac{1}{2}kT$, as it should be by the equipartition principle.

Figure 17-5 shows three oscillograms, taken at different sweep speeds, of the random output voltage of a noise generator. The source is a gas-discharge tube rather than a resistor but the nature of the random fluctuations is the same.

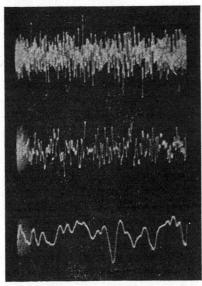

FIG. 17-5.   Single-sweep oscillograms of the output voltage of a random noise generator. The sweep speed for the middle oscillogram is 4 times, and that of the lowest is 20 times, that of the upper oscillogram. (*Courtesy of General Radio Co.*)

Problems

1. The data below were obtained in an analysis of the output of the random noise generator illustrated in Fig. 17-5. A total of 400 readings (of positive polarity only) were made of the instantaneous output voltage. If the voltage fluctuates in a truly random manner, the fluctuations follow a Gaussian distribution as given by Eq. (17-12), with v replacing δ. To see if this is the case, (a) construct a "block diagram" of the data, plotting $(\Delta N/N)/\Delta v$ vertically and centering each block on the mid-point of the corresponding voltage range. (In this calculation, let $N = 800$ rather than 400, since the general theory assumes that fluctuations of both signs are taken into account.) (b) Compute the rms voltage, v_{rms}, from the data. (Use the actual number of observations, 400.) (c) On the same diagram as in part (a), construct a graph, plotting $[1/(v_{rms} \sqrt{2\pi})] \exp(-v^2/2v_{rms}^2)$ vertically and v horizontally. Do the fluctuations appear truly random?

Voltage range, volts	Number of times observed, ΔN
0.0-0.2	75
0.2-0.4	85
0.4-0.6	66
0.6-0.8	50
0.8-1.0	42
1.0-1.2	29
1.2-1.4	22
1.4-1.6	16
1.6-1.8	6
1.8-2.0	5
2.0-2.2	3
2.2-2.4	1

2. Observations on the Brownian motion of a spherical particle of radius 0.4 micron (1 micron = 10^{-6} m) in water at $T = 300°$ K and of viscosity 10^{-3} newton-sec/m², made at intervals of 2 sec, show that its x-coordinate has changed between successive observations according to the table below.

Δx (microns)		No. of times corresponding Δx was observed
Less than ± 0.5		111
Between 0.5 and 1.5		87
-0.5	-1.5	95
1.5	2.5	47
-1.5	-2.5	32
2.5	3.5	8
-2.5	-3.5	15
3.5	4.5	3
-3.5	-4.5	2
4.5	5.5	0
-4.5	-5.5	1
Larger than ± 5.5		0

Compute (a) the average displacement in 2 sec, (b) the average value of $(\Delta x)^2$ in 2 sec, (c) Avogadro's number. (d) Construct a "block diagram" of the data above, plotting the number of observations per unit range of displacement vertically and centering each block on the mid-point of the range covered. (e) Construct on the same diagram a normal probability distribution curve, adjusted to have the same rms value of Δx.

3. The description of the General Radio Type 1390-A Random Noise Generator, which uses a gas-discharge tube as the noise source, says, in part, that the noise level at the output of the generator is about 6 mv for a one-cycle band, and that this is about 1,600,000 times the corresponding voltage for resistance noise at room temperature in a resistor of 800 ohms, equal to the output impedance of the instrument. Verify this statement.

SUGGESTED BOOKS FOR COLLATERAL READING

ALLIS AND HERLIN, *Thermodynamics and Statistical Mechanics*. McGraw-Hill, 1952.

FOWLER AND GUGGENHEIM, *Statistical Mechanics*. Macmillan, 1939.

GURNEY, *Introduction to Statistical Mechanics*. McGraw-Hill, 1949.

International Conference on the Physics of Very Low Temperatures, Proceedings of, 1949.

KEENAN, *Thermodynamics*. Wiley, 1941.

KENNARD, *Kinetic Theory of Gases*. McGraw-Hill, 1938.

LOEB, *Kinetic Theory of Gases* (2d ed.). McGraw-Hill, 1934.

PLANCK (tr. by Ogg), *Treatise on Thermodynamics*. Longmans, 1927.

SCHAEFER, *Einführung in die Theoretische Physik*, Bd. II. W. de Gruyter, 1929.

SLATER, *Introduction to Chemical Physics*. McGraw-Hill, 1939.

TOLMAN, *Statistical Mechanics with Applications to Physics and Chemistry*. Chemical Catalog Co., 1927.

TOLMAN, *The Principles of Statistical Mechanics*. Oxford-Clarendon Press, 1938.

WEBER, *Thermodynamics for Chemical Engineers*. Wiley, 1939.

ZEMANSKY, *Heat and Thermodynamics*, 3rd Edition, McGraw-Hill, 1951.

INDEX

ANSWERS TO PROBLEMS

CHAPTER 1

1. (a) 0.89 cm, 3.6 cm. (b) $t^* = -\infty$. **2.** 347.2°K. **3.** (a) $T_s = 671.69°R$, $T_i = 491.69°R$. (b) $-459.69°F$. **4.** (a) $t_{pt} = 421.4°$. (b) $t_{pt} = 284.9°$. (c) 293.6°.

CHAPTER 2

1. (a) 10^3 kgm/m³. (b) 10^{-3} m³/kgm. (c) 18×10^{-3} m³/kmole. (d) 1.29 kgm/m³, 0.77 m³/kgm, 22.4 m³/kmole. **2.** $R = 0.60$ lb-ft³/in²-lb-deg F abs = 8.3×10^3 j/kmole-deg K. **3.** 850 lb. **5.** (a) 300°K. (b) $T_b = 750°K$, $T_d = 120°K$. (c) 6.25 m³/kmole. (d) 10 m³. (e) 64 kgm. **6.** (a) 3.1 kmoles. (b) 98 kgm. (c) 215 lb. (d) 393 atm. (e) 2.8 kmoles. **7.** (a) $k = p_1^2/RT_1$. (c) 800°K. **8.** (b) 1.01×10^5 n/m². **9.** 25 cm. **10.** (a) 456°K. **11.** 14.5 cm. **12.** (a) 0.053 m³/kmole. (b) 9.4 kmoles. (c) 5.45 kmoles. **13.** (a) 480.4 atm. (b) 506 atm. (c) 414 atm. (d) 8315, 8700, 7100 vs. 6800 j/kmole-deg K. **14.** (b) 5%, 21%, 51%.

CHAPTER 3

1. 3.8×10^4 j. **2.** 1.69×10^5 j. **3.** (a) -19.5×10^4 j. (b) -27×10^4 j. (c) 150°K. (d) 7.8×10^4 n/m². **4.** $3nRT_1/2$. **5.** 3.1×10^5 j. **6.** 2.04 j. **7.** 1.13 j. **8.** (a) $w = RT \ln [(v_2 - b)/(v_1 - b)] + a[(1/v_2) - (1/v_1)]$. (b) 21.4×10^5 j. (c) 21.5×10^5 j. **9.** (a) $\beta = (1/T)[1 - (b/v)]$, $\kappa = (1/p)[1 - (b/v)]$. **10.** (a) $\beta = (1/vT)([1 + (a/vRT)]/[1/(v - b) - (a/v^2RT)])$. **11.** $\beta = -(1/\rho)(\partial\rho/\partial T)_p$, $\kappa = (1/\rho)(\partial\rho/\partial p)_T$. **12.** (a) $W = -4.6 \times 10^5$ j. (b) $W = -250$ j. (c) -0.99 m³, -5×10^{-5} m³. **13.** (b) $\kappa = 7 \times 10^{-12} + 1.83 \times 10^{-15}T$. (c) $(\partial\beta/\partial p)_T = -1.83 \times 10^{-15}$ deg⁻¹/(n/m²). (d) $\Delta\beta = -1.83 \times 10^{-7}$ deg⁻¹. **14.** (a) -3100 j. (b) -3000 j. (c) -1.5%. **15.** $\Delta T = 88$ deg. **16.** (a) $T_b = 900°K$, $T_c = 100°K$, $T_e = 193°K$. (b) 48×10^5 j, 16×10^5 j, 15.9×10^5 j, 27.4×10^5 j, 32×10^5 j.

CHAPTER 4

1. No. **2.** (a) 60 j. (b) 70 j are liberated. (c) $Q_{ad} = 50$ j, $Q_{db} = 10$ j. **3.** (a) $Q = n[a(T_2 - T_1) + b(T_2^2 - T_1^2)] + c[(1/T_2) - (1/T_1)]$. (b) $\overline{c}_p = a + b(T_2 + T_1) - c/T_1T_2$. (c) $c_p = 24.0 \times 10^3$ j/kmole-deg K, $\overline{c}_p = 24.1 \times 10^3$ j/kmole-deg K. **4.** (a) 87 j/kmole-deg. (b) 1.1×10^4 j/kmole-deg. (c) 2.75×10^5 j. (d) 3.4×10^3 j/kmole-deg. **5.** 160 cal/gm. **6.** (a) $c_p = P/n(dT/d\tau)$.

CHAPTER 5

2. $T(v - b)^{R/c_v} = \text{const}$, $T[(RT/p) - (a/RT) - (b^2p/RT) + \cdots]^{R/c_v} = \text{const}$, $[p + (a/v^2)](v - b)^{(R+c_v)/c_v} = \text{const}$. **3.** $c_v = a - (bp/T)$. **4.** (a) $19RT_1/2$, $17RT_1/2$, $18RT_1/2$. (b) $c = 3R$. **5.** (a) $c_p = 27 \times 10^3$ j/kmole-deg, $p\beta v = 0.4$ j/kmole-deg. (b) $c_p = 5R/2$, $p\beta v = R$. (c) 60%. (d) Very nearly 100%. **6.** (a) $nc_vT_0/2$. (b) $3T_0/2$. (c) $21T_0/4$. (d) $19nc_vT_0/4$. **7.** 885°K. **8.** $w = c_v(T_1 - T_2) + a[(1/v_2) - (1/v_1)]$.

10.

Process	V_2(m³)	T_2(°K)	W(j)	Q(j)	ΔU(j)
(a)	32	400	66.2×10^5	66.2×10^5	0
(b)	14	175	27.3×10^5	0	-27.3×10^5
(c)	32	400	0	0	0

11. $T_1 - T_2 = a(n_A - n_B)^2/2c_vV(n_A + n_B)$. **12.** -0.068 deg, $+0.61$ deg. **14.** (a) $a = 23 \times 10^3$, $b = 5.92$. (b) $\Delta h = 2.5 \times 10^7$ j/kmole. **15.** (a) c_p increases. (b) c_p is nearly constant. (c) c_p decreases. (d) 483 Btu/lb, 649 Btu/lb. (e) $c_p/R = 4.87$. **16.** $c_p = a + 2bT - cT^{-2}$. **17.** (a) -3.6×10^5 j/kgm. (b) -4.9×10^5 j/kgm. **19.** (a) -5.5×10^5 j. (b) -15.8×10^5 j. (c) -10.3×10^5 j. (d) 223°K. **20.** (a) 90 hp-hr. (b) 1600 lb. (c) -21°F. (d) 45 sec.

CHAPTER 6

2. (a) 1.84 ft³, 0.16 ft³. (b) 3.74 lb, 42.4 lb. **3.** (a) At about 50 atm. (c) 6 moles. (d) 7200 j. **4.** (a) 32 mm Hg. (b) 1.2×10^{-7} gm. **6.** 0.032, 0.043. **8.** (b) $RT_c/v_cp_c = e^2/2 = 3.7$. **9.** (a) At 100°F, $w = 295$ Btu/lb, $\Delta u = 742$ Btu/lb; at 212°F, $w = 352$ Btu/lb, $\Delta u = 618$ Btu/lb; at 600°F, $w = 336$ Btu/lb, $\Delta u = 213$ Btu/lb. (d) 33.3 ft³/lb (calc). **10.** (a) 977.9, 826.0, 548.5, 0 (Btu/lb). (b) 741.4 Btu/lb. **12.** -1.09 Btu/deg R.

CHAPTER 7

1. Engine satisfies 1st law but violates 2nd. **2.** 270 j, 730 j, 27%. **3.** Greater if T_1 is lowered. **5.** 1800 j. **6.** (a) 1370 j. (b) 2.7. **7.** 11.9 kwh. **8.** 8.5 watts, 0.4 cents. **10.** (a) 20.3×10^5 j, 15.9×10^5 j, 22%. (b) 68%. **11.** (a) -135 atm/deg K. (b) 270 atm. (c) 13 atm/deg K. (d) $p = 24.7$ atm. **12.** $l_{13} = 28 \times 10^5$ j/kgm. **14.** (a) 26.15. (b) 0.51 lb/in².

CHAPTER 8

1. (a) Zero. (b) 6.7 j/deg. **2.** (a) 4.2 j/deg. (b) 4.2 j/deg. **3.** (a) 780 j/deg. (b) 780 j/deg. **4.** 15 j/deg. **6.** 205 j/deg. **7.** (a) 1300 j/deg, -1120 j/deg, 180 j/deg. (b) 92 j/deg. (c) Use a series of reservoirs with temperatures between 273°K and 100°K. **8.** (a) $a \ln (T_2/T_1) + b(T_2 - T_1)$. (b) 38×10^3 j/kmole-deg. **9.** $\Delta S = 7.75 \times 10^4$ j/deg. **10.** -13.8×10^3 j/deg. **13.** (a) $Q_2 = +1200$ j, $Q_3 = -200$ j. (b) -3 j/deg, $+4$ j/deg, -1 j/deg. (c) Zero.

CHAPTER 9

2. (a) Zero.   (b) $-T(dB/dT)$.   **3.** (a) $(\partial c_p/\partial p)_T = 0$.   (b) $(\partial c_p/\partial p)_T \neq 0$.
4. (a) $c_v = a + bT - R$.   (b) $s = s_0 + a \ln (T/T_0) + b(T - T_0) - R \ln (p/p_0)$.
5. -1.92×10^5 j/deg.

6.

	p(n/m^2)	V(m^3)	T(°K)
a	2×10^5	3	100
b	4×10^5	6	400
c	2×10^5	6	200

Path	W(j)	Q(j)	ΔU(j)	ΔS(j/deg)
ab	9×10^5	54×10^5	45×10^5	$36 \times 10^3 \times \ln 2$
bc	0	-30×10^5	-30×10^5	$-15 \times 10^3 \times \ln 2$
ca	-6×10^5	-21×10^5	-15×10^5	$-21 \times 10^3 \times \ln 2$
Σ	3×10^5	3×10^5	0	0

7. (a) $nR \ln 2$.   (b) $nR \ln 2$.   (c) $nR \ln 2$.   (d) Zero.   **8.** (a) 754°K.
(b) 757°K.   **9.** (a) $T_2 = T_1$, $\Delta s = 25 \times 10^3$ j/kmole-deg.   (b) $T_2 - T_1 = -33$
deg, $\Delta s = 22.3 \times 10^3$ j/kmole-deg.   **10.** Let $\beta_{\text{liq}} = 4.3 \times 10^{-4}$ deg^{-1}. (a) Q (gas)
$= -4.6 \times 10^5$ j, Q (liq) $= -12.9 \times 10^5$ j.   (b) ΔU (gas) $= 0$, ΔU (liq) $= -12.9$
$\times 10^5$ j.   **12.** (a) $w = -4.5$ j/kgm.   (b) $q = -153$ j/kgm.   (c) $\Delta u = -148$
j/kgm, $+0.41$ deg.   **13.** (a) -0.43 deg.   (b) Zero.   (c) $+3.5$ deg.   **14.** (a)
-0.48 deg.   (b) $+0.10$ deg.   (c) $+3.6$ deg.   **15.** $c_p - c_v$ (calc) $= 0.39 \times 10^3$
(200°K), $c_p - c_v$ (calc) $= 4.0 \times 10^3$ (1200°K).   **16.** $0.404 R$.   **17.** -1.1°C, 410
atm.   **19.** $h = 1412$ Btu/lb, $s = 1.657$ Btu/lb-deg F abs, $g = -673$ Btu/lb.
20. $\Delta u = 830$ Btu/lb, $\Delta s = 1.2$ Btu/lb-deg F abs, $\Delta h = 910$ Btu/lb, $\Delta g = 0$.
21. (a) $v = 30$ m^3/kmole, v (ideal gas) $= 31$ m^3/kmole.   (b) $\Delta U = 499$ cal, $\Delta S =$
1.44 cal/deg, $\Delta H = 539$ cal, $\Delta G = 0$.   **22.** (b) 7.1×10^{-4} mm Hg.   (c) 1.4×10^3
atm.   **24.** (a) $\mu = 0$.   (b) $\mu \approx \dfrac{2a - RTb}{v^2 c_p}$.   **25.** $l = R(BC - AD)T^2/(C + DT)^2$.
26. 2.13×10^8 j/kmole.   **27.** (c) 2.79°K.

CHAPTER 10

1. (g) 7.91×10^5 j.   (h) -2.08×10^5 j.   (i) 5.83×10^5 j.   (j) 29.3% vs. 31%
(difference due to computational errors).   (k) 27%.   (l) Let $n = 1$ mole.
48.9×10^5 j, 43.1×10^5 j, 1.13.   (m) 5.83×10^5 j.   (n) 29%.   (o) 6.1%.
2. (a) 400 Btu/lb.   (b) 310 Btu/lb.   **3.** $\eta_1 = 42\%$, $\eta_2 = 64\%$.   **4.** (a) 3.7.
(b) 1.1.   **5.** $Q_1 = -1200$ j, $Q_2 = +1800$ j, $Q_3 = -600$ j.

CHAPTER 11

1. (a) 1.7×10^{-6} m.   (b) About 4×10^6 molecules.   2. (a) 3.1×10^{19} molecules/m³.   (b) 3.1×10^{10} molecules.   3. (a) 5.6×10^{-6}.   (b) 7.9×10^{-6}.
4. (a) 1.2×10^{-5}.   (b) 4.4×10^{-3}.   5. 3.2 m/sec, 3.36 m/sec.   6. (a) 10 m/sec.
(b) $\bar{v} = 7.5$ m/sec, $v_{rms} = 7.9$ m/sec.   (c) $\bar{v} = 8.3$ m/sec, $v_{rms} = 8.7$ m/sec.
(d) $\bar{v} = 5$ m/sec, $v_{rms} = 7.1$ m/sec.   7. (a) 6.2×10^{-21} j.   (b) 1930 m/sec,
480 m/sec, 193 m/sec.   8. (a) 112 m/sec.   (b) 520 m/sec.   (c) 215 m/sec.
9. (a) 7700°K.   (b) 7.7×10^{6}°K.   (c) 7.7×10^{9}°K.   10. $p = \frac{1}{3}\Sigma n m \bar{v^2}$.   11.
Force per unit length $= n m \bar{v^2}/2$.   12. (a) 3.5×10^{23} impacts/cm²-sec.   (b) 130 m.
13. 19×10^{27} coll/sec.   14. (a) 1.95×10^{19} molecules/cm³.   (b) 3.2×10^{23}
molecules/cm²-sec.   (c) same as (b).   (d) Heat of vaporization, per molecule,
about 10 times mean kinetic energy.   15. (a) 9.3×10^{-6} gm/cm²-sec.   (b) About
99% of (a).   16. $t = 4V/\bar{v}A$.   17. (a) 12.6×10^{16} molecules.   (b) 2×10^{-3}
mm Hg.   18. $p = (p_0/2)[1 + \exp(-A\bar{v}t/2V)]$.   19. $pV/T = (nR) + (b'p/T)$.
20. (b) 2.9×10^{-10} m, 1.6×10^{-10} m.   21. (a) 0.14 gm/cm³.   (b) 3.3×10^{-10} m.

CHAPTER 12

4. (a) 12.5×10^{23} molecules.   (b) 26×10^{20} molecules.   (c) 54×10^{17} molecules.
(d) 20×10^{23} molecules.   5. (a) 0.52 molecule.   (b) The M-B distribution function only has significance when applied to large numbers of molecules.   6. (a)
$0.83\, v_m$.   (b) $0.83\, v_m$.   7. (a) $v_m = 386$ m/sec, $\bar{v} = 435$ m/sec, $v_{rms} = 482$ m/sec.
(b) 224 m/sec, 709 m/sec, 2240 m/sec.   8. (a) 2.08×10^{-3}.   (b) 8.3×10^{-3}.
(c) 6.7×10^{-8}.   10. (a) 0.166.   (b) 0.163.   (c) 0.162.   11. 1.6×10^{-12}.
12. (a) $N[1 - \mathrm{erf}(x) + 2xe^{-x^2}/\sqrt{\pi}]$.   (b) 0.576.   (c) 0.046.   13. (a) 0.422,
0.078, 0.500.   (b) 0.424, 0.576, 1.000.   14. 0.843.   15. (a) 6.5×10^{18}.   (b)
1.6×10^{26}.   (c) 5.7×10^{26}.   16. $[n v_m \exp(-x^2 v^2{}_m)]/2\sqrt{\pi}$.   17. $(1/v)_{av} = 2/v_m\sqrt{\pi}$.
18. (a) $0.72\, v_m$.   (b) $1.44\, v_m$.   19. $W_m = kT/2$; no.   20. (b) $k = N/V$.   (c)
$\bar{v} = V/2$, $v_{rms} = V/\sqrt{3}$.   21. (b) $k = 2N/V^2$.   (c) $\bar{v} = 2V/3$, $v_{rms} = V/\sqrt{2}$,
$v_m = V$.   22. 8.7×10^{-3} m, 12.3×10^{-3} m.   23. (a) 198 m/sec.   (b) 13
mgm/hr.   (c) 120 sec.   24. 3.26 sec.   25. (a) 4.6 μgm/sec.   (b) 3.5×10^{11}
molecules/sec, 1.2 μμgm/sec.   (c) 1.7×10^8 molecules.   (d) 3.3×10^{-8} mm Hg.
26. 0.083 mm, 2.4×10^{-3} deg.   27. (a) 18.   (b) $c_v = 9R$, $\gamma = 1.11$.   29. (a)
6.35×10^{13} neutrons/m³.   (b) 2.63×10^{-11} n/m².

CHAPTER 13

1. (a) 6.6×10^9 coll/sec.   (b) 6.6×10^3 coll/sec.   2. (a) 1.93×10^2 n/m².
(b) 3.8×10^4 coll/m.   3. (a) 5.5×10^9 coll/sec.   (b) 2.8×10^{23} coll/cm²-sec.
(c) 2.4×10^{22} molecules.   4. (a) 3679.   (b) 1350.   (c) 68.   (d) 2390.   (e) 368.
(f) 74.   (g) Impossible to compute from theory.   5. 30×10^{-6} sec.   6. (a)
3×10^4 m.   (b) Practically 100%.   7. About 5×10^{-4} mm Hg.   8. (a) 10 cm.
(b) 60 μa.   9. (a) 1.8×10^{-10} m.   (b) 1.3×10^{-10} m.   10. 8.12, 8.45, 9.59, 10.3,
11.5.   11. (a) 0.34×10^{-9} m.   (b) 200.   (c) 2.3 m/sec.   (d) 200.   (e) 2.2×10^4
12. (a) 6.   (b) 6.   (c) 6.   13. (b) 1.42×10^4 collisions.   (c) 7.2×10^9
collisions/sec.   (d) 2 μsec.   14. (a) -1.33×10^{25} (molecules/m³)/m.   (b)
$1.18 \times 10^{23} + 4.5 \times 10^{15}$ molecules/sec.   (c) $1.18 \times 10^{23} - 4.5 \times 10^{15}$ molecules/sec.   (d) 9×10^{15} molecules/sec, 0.69 μgm/sec.

CHAPTER 14

1. (a) 10^{57}.   (b) 0.93, 0.47, 7.4×10^{-4}.   **2.** 14%, 0.25%.   **3.** $\delta N_1 = -2$, $\delta N_2 = +4$.   **4.** (a) $W = \exp(12.8 \times 10^6)$.   (b) 1.   **5.** (a) $-2(dN)^2/N_i$. (b) $\exp(-5.38 \times 10^{15})$.   (c) -7×10^{-8} j/deg.   (d) 3.04×10^9 molecules.

CHAPTER 15

1. (a) $Z = 2\pi A kT / Hm$.   (b) Force per unit length $= NkT$.   **2.** $\rho = \rho_0 \exp$ $(m\omega^2 r^2 / 2kT)$.   **3.** (b) $p^{(1-\gamma)} = \dfrac{(\gamma - 1) Mg}{RK} Z + \text{const}$, where $K = T_p^{(1-\gamma)/\gamma}$. **5.** kT.   **6.** $c_A = R$.   **7.** 865, 117, 16.   **8.** (a) 1.14×10^3 j/kmole-deg.   (b) 2.74×10^3 j/kmole-deg.   **9.** (a) $\Theta_E = 116°K$.   **10.** (a) $x = 5.2$.   (b) $M/M_{sat} =$ 0.81.   **11.** (a) $C = 5.28 \times 10^{-4}$.   (b) $\mu = 2.54 \times 10^{-23}$ amp-m².   **12.** $(N_1 - N_2)/$ $N_1 = 1.35 \times 10^{-4}$.

CHAPTER 16

1. (a) 1.   (b) 36.   (c) 16.   **2.** (a) $\bar{v} = 3v_{mo}/4$.   (b) $v_{rms} = (\sqrt{3/5})v_{mo}$. (c) $\overline{(1/v)} = 3/2v_{mo}$.   **3.** (a) $w_{mo} = 10.8$ ev.   **5.** (a) $c_v = 0.142R$.   (b) 4.7%. **6.** 3×10^{15} amp/m².   **7.** 360,000 atm.   **8.** About 6×10^{-9}.

CHAPTER 17

1. (b) $v_{rms} = 0.79$ volt.   **2.** (a) $\overline{\Delta x} = 0$.   (b) $\overline{\Delta x^2} = 1.78 \times 10^{-12}$ m².   (c) 7.4×10^{26} molecules/kmole.

SELECTED DIFFERENTIALS FROM A CONDENSED COLLECTION OF THERMODYNAMIC FORMULAS

by P. W. Bridgman

Any partial derivative of a state variable of a thermodynamic system, with respect to any other state variable, a third variable being held constant [for example, $(\partial u/\partial v)_p$] can be written, from Eq. (4-13), in the form

$$(\partial u/\partial v)_p = \frac{(\partial u/\partial z)_p}{(\partial v/\partial z)_p},$$

where z is any arbitrary state function. Then if one tabulates the partial derivatives of all state variables with respect to an arbitrary function z, any partial derivative can be obtained by dividing one tabulated quantity by another. For brevity, derivatives of the form $(\partial u/\partial z)_p$ are written in the table below in the symbolic form $(\partial u)_p$. Then, for example,

$$\left(\frac{\partial u}{\partial v}\right)_p = \frac{(\partial u)_p}{(\partial v)_p} = \frac{c_p - p(\partial v/\partial T)_p}{(\partial v/\partial T)_p},$$

which agrees with Eq. (5-24). Ratios (not derivatives) such as $d'q_p/dv_p$ can be treated in the same way. For a further discussion, see *A Condensed Collection of Thermodynamics Formulas* by P. W. Bridgman (Harvard University Press), from which the table below is taken.

p constant

$(\partial T)_p = 1$

$(\partial v)_p = (\partial v/\partial T)_p$

$(\partial s)_p = c_p/T$

$(\partial q)_p = c_p$

$(\partial w)_p = p(\partial v/\partial T)_p$

$(\partial u)_p = c_p - p(\partial v/\partial T)_p$

$(\partial h)_p = c_p$

$(\partial g)_p = -s$

$(\partial f)_p = -s - p(\partial v/\partial T)_p$

h constant

$(\partial p)_h = -c_p$

$(\partial T)_h = v - T(\partial v/\partial T)_p$

$(\partial v)_h = -c_p(\partial v/\partial p)_T - T(\partial v/\partial T)_p^2$
$\qquad\qquad + v(\partial v/\partial T)_p$

$(\partial s)_h = vc_p/T$

$(\partial q)_h = vc_p$

$(\partial w)_h = -p[c_p(\partial v/\partial p)_T + T(\partial v/\partial T)_p^2$
$\qquad\qquad - v(\partial v/\partial T)_p]$

T constant

$(\partial p)_T = -1$

$(\partial v)_T = -(\partial v/\partial p)_T$

$(\partial s)_T = (\partial v/\partial T)_p$

$(\partial q)_T = T(\partial v/\partial T)_p$

$(\partial w)_T = -p(\partial v/\partial p)_T$

$(\partial u)_T = T(\partial v/\partial T)_p + p(\partial v/\partial p)_T$

$(\partial h)_T = -v + T(\partial v/\partial T)_p$

$(\partial g)_T = -v$

$(\partial f)_T = p(\partial v/\partial p)_T$

g constant

$(\partial p)_g = s$

$(\partial T)_g = v$

$(\partial v)_g = v(\partial v/\partial T)_p + s(\partial v/\partial p)_T$

$(\partial s)_g = \dfrac{1}{T}[vc_p - sT(\partial v/\partial T)_p]$

$(\partial q)_g = -sT(\partial v/\partial T)_p + vc_p$

$(\partial w)_g = p[v(\partial v/\partial T)_p + s(\partial v/\partial p)_T]$

<u>s constant</u>

$(\partial p)_s = -c_p/T$

$(\partial T)_s = -(\partial v/\partial T)_p$

$(\partial v)_s = -\dfrac{1}{T}[c_p(\partial v/\partial p)_T \mp T(\partial v/\partial T)_p^2]$

$(\partial q)_s = 0$

$(\partial w)_s = -\dfrac{p}{T}[c_p(\partial v/\partial p)_T + T(\partial v/\partial T)_p^2]$

$(\partial u)_s = \dfrac{p}{T}[c_p(\partial v/\partial p)_T + (T\partial v/\partial T)_p^2]$

$(\partial h)_s = -vc_p/T$

$(\partial g)_s = -\dfrac{1}{T}[vc_p - sT(\partial v/\partial T)_p]$

$(\partial f)_s = \dfrac{1}{T}[pc_p(\partial v/\partial p)_T + pT(\partial v/\partial T)_p^2$
$\qquad\qquad + sT(\partial v/\partial T)_p]$

<u>v constant</u>

$(\partial p)_v = -(\partial v/\partial T)_p$

$(\partial T)_v = (\partial v/\partial p)_T$

$(\partial s)_v = \dfrac{1}{T}[c_p(\partial v/\partial p)_T + T(\partial v/\partial T)_p^2]$

$(\partial q)_v = c_p(\partial v/\partial p)_T + T(\partial v/\partial T)_p^2$

$(\partial w)_v = 0$

$(\partial u)_v = c_p(\partial v/\partial p)_T + T(\partial v/\partial T)_p^2$

$(\partial h)_v = c_p(\partial v/\partial p)_T + T(\partial v/\partial T)_p^2$
$\qquad\qquad - v(\partial v/\partial T)_p$

$(\partial g)_v = -v(\partial v/\partial T)_p - s(\partial v/\partial p)_T$

$(\partial f)_v = -s(\partial v/\partial p)_T$

DEFGH798765432